Critic Check
338 Main-Conn.

Aa

Ca

D

E

m

Basic Concepts
of Mathematics

by

G. CUTHBERT WEBBER

H. Fletcher Brown Professor of Mathematics

University of Delaware

and

JOHN A. BROWN

Professor of Education and Mathematics

University of Delaware

ADDISON-WESLEY PUBLISHING COMPANY, INC.

READING, MASSACHUSETTS · PALO ALTO · LONDON

This book is in the

ADDISON-WESLEY SCIENCE AND MATHEMATICS

EDUCATION SERIES

Consulting Editors

RICHARD S. PIETERS   PAUL ROSENBLOOM

GEORGE B. THOMAS, JR.   JOHN WAGNER

Preface

Basic Concepts of Mathematics has grown out of a junior-year course developed at the University of Delaware for prospective elementary school teachers. Much of the material has been course-tested both with those groups and groups of teachers-in-service. With the possible exception of a portion of Chapter 3, the development of ideas is just as useful and important for persons desiring a sound background in, and a suitable explanation of, the structure of both arithmetic and algebraic concepts; accordingly, this development is suitable for many liberal-arts education programs.

The primary purpose is to develop understanding of basic mathematical concepts on the part of the reader. To this end definitions and theorems are motivated through a discussion of background, reasons are given for choosing definitions, and examples are used to make theorems meaningful before proofs are attempted. Intuitive approaches and informal discussions are used to introduce properties and theorems; in most instances, this discussion is followed by a proof. Questions are placed throughout the textual material to encourage the reader to develop his power to reason and to read critically; at times these questions appear as a set of "development exercises" within the text. Basic forms of reasoning, proof if you will, are discussed throughout and in summatory form in the last chapter.

The first seven chapters may well constitute a one-semester three-hour course. Herein the properties of natural numbers are developed and applied to an extension of the four basic operations upon these numbers; in the early work, set concepts are used as a basis for the development. In Chapter 7 both the arithmetic and algebraic aspects of "common fractions" are explored.

A logical treatment of real numbers is always a vexing task in an elementary course since only an introduction to this somewhat difficult area can be attempted. The treatment in Chapter 11 should serve to develop an understanding of real numbers in terms of concepts which will be stepping stones in a later, more complete discussion. Moreover, this treatment aids understanding of the number line and its application in Chapter 12, "Measurement: A Mathematical Approach."

Throughout, no distinction is made between arithmetic and algebra; there is a natural flow from one to the other. Moreover, the reader soon realizes that there are reasons for the "usual" operations with numbers, that there is a structure to elementary mathematics which, when comprehended, can eliminate both misunderstanding and lack of understanding.

Much has been written about "new mathematics" in recent years; it might be advisable to characterize this "new mathematics" as a new approach, a different emphasis. There is emphasis on structure and development to give coherence and meaning to what has often been a set of isolated concepts and techniques. In this book "modern" ideas that serve a purpose are introduced; moreover, they are introduced where needed and are then used. Certain concepts which one might expect to find have not been included since they were not deemed necessary or advisable for the development.

Comprehension of the ideas delineated in this book, especially in Chapters 3, 4 and 7, should serve to enable the teacher of an elementary grade to present arithmetic in a meaningful manner, rather than as a set of isolated techniques to be performed mechanically. Moreover, this material gives background necessary for presenting many topics not found in a traditional curriculum but being recommended for inclusion in the early grades. Also, junior and senior high school teachers of mathematics will find this material of great service as background for courses being recommended for those school areas. Although these recommendations, at both the elementary and secondary levels, are coming from several curriculum study groups, all are based on a common mathematical structure, that of the real number system. It is this structure which is emphasized herein.

Both authors served on the writing team of the School Mathematics Study Group (SMSG); the influence of that group is obvious both as to inclusion of topical material and as to the general philosophy. Certain ideas developed by that group have been adapted for use herein; it is our pleasure to express gratitude for permission to make use of these ideas.

Colleagues have been most helpful, in particular Professors Willard E. Baxter, Robert W. Kennard and E. Vernon Lewis, both in criticizing manuscript and offering suggestions; to them we extend our thanks. The constructive criticism of those who reviewed the manuscript and the cooperation of the staff of Addison-Wesley Publishing Company, Inc., have contributed greatly to the end result.

<table>
<tr><td>Newark, Delaware</td><td>G.C.W.</td></tr>
<tr><td>February 1963</td><td>J.A.B.</td></tr>
</table>

Contents

CHAPTER 1

Numeral Systems

Numbers are interesting! Numbers are useful! The very young child seems to be fascinated by counting and later by discovering what he can do with numbers. From early times man has had need for numbers, whether to count his possessions or to assist in barter arrangements.

1-1 PRIMITIVE ASPECTS OF NUMBER

A primitive "lord of the manor" who desired to determine how many cows he possessed might well have had them pass before him. As each cow passed he could have made a mark in the dirt or on a stick until eventually he represented the count of his herd as

$$| | | | | | | | | | | | | | | | | | | | | | | | | \cdot$$

He might soon get the idea that this marking procedure could be improved by representing the count in groups:

$$| | | | | \quad | | | | | \quad | | | | | \quad | | | | | \quad | | \cdot$$

This particular grouping might well have come about through use of the fingers on a hand. If he desired to communicate his count verbally to another person he needed words. When grouping was not used he needed a word for each possible count, like our one, two, three, four, . . . , twenty-one, twenty-two, etc. The choice of words is entirely arbitrary and has varied both in time and with various languages. Our early man who used the grouping procedure above would note that he needed only a few words; for the above example he needed words like one, two, three, four, and five only. Then he could state his result as "four fives and two." These words would serve until he counted "five fives and five"; then he would realize the need for something additional. Since grouping was so successful, possibly the use of larger groups would continue that success. In counting these "fives" by using his fingers (on one hand) it would seem logical to take five fives as the next larger group. Let us call this a "squiggle." Then the count

$$||||| ~ ||||| ~ ||||| ~ ||||| ~ ||||| ~ ||||| ~ ||||| ~ |||$$

would be grouped as

$$(||||| ~ ||||| ~ ||||| ~ ||||| ~ |||||) ~ ||||| ~ ||||| ~ |||$$

and communicated orally as "one squiggle, two fives, and three." Our early man is advancing! If he had need for it, he probably would put five squiggles in the next larger group and coin a word for it, say "crunch." And so on indefinitely, introducing new group sizes and coining new words as they are needed.

The next step would probably be communication by "writing." Of course the words could be written, as in the preceding discussion, but symbols in place of words would probably occur to him as a simplifying measure. A picture of a hand for "five" would serve but would be cumbersome. He might decide to use $\square$ for "five," $\triangle$ for "squiggle," and $*$ for "crunch." Then he could write the number of the first example as $\square\square\square||$ and the number of the second example as $\triangle\square\square|||$. A number which we would write as 191 he would write as $*\triangle\triangle\square\square|$.

Symbols for numbers are called *numerals*. Numerals introduced in the above system are $|$, $\square$, $\triangle$, and $*$. This system has two main features which we can call repetition and addition.

Repetition. A symbol is repeated to indicate the presence of more than one group of a particular size.

Addition. Addition is employed both within group sizes, e.g., $\square\square\square = 5 + 5 + 5$, and between group sizes, e.g., $\triangle\triangle\square\square = 50 + 15$.

Would $\triangle\triangle\square\square$ represent the same number as $\square\triangle\square\triangle$? Certainly it would, since a particular symbol always represents the same group size, no matter where it is placed. As a consequence, addition in such a system is very simple. To find

$$\triangle\triangle\square\square\square|||| + \triangle\triangle\triangle\square\square\square||,$$

"sweep together" the symbols to obtain

$$\triangle\triangle\triangle\triangle\triangle\square\square\square\square\square\square||||||;$$

then use conversion equations:

$$||||| = \square, \qquad \square\square\square\square\square = \triangle, \qquad \triangle\triangle\triangle\triangle\triangle = *, \text{ etc.}$$

The result is $*\triangle\square\square|$.

It would be an easy matter to construct one of those "beads strung on wires within a frame" contraptions known as an *abacus* to assist with computations in this system. How many beads would be needed on each wire? Either four or five beads would suffice; we shall use five beads on each wire. For simplicity, wires will be represented by lines and beads by vertical marks, the group size being indicated at the left. Let us perform the above addition. We represent one number on the abacus, say △ △ ☐ ☐ ☐ | | | |, and obtain the diagram in Fig. 1–1. On each line the *unused* beads are shown

FIGURE 1–1   FIGURE 1–2

on the right. Then add, in turn, two | beads, three ☐ beads, and three △ beads. The order in which this is done is immaterial, though we will start with the smallest denomination and proceed upward. Conversion should be carried out as we proceed, since there are only five beads on each wire. When adding to the lowest wire, only one bead can be added before a conversion takes place; "adding" means to move a bead to the left. This produces the diagram in Fig. 1–2. To obtain the diagram in Fig. 1–3, add three beads to the ☐ wire in Fig. 1–2. Then add three beads to the △ wire in Fig. 1–3 to produce Fig. 1–4. The result is, as before, * △ ☐ ☐ |.

FIGURE 1–3   FIGURE 1–4

Think through the above ideas carefully, since they are basic and applicable to most systems. Do not belittle the use of an abacus; it can help to clarify ideas. Moreover, an abacus operator can work much more rapidly than most people realize; computer operators have been outdone by abacus operators.

The grouping in fives used above was natural though not necessary. It would have been just as natural to group in tens, because of man's ten fingers. Obviously this is the basis of "our" numeral system; as will be seen, other peoples have grouped in tens too. Would it not have been almost as natural to group in twenties (except that most people have more difficulty wiggling an individual toe than an individual finger)?

In succeeding sections we will take a cursory look at a few numeral systems of historical interest, not because we are greatly interested in being able to compute in those systems, but rather because the basic principles are of paramount importance.

PROBLEM SET 1–1

1. Write the following Hindu-Arabic numerals in the "fives" notation of this section. [*Hint:* Consider 178 as 125 + 50 + 3.]

   (a) 178   (b) 67   (c) 283   (d) 399   (e) 562
   (f) 624   (g) 526   (h) 434   (i) 476

2. (a) What would be the next larger group size beyond that represented by ∗?
   (b) Use ∼ as the numeral for that group size and write both 682 and 750.
   (c) Write the conversion equation for this new unit.

3. Use a line abacus to add the following and show progressive diagrams for the various stages.

   (a) △ △ □ □ □ □ | + □ | | (b) △ □ □ | | | + ∗ △ □ | | | |
   (c) △ △ △ □ □ + △ △ □ □ □ | | |

4. In problem 3(c) which numeral should be placed on the diagram first? Why?

5. For the "fives" system, is any symbol needed to represent the fact that there are no groups of a particular size? Why?

6. Why would four beads per wire suffice for an abacus for the "fives" system?

1–2 EGYPTIAN NUMERALS

One system of numerals used by the Egyptians about 3000 B.C. was quite similar to the "fives" system of the previous section. The chief difference is that the group sizes were based on "ten-ness," i.e., they corresponded to our ten, hundred, thousand, etc. As might be expected, their symbols were pictorial in nature; you can use your imagination as to what they might have represented. The following are simplified forms of these symbols.

One	Ten	Hundred	Thousand	Ten thousand	Hundred thousand	Million
|	∩	᧐	⚸	⫯	⫰	ᛘ

The principles of repetition and additivity were basic in the use of these symbols. Hence our numeral 21468 would have been written as follows. Would the order and arrangement of these symbols be material?

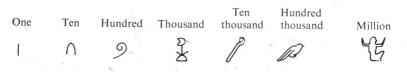

1–3 ROMAN NUMERALS

The Roman numeral system is an enigma, in some respects. It seems to have been used in business transactions as late as 1600 A.D., even though the Hindu-Arabic system (our system) was in vogue at that time. Why was it used for such a long period? The probable reasons are twofold: first, Roman influence on Western civilization was great and long lasting even though mathematical contributions were relatively slight; second, the system is simple to understand and manipulation with numbers requires little basic knowledge. Since, until relatively modern times, most people had little education, ease of operation would be conducive to the retention of a system even though the operations were time consuming.

One might say that the Roman system is based on "ten-ness" in that there are symbols for one, ten, hundred, thousand, etc. In modern dress these are

one	ten	hundred	thousand
I	X	C	M

However, group sizes of five, fifty, and five hundred were also used, with symbols

five	fifty	five hundred
V	L	D

The use of these latter symbols destroyed, in part, the basic "ten-ness" concept. Earlier symbol forms differed in many respects from those listed.

In olden times the writing of Roman numerals was based entirely on the principles of repetition and addition. Our numbers 297 and 1974 would have been written as

CCLXXXXVII,

MDCCCCLXXIIII.

Note the use of the principles of repetition and addition; for instance,

CCLXXXXVII   means $200 + 50 + 40 + 5 + 2.$

The arrangement of symbols is immaterial, as for systems discussed previously; for example, XVI would mean the same as IVX. This being so, the addition of numbers could be effected by the "sweeping together" and conversion operations discussed in Section 1–1.

In later times another principle was used, that of subtraction. Instead of writing four as IIII, it was written IV; this is based on $4 = 5 - 1$, subtraction being indicated by placing a "lesser" symbol to the left of a "larger" symbol. In this form of Roman numerals,

$$\left.\begin{array}{r} 9 \\ 40 \\ 90 \\ 400 \\ 900 \end{array}\right\} \quad \text{was written} \quad \left\{\begin{array}{l} \text{IX,} \\ \text{XL,} \\ \text{XC,} \\ \text{CD,} \\ \text{CM.} \end{array}\right.$$

In applying this principle certain rules were followed.

(a) Only the symbols for one, ten, and hundred could precede symbols for larger units.
(b) I   could precede only   V   or   X;
X   could precede only   L   or   C;
C   could precede only   D   or   M.
Thus, I, X, or C could precede only the symbols for the next two larger units.

That further use of this principle could lead to difficulty can be seen by considering IXC. Does it mean I(XC) = one before ninety = 89, or (IX)C = nine before one hundred = 91?

Naturally this mode of expression saved time and effort in writing numbers, for example,

$$\text{MDCCCCLXXIIII} \quad \text{became} \quad \text{MCMLXXIV.}$$

However, this gain was offset by certain losses. On the one hand addition became complicated, as will be noted in the problems. On the other hand, we have lost the freedom of writing symbols in any order.

A multiplicative principle came into use during the Middle Ages for writing large numbers; a bar placed over a symbol indicated multiplication by <u>1000</u>. For example, $\overline{X} = 10,000$; $\overline{C} = 100,000$, $\overline{M} = 1,000,000$. With these symbols, 221,341 would be written $\overline{CC}\overline{XX}MCCCXLI$.

There is a distinction between a number and a numeral. In this chapter we are considering various systems of numerals for the same numbers. When something is written, that "something" is a numeral, not a number. At times it is difficult to be precise in the use of the words "number" and "numeral" without being repetitive and introducing awkward sentence constructions. Let us try to be at least moderately precise in this respect.

PROBLEM SET 1–3

1. Write the following, using the Egyptian numeral system.

(a) 52   (b) 74   (c) 379   (d) 2645   (e) 12346

2. Explain how to add numbers in the Egyptian system.

3. Explain how to perform 248 − 125 and 243 − 168 in the Egyptian system.

4. Write the following in Roman numerals, both with and without use of the subtractive principle.

   (a) 257   (b) 249   (c) 464   (d) 2929   (e) 1950   (f) 3494

5. Write the conversion equations for Roman numerals.

6. Explain the basic principles of adding two numbers written in Roman numerals, assuming that the subtractive principle has not been used in writing the numerals.

7. Perform the indicated operations using Roman numerals.

   (a) CXVI + LXXVIII   (b) LXVII + CLXV
   (c) DCCXXXXV + CLXVII   (d) MDCC + CCCVI
   (e) LXVII − XXXVII   (f) MDCC − CCCVI
   (g) LXII − XXXVII   (h) CLXV − LXVII

8. Explain why addition is more complicated when the subtractive principle is used in writing Roman numerals.

9. If numbers are written in Roman numerals using the subtractive principle, what do you think would be the most convenient method of adding them?

10. Use your answer to Problem 9 to perform the following operations.

    (a) XCIV + XLIX   (b) CMXCIX + MCDXXIV

11. Explain the construction of an abacus for Roman numerals.

1–4 BABYLONIAN NUMERALS

The Babylonians introduced one of the two basic steps leading from the type of system discussed previously to a system such as the one we use daily. This step was the introduction of the concept of "position."

Basically, only two symbols were used, ▼ for one and ⟨ for ten. Numerals for numbers from one to fifty-nine were built up, as in previous systems, by using the principles of repetition and addition. For example, eleven and fifty-nine would be written

$$ \langle\ \blacktriangledown \quad \text{and} \quad \begin{matrix} \langle\ \langle\ \langle \\ \langle\ \langle \end{matrix} \quad \begin{matrix} \blacktriangledown\blacktriangledown\blacktriangledown\blacktriangledown\blacktriangledown \\ \blacktriangledown\blacktriangledown\blacktriangledown\blacktriangledown \end{matrix} $$

This system uses a basic group size of sixty, i.e., sixty plays the role that five played in Section 1–1. Hence, a number is thought of as ... + so many sixty-sixties + so many sixties + so many ones. The new principle enters at this stage; they did not introduce new symbols for sixty, sixty-sixties, etc., but rather used the same symbol for ten sixties as for ten ones or ten sixty-sixties. The *position* of the symbol was supposed to indicate which group size was intended. For example, eleven sixties + twelve ones would be written ⟨ ▼ ⟨ ▼ ▼. The fact that a ▼ precedes a ⟨, above, was used to indicate that ⟨ ▼ referred to a larger group size than did ⟨ ▼ ▼. Not too bad so far, but suppose you wrote ten sixties + ten as ⟨ ⟨. How could you distinguish this from the numeral for twenty? Some sort of "separator" is needed, and they did introduce such in the later years of their civilization. We will use a comma as separator, so that

$$\text{ten sixties} + \text{ten} \quad \text{is} \quad ⟨ , ⟨$$
$$\text{twenty} \quad \text{is} \quad ⟨ ⟨$$

In ⟨ , ⟨ the same symbol is used to denote ten sixties as to denote ten ones; the position of the symbol denotes which group size is intended.

How did the Babylonians write ten sixty-sixties + ten? Very simple, by merely leaving a space they indicated the lack of sixties: ⟨   ⟨ But then, how about ten sixty-sixty-sixties + ten? They had no way of distinguishing between such numbers, since the length of the gap would hardly suffice for this purpose. This lack of a symbol to indicate that a certain group size is missing led to untold ambiguities. Suppose they had used a rectangle, □, to indicate that a group size was missing, i.e., as a placeholder. Then the notations

⟨ , ⟨	for	ten sixties + ten,
⟨ □ ⟨	for	ten sixty-sixties + ten,
⟨ □ □ ⟨	for	ten sixty-sixty-sixties + ten

would have been much clearer.

In Babylonian notation, ⟨ , ⟨ could mean any one of the following numbers:

> ten sixties + ten, or
>
> ten sixty-sixties + ten sixties, or
>
> ten sixty-sixty-sixties + ten sixty-sixties.

Again it was the lack of a symbol for a placeholder which caused the confusion. With a placeholder symbol the above numbers could be written

⟨ , ⟨	for	ten sixties + ten,
⟨ , ⟨ □	for	ten sixty-sixties + ten sixties,
⟨ , ⟨ □ □	for	ten sixty-sixty-sixties + ten sixty-sixties.

What a world of difference one simple idea can make!

The Babylonian positional numeral system was in vogue quite early, about 1800 B.C. Even so, the Greeks made little use of this idea. Their primary numeral systems were two in number, one something like the Roman numerals and one using letter symbols for numbers. However, there is some evidence that certain Greeks used a positional system and even used a placeholder symbol like our symbol for zero. The use of the "position" concept led to economy of symbolism, but this economy was anything but effective until the "placeholder" concept came into use.

PROBLEM SET 1–4

1. (a) Write twelve in Babylonian notation. (b) Name two other numbers with which this could be confused.

2. The following numbers are in "our" notation. Write them in Babylonian notation, using a separator where needed (1) without using a placeholder, and (2) using a placeholder, where needed.

   (a) 72   (b) 60   (c) 3612   (d) 7224   (e) 7264   (f) 7200

3. Write a numeral in Babylonian notation for which (a) a separator is needed but not a placeholder; (b) a placeholder has the effect of a separator.

1–5 HINDU-ARABIC NUMERAL SYSTEM

The Hindu-Arabic numeral system is our numeral system! What are its basic features?

First and foremost, no symbols other than 0, 1, 2, 3, 4, 5, 6, 7, 8, and 9 are needed in order to write a symbol for any number, no matter how large it may be. In the "fives" system, discussed in Section 1–1, it would be necessary to concoct more and more symbols as we needed to write larger numbers. In addition to those previously introduced, symbols for group sizes 5^4, 5^5, 5^6, etc., would also be needed.

Second, the group sizes are ten, ten tens or hundred, ten hundreds or thousand, etc.; thus the system is based on "ten-ness."

Third, the Hindu-Arabic system is positional in that the 3 in 43 means three ones, in 534 it means three tens, in 367 it means 3 hundreds, etc.

Fourth, it is not repetitive. We do not write the symbol for ten twice to get the symbol for twenty. Rather, this is indicated by using the symbol 2 in the tens position.

Fifth, it is additive. For example, 346 means 3 hundreds + 4 tens + 6 ones.

Sixth, we use zero, 0, as a placeholder. Actually, this symbol not only keeps other symbols in proper location but also indicates that there are no groups of a certain size present in the number; for example, 3040 means 3 thousands + 0 hundreds + 4 tens + 0 ones. The use of zero as a placeholder is incidental to its use as expressed in the preceding sentence; the latter expresses more nearly its real meaning, as will be seen later.

Accordingly, the Hindu-Arabic system is based on group size ten and uses
  (1) the principle of position,
  (2) the principle of addition,
  (3) nonrepetition of symbols (in the previous sense),
  (4) a placeholder.
A more extensive discussion of position is given in Chapter 4; at that stage we will have a better command of the basic ideas of number and of the fundamental operations.

Why is this system called Hindu-Arabic? The Hindus developed ten symbols similar to our 0, 1, 2, 3, 4, 5, 6, 7, 8, and 9; moreover, they used the symbol "0" in much the way we do. This symbol appeared before 600 A.D., but not much before that time. The Arabic contribution was to disseminate knowledge of this system. They used it and taught it to others as they migrated to various parts of Europe after 1000 A.D. Gradually it displaced the Roman numerals as a method of writing, and its facility in computation led to the displacement of "abacuslike" computational procedures.

A few comments on certain words and their usage would seem to be appropriate. Figure 1–5 gives the names of the "positions" in a numeral.

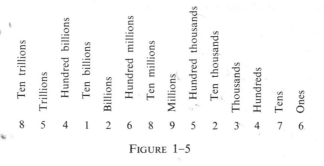

FIGURE 1–5

At first the place-value words go "up by powers of ten":

ten	is	ten times one,
hundred	is	ten times ten,
thousand	is	ten times hundred.

Then the words "go up by thousands" in that

million	is	thousand times thousand,
billion	is	thousand times million,
trillion	is	thousand times billion, etc.

In the above tabulation the names of certain place values have been raised to show this progression of ideas and the "filling in" of intermediate group-size names.

It is interesting to note that the above progression of ideas is not used in all countries. For instance, in England the "billion" is a million million and hence is equivalent to our trillion.

How do you read "432"? Quite possibly you say "four hundred and thirty-two." This is quite common even among mathematicians. The word "and" is generally interpreted in mathematics as "plus," so that it is quite correct to read 432 as 400 + 32. However, if you read 432000 as "four hundred and thirty-two thousand," this wording might be interpreted as 400 + 32000 which certainly is not intended. Since there is a possibility of misinterpretation, it is advisable to omit the word "and"; read 432 as "four hundred thirty-two."

PROBLEM SET 1-5

1. How many beads could appear on each wire of an abacus constructed for the Hindu-Arabic system? Explain why nine beads will suffice.

2. Use "line diagrams," as in Section 1-1, to describe how to perform 643 + 527, using an abacus. In this and the following problems use nine beads on each wire.

3. Use sequential line diagrams, as in Section 1-1, to perform the following operations.
   (a) 347 + 65   (b) 126 + 748   (c) 1735 + 697
   (d) 2573 + 89   (e) 471 + 8046   (f) 7804 + 3008

4. (a) Describe how to perform 2 × 32, using an abacus.
   (b) Describe how to perform 3 × 32, using an abacus.
   (c) Describe how to perform 10 × 32, using an abacus, (1) the long way, (2) the short way.
   (d) Explain why the "short" procedure in part (c) works.
   (e) Describe how to perform 12 × 32, using an abacus. Explain why the procedure works.
   (f) Repeat part (e) for 13 × 74, and 123 × 68.

5. Describe how to perform the following, using an abacus.
   (a) 15 − 4   (b) 15 − 7   (c) 25 − 13   (d) 25 − 18

6. Describe how to use an abacus to perform the following; explain the procedure.
   (a) 15 ÷ 5   (b) 24 ÷ 8   (c) 54 ÷ 6   (d) 120 ÷ 6

7. Try to devise a short procedure for Problem 6(d). Explain the procedure.

8. Use the procedure of Problem 7 to perform the following.
   (a) 264 ÷ 6   (b) 105 ÷ 7   (c) 88 ÷ 4   (d) 152 ÷ 8

9. Suppose you have two boxes, call them A and B, with marbles in each.
  (a) How could you determine whether or not A contains exactly as many marbles as B? Two ways.
  (b) One of the methods used in (a) was probably used by early man before he learned to count. Discuss this.
  (c) How could you explain to someone what "A has more than B" means without using a counting procedure.

1–6 BASE FIVE NUMERAL SYSTEM

Let us assume that the primitive "lord of the manor" in Section 1–1 had discovered the principles basic to the Hindu-Arabic system of numerals, namely, position, zero, and addition. What would his system have looked like? Would it have been as useful as the Hindu-Arabic system? What symbols would he have needed? He would have needed symbols to denote $|, | |, | | |, | | | |$, and also a "zero." Naturally, to denote these he could have concocted any symbols he desired; to simplify matters let us agree to use 1, 2, 3, 4, and 0. Table 1–1 lists what he would say and write in his counting

Table 1–1

Say	Write
One	1
Two	2
Three	3
Four	4
One five and zero	10 (read "one zero")
One five and one	11 (read "one one")
$\vdots$	$\vdots$
One five and four	14
Two fives and zero	20

procedure, using these symbols. Eventually he would reach 100 for "1 twenty-five and 0 fives and 0 ones." What is the next numeral? Compare the use of these symbols with the use of symbols in Section 1–1 and note the decrease in complexity.

This system of numerals will be called the *base five* numeral system. Since the system is based on "five-ness," five is called the *base* of the system. To denote the fact that 24 is in base five numerals rather than the Hindu-Arabic system (base ten), it will be written 24(five); this must be read as "two four, base five" so as not to confuse it with 24(ten).

Let us suppose that our early man has counted both his cattle and his horses; he has 23(five) cows and 11(five) horses, say. How could he determine the total number of animals he possesses? He could start from the beginning to obtain a complete count. However, he might soon get an idea to shorten the procedure, that of "regrouping":

(2 fives and 3 ones)   together with   (1 five and 1 one)

would be the same as

(2 fives and 1 five)   and   (3 ones and 1 one).

If he used the notion of placing each set of five animals in a corral, he would "move together" the 3 individual cows and the 1 individual horse and say that there were now 4 individual animals and 3 corrals of five each. Hence he would be developing the idea of addition,

23(five) + 11(five) = 34(five).

Eventually he would see the need for addition combinations from $0 + 0$ to $4 + 4$. These combinations could be gathered together in an *addition table*, such as Table 1–2. To find $2 + 4$ from Table 1–2, locate 2 in the left column

Table 1–2. Base five addition table.

+	0	1	2	3	4
0	0	1	2	3	4
1	1	2	3	4	10
2	2	3	4	10	11*
3	3	4	10	11	12
4	4	10	11	12	13

and 4 in the top row. Then read the number which appears at the intersection of the row corresponding to 2 and the column corresponding to 4; the result, 11, is starred in the table. That 3(five) + 3(five) = 11(five) would be arrived at by an actual regrouping into 1 corral of five and 1 one. This same regrouping procedure would yield

23(five) + 14(five) = (2 + 1)fives + (3 + 4)ones
= (2 + 1)fives + (1 five and 2 ones)
= (2 + 1 + 1)fives + 2 ones
= 42(five).

ILLUSTRATIVE EXAMPLE.   Perform the operation 234(five) + 144(five), showing all steps.

Solution.

```
    ③ ② ①
    2  3  4     ① 4 + 4 = 13,   carry 1 five,
(+) 1  4  4     ② 3 + 4 + 1 = 13,   carry 1 twenty-five,
    4  3  3     ③ 2 + 1 + 1 = 4.
```

Our primitive man would say automatically $4 + 4 = 13$, and if we worked with this numeral system long enough, we could do the same. Such is not our purpose, so, if you desire, you may use a hybrid type of thinking and say

$$4 + 4 = \text{eight}$$
$$= 1 \text{ five} + 3 \text{ ones}.$$

This will speed up your thinking and at the same time reinforce the notion of "five-ness."

How would you compute $4(\text{five}) - 1(\text{five})$? Couldn't this be transformed from

$$4 - 1 = \text{what} \quad \text{to} \quad 1 + \text{what} = 4?$$

The addition combinations would yield the result 3. To calculate $32 - 14$, the "borrow" procedure could be used:

② ①   ① Borrow a five; $4 + \text{what} = 12$; answer 3.
3 2   ② 2 fives remain; $1 + \text{what} = 2$; answer 1.
$(-)1$ 4
‾‾‾‾‾‾
1 3

Additions and subtractions in base five numerals are as easy as in base ten numerals. You probably doubt this but you should examine your reasons. Naturally, we are so accustomed to working in base ten that anything else seems awkward. However, if you had used the base five from your early days you would feel "at home" using it now, and computations in that system would be performed quickly and accurately.

Our primary goal is to study the base ten or decimal system, not to become facile in manipulating in base five. Why, then, do we bother with the base five system? Computations in the decimal system have become so mechanical for most of us that it is difficult to think about what we are doing. Working in a less familiar situation forces us to think about why things are being done as they are. Having thought through these concepts, we can then apply this knowledge to the familiar base ten system of numerals.

PROBLEM SET 1–6

1. Group the following for counting in base five and then write the numeral for the number.

|||||||||||||||||||||||||||. — 3 4

2. What do the following numerals mean?
   (a) 42(five)   (b) 234(five)   (c) 302(five)   (d) 2004(five)

$4(5^{'}5) + 2$ more

$2(25)$ $3(5) + (4$ $=69$

3. Write the next "succeeding" base five numeral for each of the following.

(a) 44   (b) 404   (c) 440   (d) 40040

4. Perform the indicated operations; use statements, as in the illustrations, to explain the steps.

(a) 24(five) + 32(five)   (b) 102(five) + 43(five)
(c) 234(five) + 112(five)   (d) 2434(five) + 1322(five)
(e) 3041(five) + 4234(five)   (f) 44444(five) + 334320(five)
(g) 42(five) − 21(five)   (h) 32(five) − 24(five)
(i) 430(five) − 143(five)   (j) 4020(five) − 3432(five)

1–7   BASE FIVE MULTIPLICATION

What is needed for multiplication? We need basic multiplication combinations, of course, like 3×4; actually we need combinations from 0×0 to 4×4. These combinations, which are given in Table 1–3, could, for

Table 1–3. Base five multiplication table.

×	0	1	2	3	4
0	0	0	0	0	0
1	0	1	2	3	4
2	0	2	4	11	13
3	0	3	11	14	22
4	0	4	13	22	31

example, be obtained by thinking of 3×4 as meaning $4 + 4 + 4$; that is, multiplication can be expressed in terms of addition. This would yield $3 \times 4 = 22$(five). Again, to avoid having to memorize a table we could interject a thought in base ten:

$$3 \times 4 = \text{twelve} = 2 \text{ fives} + 2 \text{ ones} = 22(\text{five}).$$

ILLUSTRATIVE EXAMPLE. Multiply 21(five) by 2(five).

Solution. This could be thought of as 2(2 fives + 1 one) so that each of 2 fives and 1 one should be multiplied by 2. The result is 4 fives + 2 ones, or 42(five). Let us use the same idea in multiplying 34 by 2, the procedure being set up in a somewhat expansive form:

② ①

  3 4   ① $2 \times 4 = 13$(five); the 1 is written in the "fives column."

 × 2   ② $2 \times 3 = 11$(five); 11 is the number of fives, so that

  1 3   (1 five + 1 one) fives =

1 1   1 twenty-five + 1 five.

1 2 3

The thinking behind these steps will be discussed in detail later. Until then we will proceed somewhat mechanically; problems like 24(five) × 32(five) will be worked but not discussed at this stage. Division problems will not be considered until later.

PROBLEM SET 1–7

1. Perform the indicated operations.
   (a) 24(five) × 3(five)   (b) 103(five) × 4(five)   (c) 344(five) × 2(five)

2. Perform the operations indicated. Assume that when the multiplier has two or more digits the formal procedure is the same as in base ten.
   (a) 42(five) × 43(five)   (b) 1404(five) × 203(five)
   (c) 3421(five) × 430(five)   (d) 2044(five) × 412(five)
   (e) 1420(five) × 40(five)   (f) 30201(five) × 132(five)
   (g) 43012(five) × 303(five)   (h) 4444(five) × 34(five)

1–8   OTHER BASES

We have seen that both base five and base ten can be used for representing numbers, and that it is as easy to compute using one system as the other. What about other bases? Suppose our primitive man had three fingers missing from one hand. What group size, other than five, would be natural for him to use? It is hoped that you said "seven."

DISCUSSION EXERCISES

1. What symbols would be needed for base seven?
2. What would 12(seven) mean?
3. Write the base seven numeral used in counting | | | | | | | | | | | | | | | | | | | | | | | .
4. Name the first four group sizes used in this numeral system.
5. What would 3625(seven) mean?
6. Show that 6 + 5 = 14(seven) and 3 + 6 = 12(seven).
7. Construct an addition table for base seven.
8. Show that 6 × 5 = 42(seven) and 4 × 5 = 26(seven).
9. Construct a table for base seven multiplication.

If you thought through the above exercises carefully you should realize that a base seven numeral system is not only feasible but, again, quite similar to the decimal system.

What base does the word "dozen" and the relationship "12 inches is a foot" suggest to you? For base twelve, symbols are needed for zero, one, two, . . . , ten, and eleven. As before, we could use 0, 1, 2, . . . , 8, 9 for zero, one, two, . . . , eight, and nine. But what about "ten"? Would 10 serve? No, because "10" means 1 twelve + 0 ones in base twelve. New symbols are needed for ten and eleven. Anything would do; suppose we use "T" for "ten" and "E" for "eleven." With this agreement,

$$3T5(\text{twelve}) \quad \text{would mean} \quad 3 \text{ twelve}^2 + \text{T twelves} + 5 \text{ ones.}$$

DISCUSSION EXERCISES

1. Write the base twelve numeral for | | | | | | | | | | | | | | | | | | | | | | | | | | | | | | | | .

2. Show that T + T = 18(twelve), E + E = 1T(twelve). Find T + E.

3. Construct the complete addition table for the base twelve system. Devise a "shortcut" procedure for the construction.

4. Construct the complete multiplication table for base twelve [typical entries, $7 \times 9 = 53(\text{twelve})$, $E \times E = T1(\text{twelve})$]. Devise a "shortcut" procedure for the construction.

There are indications that other bases have been used at one time or another. We have seen the use of base sixty in the Babylonian system; this base is still used to some extent in angle and time measurement:

$$60 \text{ seconds} = 1 \text{ minute} \quad \text{and} \quad 60 \text{ minutes} = 1 \text{ degree,}$$
$$60 \text{ seconds} = 1 \text{ minute} \quad \text{and} \quad 60 \text{ minutes} = 1 \text{ hour.}$$

The French word "quatre-vingt" for "four twenties" is an indication of the use of twenty as a base.

The relationships between pint, quart, half-gallon, and gallon,

$$2 \text{ pt} = 1 \text{ qt}, \quad 2 \text{ qt} = 1 \text{ half-gal}, \quad 2 \text{ half-gal} = 1 \text{ gal,}$$

form an application of a scale with base two. For reasons to be mentioned later, this scale is sufficiently important to warrant discussion.

DISCUSSION EXERCISES

1. What symbols would be needed for base two?

2. What would 101(two) mean?

3. Write the numeral in base two notation to be used to give a count of | | | | | | | | | | | | | | | | | | | | | .

4. Construct addition and multiplication tables for base two numerals.

5. (a) Write the decimal system numeral for the set of Problem 3.
   (b) How many digits are there in the numeral just written?
   (c) How many digits are there in the numeral written in Problem 3?
   (d) Compare the answers to parts (b) and (c). Does this suggest an advantage which the decimal system has over base two?
   (e) In line with the answer to part (d) can you suggest what happens as the base size increases?

6. (a) How many addition combinations have to be learned for base two?
   (b) How many addition combinations would have to be learned for base ten?
   (c) Would it be easier to learn to add in base two or base ten? Why?

PROBLEM SET 1-8

1. Perform the operations indicated.
   (a) 625(seven) + 304(seven)   (b) 5026(seven) + 6365(seven)
   (c) 1240(seven) + 5456(seven)   (d) 3064(seven) + 666(seven)
   (e) 62(seven) × 4(seven)   (f) 26(seven) × 56(seven)
   (g) 240(seven) × 235(seven)   (h) 4623(seven) × 604(seven)
   (i) 654(seven) − 432(seven)   (j) 654(seven) − 465(seven)
   (k) 305(seven) − 154(seven)   (l) 624(seven) − 356(seven)

2. Perform the operations indicated.
   (a) T38(twelve) + 3E7(twelve)   (b) 347E(twelve) + 90T6(twelve)
   (c) 3009(twelve) + T3T7(twelve)   (d) 8436(twelve) + ETTE(twelve)
   (e) 4T(twelve) × 8(twelve)   (f) 84(twelve) × T7(twelve)
   (g) 3E9(twelve) × 8E(twelve)   (h) 90T8(twelve) × 309(twelve)
   (i) 43T(twelve) − 156(twelve)   (j) 9E8(twelve) − 46T(twelve)
   (k) T10(twelve) − 3E7(twelve)

3. Perform the operations indicated.
   (a) 1011(two) + 1101(two)   (b) 1010(two) + 11101(two)
   (c) 101(two) × 110(two)   (d) 1101(two) × 1011(two)
   (e) 1101(two) − 110(two)   (f) 1001(two) − 101(two)

4. (a) State one disadvantage which the base twelve numerals would have over base ten numerals.
   (b) Guess at a possible advantage that the base twelve system would have over the base ten system.

1-9 CHANGE OF BASE

In Problem 4(b) above you were asked to "guess"; we should be able to do better than that. Suppose we have a set of objects which have been counted and, in base five, the numeral is 342(five). What would be the corresponding numeral in base ten? Now,

$$342(\text{five}) = 3 \text{ twenty-fives} + 4 \text{ fives} + 2 \text{ ones}$$
$$= 3(25) + 4(5) + 2 \qquad (\text{in base ten})$$
$$= 75 + 20 + 2 \qquad (\text{in base ten})$$
$$= 97(\text{ten}).$$

In similar fashion the numeral for a number in any base can be converted to the corresponding numeral in base ten.

Now consider the converse problem. Suppose that we have a number whose numeral in base ten is 312(ten) and we wish to obtain the corresponding numeral in base five. Think basically; we have "three hundred twelve" objects and desire to use group sizes of five, twenty-five, one hundred twenty-five, six hundred twenty-five, etc. Would there be any groups of six hundred twenty-five? No, that group size is too large; one hundred twenty-five is the largest group size we need to use. How many one hundred twenty-fives would there be? Couldn't this be determined by dividing 312 by 125, in base ten? The result is 2, so that $312 = 2 \cdot 125 + 62$. In similar fashion the number of twenty-fives in 62(ten) can be determined. Finally,

$$312 = 2 \cdot 125 + 2 \cdot 25 + 2 \cdot 5 + 2 = 2222(\text{five}).$$

ILLUSTRATIVE EXAMPLE. Convert 1471(ten) to a numeral in base twelve and also to a numeral in base two.

Solution.

Base twelve. Group sizes needed are one, twelve, and one hundred forty-four;

$$1471(\text{ten}) = \text{ten}(\text{one hundred forty-fours}) + 31$$
$$= \text{T}(\text{one hundred forty-fours}) + 2(\text{twelves}) + 7(\text{ones})$$
$$= \text{T27(twelve).}$$

Base two. Group sizes needed are the following (words are too clumsy here; use decimal scale notation):

$$1, \quad 2, \quad 4, \quad 8, \quad 16, \quad 32, \quad 64, \quad 128, \quad 256, \quad 512, \quad 1024.$$

Hence,

$$1471(\text{ten}) = 1 \cdot 1024 + 447$$
$$= 1 \cdot 1024 + 0 \cdot 512 + 1 \cdot 256 + 191$$
$$= 1 \cdot 1024 + 0 \cdot 512 + 1 \cdot 256 + 1 \cdot 128 + 63$$
$$= 1 \cdot 1024 + 0 \cdot 512 + 1 \cdot 256 + 1 \cdot 128 + 0 \cdot 64$$
$$+ 1 \cdot 32 + 1 \cdot 16 + 1 \cdot 8 + 1 \cdot 4 + 1 \cdot 2 + 1$$
$$= 10110111111(\text{two).}$$

The preceding example will enable us to take some of the guesswork out of Problem 4(b) of the last problem set. Here, for the same number, the numeral requires:

Base two	Base ten	Base twelve
eleven digits	four digits	three digits

This illustrates the following statement.

As the base size increases, the number of digits required for a specific number decreases.

PROBLEM SET 1–9

1. Change the following to numerals in the decimal system.
   (a) 101101(two)   (b) 36142(seven)   (c) 3T4E(twelve)
   (d) 4732(eight)   (e) 2101(three)   (f) 3213(four)
   (g) 9E34(twelve)   (h) 6705(eight)

2. Change the following decimal numerals to numerals in the base indicated.
   (a) 943 to base twelve   (b) 74 to base two
   (c) 630 to base seven   (d) 4301 to base five
   (e) 463 to base two   (f) 463 to base three
   (g) 9784 to base twelve   (h) 9784 to base nine

3. (a) If 0, 1, 2, 3, 4, and 5 are symbols used in a numeral system, what can be said about the possible base, or bases? 6 or Greater Base
   (b) If 0, 1, 2, 3, 4, and 5 are *all* the symbols used in a numeral system, is the base unique? If so, name it. 6

4. A numeral could be converted from base seven to base twelve, say, by first converting from base seven to base ten and then from base ten to base twelve. Convert the following as indicated.
   (a) 4130(five) to base twelve   (b) T13(twelve) to base seven
   (c) 11011(three) to base five   (d) 613(seven) to base two

5. Which would require a smaller number of digits, a numeral in
   (a) base twenty or base ten?
   (b) base five or base seven?
   (c) base twelve or base seven?

1–10   APPLICATIONS

Today the use of high-speed computers is commonplace. Basically, these machines add, but they do it so rapidly that a lengthy computation can be carried out in a very short time. In what numeral system do these machines

Read *binary* *no. System*

do their "thinking"? Usually it is not base ten as might be expected, but rather base two. These machines have in their interiors a host of electrical components which work like a radio tube. Such a component has only two possible states, either it is conducting current or it is not. Suppose we assume that conducting current corresponds to 1 and not conducting current corresponds to 0. If there are six of these devices and their states are indicated by ● and 0 for conducting and not conducting, respectively, then we can represent the numeral 101101(two) by a diagram such as

● 0 ● ● 0 ●

Accordingly, the base two numeral system is of great importance.

Here is a "mystery" game which has some actual mathematics behind it. Write each decimal number from 1 to 31, inclusive, in the base two system. The decimal number 27, for instance, would have five digits in base two:

$$4\ 3\ 2\ 1\ 0$$
$$27(\text{ten}) = 1\ 1\ 0\ 1\ 1(\text{two}).$$

The positions of these digits, from left to right, could be named 4, 3, 2, 1, and 0, as shown in the diagram. Now take five blank cards, and write at the top of each card one of the "names" 0, 1, 2, 3, and 4. On card 4 write each number from 1 to 31 whose base two numeral has 1 in position 4. On card 3 place each such number whose numeral has 1 in position 3; then continue in similar fashion with the other cards. They should look like those shown in Fig. 1–6. Place the cards facing a person who does not know how they

4		3		2		1		0	
16	24	8	24	4	20	2	18	1	17
17	25	9	25	5	21	3	19	3	19
18	26	10	26	6	22	6	22	5	21
19	27	11	27	7	23	7	23	7	23
20	28	12	28	12	28	10	26	9	25
21	29	13	29	13	29	11	27	11	27
22	30	14	30	14	30	14	30	13	29
23	31	15	31	15	31	15	31	15	31

FIGURE 1–6

were constructed; you stand behind them. Ask your companion to choose any number from 1 to 31, inclusive, and to tell you on which cards the number appears. Suppose he says it is on card 3; you know that the number chosen has a 1 in position 3 of its base two numeral. If he says the number appears on cards 3, 2, 1, and 0 only, the base two numeral must be 01111; hence the number is $1 \cdot 8 + 1 \cdot 4 + 1 \cdot 2 + 1 = 15$. Try it! A set of six such cards would suffice for what numbers? Why were the digit positions "named" 0, 1, 2, 3, and 4, instead of 1, 2, 3, 4, and 5?

SUGGESTED READING

CAJORI, FLORIAN, *A History of Mathematical Notations.* Chicago, Illinois: The Open Court Publishing Co., 1928–9.

DUBISCH, R., *The Nature of Number: An Approach to Basic Ideas of Modern Mathematics.* New York: Ronald Press Co., 1952.

EVES, H., *An Introduction to the History of Mathematics.* New York: Rinehart, 1953.

LARSEN, HAROLD D., *Arithmetic for Colleges.* New York: Macmillan Co., 1950. Chapter 1.

MUELLER, F., *Arithmetic: Its Structure and Concepts.* New York: Prentice Hall, 1956. Chapter 1.

SMITH, D. E., and J. GINSBURG, *Numbers and Numerals.* Washington, D.C., NCTM.

SWAIN, R., *Understanding Arithmetic.* New York: Rinehart, 1957. Chapter 1.

CHAPTER **2**

Sets and Numbers

In this chapter the concept of set is introduced to enable us to clarify our idea of number. As a result of this clarification, operations which have been performed without reason, or without realization, will become clearer. This will prove to be a foundation for removing misunderstanding and lack of understanding. As we proceed, it must be remembered that in order to understand it is necessary to discuss in considerable detail, to be precise, to take a "long way around." Only after we follow through a detailed discussion will it be feasible or advantageous to shorten the procedure; only after we learn ideas thoroughly should "cut-and-dried" procedures or calculations be performed.

2–1 SETS

Probably an individual's earliest experience with numbers came about through associating a word, such as "three," with a certain collection, or set, of objects. This may have been a set of marbles or of persons or of houses, etc., usually specific objects in an early experience. A *set* is merely a collection of things, these "things" being called the *elements* of the set. The elements *belong to* the set, and the set *consists of* its elements. In actuality we are assuming that we "know" what is meant by a "set," or "collection," and the phrase "belong to."

These ideas are more common than may appear at first mention. We speak of a herd of cows, by which is meant the collection as a whole, not the individual cows. Likewise, we refer to a flock of birds, a class of boys, a family of persons. The points on a line form a set; sometimes we wish to refer to individual points, or members of the set; at other times we wish to refer to the collection as a whole. It is important that we distinguish between the set and its members, between the herd and individual cows, between the class and individual members of that class.

Suppose a set consists of the boys Harry, George, and Mike. This set could be denoted by {Harry, George, Mike} ; the members of the set (or more precisely, symbols to represent these members) are enclosed within braces. Capital letters will also be used to denote sets; the above set might be de-

23

noted by A. Would {George, Mike, Harry} be the same set A? Of course it would; the order in which the elements are named is immaterial. We will consider only sets of distinct elements, that is, no two elements of a given set will be the same.

Sets having the same elements are said to be *equal* and the symbol "$=$" is used to denote this. Hence,

$$A = \{\text{George, Mike, Harry}\} = \{\text{Harry, George, Mike}\}.$$

Quite often the members of a set will possess a common property, in which case this property can be used in denoting the set. For instance, if Harry, George, and Mike are the only persons sitting in the front row of a certain class, then

$$A = \{\text{all persons sitting in the front row of this class}\}.$$

This device can save time and space; e.g., the notation {all letters of our alphabet} is much shorter than {a, b, c, d, e, f, g, h, i, j, k, l, m, n, o, p, q, r, s, t, u, v, w, x, y, z} and is equally descriptive. Sometimes this is written {a, b, c, ..., z}, where the dots mean that we continue writing "in this fashion" from c to z; since "in this fashion" can be ambiguous, this last notation is not the best method to use.

2–2 MATCHING

At first glance the sets

$$A = \{\text{Harry, George, Mike}\},$$
$$B = \{x, y, z\},$$
$$C = \{\text{horse, book, dog}\}$$

do not seem to have anything in common. Certainly no two of these sets are equal. Do they have a common property? To each element of A a string could be attached, the other end of each string being attached to one, and only one, element of B (in diagrams these strings will be represented by lines); for instance,

Here, to each element of B there is attached a string which comes from one, and only one, element of A, and conversely. In these circumstances set A is said to *match* set B. In this matching, elements Harry and x are said to

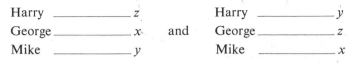

correspond; likewise, George and *y* would be corresponding elements. There are other ways of matching *A* to *B*, for example,

Harry	—————— *z*		Harry	—————— *y*
George	—————— *x*	and	George	—————— *z*
Mike	—————— *y*		Mike	—————— *x*

Find other ways of matching *A* to *B*. Likewise *A* and *C* match, and so do *B* and *C*. The sets *A*, *B*, and *C* are matching sets; this is a property common to *A*, *B*, and *C*.

Could sets *B* and *D* = $\{p, q, r, s\}$ be matched? Why? You probably found that no matter how you tied strings in the "approved fashion" there was always one element of *D* left over, or not attached. Hence *B* and *D* do not match. The following is not an approved fashion of tying strings (why?):

So sets *A*, *B*, and *C* do have a common property, the property of matching each other, and this property is not shared by set *D*.

Problem. Construct two sets, one of which matches *A* and the other matches *D* (*A* and *D* were defined previously); show the matchings. Determine whether the set *E* = $\{1, m, \text{rat}, \text{girl}, \text{hat}\}$ matches *D*, and show why it does or does not.

2–3 NUMBER

Consider those sets which match the set consisting of a triangle, the set *F* = $\{\triangle\}$. Name three sets which match *F*. The fact that they match *F* will be expressed by saying that they have the *number* "one" associated with them; the notation for one will be the usual "1," or $n(F)$ when a general form of notation is desirable.

The elements of the sets *G*, *H*, and *I*, which follow, are distinct triangles. Accordingly, those sets which match *G* = $\{\triangle, \triangle\}$ will be said to have the number two associated with them. Hence two = $n(G)$ or 2, to use the usual symbol; also, $n(X) = 2$ for any set *X* which matches *G*. We could continue in this fashion with *H* = $\{\blacktriangle, \blacktriangle, \blacktriangle\}$ and three = $n(H) = 3$; then *I* = $\{\triangle, \triangle, \triangle, \triangle\}$ and four = $n(I) = 4$, etc. The word "four" and the symbol "4" have been coined for use with any set which matches set *I*. Continuing in this fashion, other words and symbols are coined to denote further numbers. The symbols for the elements of sets G, H, and I are supposed to represent different triangles; hence these are sets of distinct elements.

In terms of the notation introduced in Section 2–2,

$$n(A) = n(B) = n(C) = 3, \qquad n(D) = 4, \qquad n(E) = 5.$$

Note that no attempt has been made to say what a particular number is, but a serious attempt has been made to state precisely a property characteristic of the number. It is impossible to define everything, as careful thought should convince you; this idea will be expanded in Chapter 15. However, this discussion will enable us to develop properties of, and operations with numbers which should result in a clearer "picture" of arithmetic. The term "one-to-one correspondence" is frequently used, instead of the word "matching."

Symbols $a_1, a_2, a_3, \ldots$ (read a_1 as "a sub one"; "sub" is an abbreviation for "subscript") could be used to represent different things just as readily as a, b, c, ... Moreover, there are advantages to the subscript notation. If we denote $\{a_1\}$ by S_1, $\{a_1, a_2\}$ by S_2, $\{a_1, a_2, a_3\}$ by S_3, $\{a_1, a_2, a_3, a_4\}$ by S_4, etc., then $n(S_1) = 1, n(S_2) = 2, n(S_3) = 3, \ldots, n(S_k) = k$ (k may be any number such as 1, 2, 3, etc.). These S sets (S for standard) are introduced for purposes of comparison; if $n(H) = 1$, then H may be compared with S_1 by matching; if we need a set whose number is 4, then S_4 may be used. These standard sets will prove to be handy for reference.

Two points for thought!

(1) If S represents a set, then $n(S)$ is a number. A number is not the same as a set; hence $n(S) \neq S$. Read and write notation carefully.

(2) The use of "=" in connection with sets may seem strange at first. When $S_2 = \{a_1, a_2\}$ is written, we mean that S_2 and $\{a_1, a_2\}$ are two symbols for the same thing. As you progress in mathematics you will find that this equality symbol may mean different things in different situations.

The number of a given set can be found by matching the given set with an S set. For example, if $X = \{1, 5, 7, 13, 22, 156\}$, then X can be matched with S_6 (do it!); hence $n(X) = n(S_6)$. Since $n(S_6) = 6$, then $n(X) = 6$. The numbers which have been introduced are called *natural numbers*. In one sense a natural number characterizes the "size" of a set.

PROBLEM SET 2–3

1. Write a notation for each of the following sets.
   (a) The numbers between 2 and 9 (does not include either 2 or 9).
   (b) The members of your *immediate* family.

(c) The letters of our alphabet between c and k.

(d) The persons in one of your classes. (Don't despair; do it an easy way!)

2. A room is "full" of men and women. State two ways you could determine whether or not there are more men than women. Which is easier?

3. Match each set of parts (a), (b), and (c) of Problem 1 with an S set. Write the number of each of these sets in three ways.

4. For $A = \{r, s, t\}$ and $B = \{x, y, z\}$, (a) write all the different matchings of A with B. (b) How many matchings are possible?

5. Find the number associated with each of the following sets (use S sets and show details).

(a) $A = \{Mary, Joan, Henry, Ted, Oren\}$

(b) $B = \{p, q, r, s, t, u, v\}$

(c) $C = \{13, 3, 1, 7, 12, 57, 63, 2\}$

(d) $D = \{$the numbers between 11 and 19$\}$

(e) $E = \{III, V, X, IV, XI, VII\}$

6. (a) In Problem 5, does set B equal set D?

(b) What relationship exists between these sets? *have same no, property*

(c) Express this relationship in terms of numbers. $N(B) = N(D) = N(s) = 7$

7. (a) What is meant by the symbol 6? (b) What is meant by the symbol 10?

8. Using the notation of Problem 5, (a) does $A = 5$ have meaning? Why?

(b) Write a meaningful relationship between A and 5; between B and 7; between E and 6.

9. If X denotes a set, what would $n(X) = 4$ mean? What would $n(Y) = 7$ mean?

10. Use sets A and B of Problem 4 in answering the following questions. Write the elements of set A. When we attempt to match set B with set A:

(a) How many choices are there for the element of B which is to be attached to r by a "string"?

(b) Having chosen the element to be attached to r, write each way an element of B could be paired with s. How many pairings are possible?

(c) In part (b) would the answer be the same for each choice of element paired with r?

(d) In how many different ways could elements be chosen from B to be paired with *both* r and s?

(e) For each way in which elements of B could be chosen to be paired with both r and s how many choices are there for the element to be paired with t?

(f) What is the number of different matchings of B with A?

11. Use the scheme devised in Problem 10 to find the number of matchings of the following sets.

(a) $X = \{a, b, c, d\}$ with $Y = \{x, y, z, w\}$ → $4 \times 3 \times 2 \times 1$

(b) $S_5 = \{a_1, a_2, a_3, a_4, a_5\}$ with $T = \{x_1, x_2, x_3, x_4, x_5\}$

in 0 →

2–4 SUBSETS AND INEQUALITY

If each element of set B is also an element of set A, then B is said to be a *subset* of A. Hence $\{2, 5, 7\}$ is a subset of $\{2, 4, 5, 7\}$ and $\{$Mary, Joan$\}$ is a subset of $\{$Clarice, Mary, Ann, Joan$\}$. According to this definition, would $\{2, 5, 7\}$ be a subset of $\{2, 5, 7\}$? Of course, since each set is a subset of itself. The symbol $\subseteq$ will be used to express the subset relationship;

$$B \subseteq A \qquad \text{means} \qquad B \text{ is a subset of } A,$$

including the possibility that $B = A$.

If B is a subset of A but does not include all elements of A, then B is called a *proper subset* of A; this relationship is denoted by $B \subset A$. Hence $\{2, 5, 7\}$ is a proper subset of $\{2, 5, 6, 7\}$. Is set A a proper subset of itself? Pictorially the proper subset relationship is shown by

where A is the set of all points inside the outer curve and B is the set of all points inside the inner curve.

If X matches a proper subset of Y, then $n(X)$ is said to be *less than* $n(Y)$, or, in symbols, $n(X) < n(Y)$. Thus

$$n(X) < n(Y) \qquad \text{means} \qquad X \text{ matches a proper subset of } Y.$$

Suppose that $A = \{a, b, c, d\}$ and $B = \{u, v, w, r, s\}$. Now, A matches $C = \{u, v, w, r\}$, so that $n(A) = n(C)$. Also, $C \subset B$, so that $n(C) < n(B)$; consequently, $n(A) < n(B)$. Note that C was selected as a subset (any subset) of B which matches A.

Problem. Show that $n\{3, 7, 11, 13, 2\} < n\{1, 4, 6, 3, 14, 17, 20\}$.

Let us show that $1 < 2$. Now $1 = n(S_1)$ and $2 = n(S_2)$. Since S_1 is a proper subset of S_2, then S_1 matches a proper subset of S_2. Hence $n(S_1) < n(S_2)$, from which it follows that $1 < 2$. The same procedure could be used to show that $2 < 3$; show this. In similar fashion, show that $3 < 4$. Extending these results, we see that

$$1 < 2 < 3 < 4 < 5 < 6 < \cdots .$$

Are the numbers 3 and 5 equal, or is one of them less than the other? Since $3 = n(S_3)$ and $5 = n(S_5)$, the set S_3 should be compared with S_5; comparison shows that $n(S_3) \neq n(S_5)$. Actually, S_3 matches a proper subset of S_5, so that $n(S_3) < n(S_5)$. Hence $3 < 5$. To obtain information concerning 3 and 5, sets S_3 and S_5 were used. Why?

Note that when the idea of "less than" is defined precisely it is not difficult to show that one specific natural number is less than another such number. Note also that the definition used is merely a precise form of our intuitive notion of "less than."

The symbol $7 > 5$ will be defined to mean the same as $5 < 7$.

ILLUSTRATIVE EXAMPLE. Show that $6 > 2$.

Solution. If it is shown that $2 < 6$, the desired result will follow. Now,

$$2 = n(S_2) \quad \text{and} \quad 6 = n(S_6);$$

also,

$$S_2 \subset S_6.$$

Hence S_2 matches a proper subset of S_6, so that

$$n(S_2) < n(S_6);$$

accordingly,

$$2 < 6.$$

2–5 NULL SET AND ZERO

Consider the following descriptive phrases:
(a) all males in classroom 100,
(b) all people in classroom 100 between the ages of 6 and 60,
(c) all people in classroom 100 whose ages are less than 21,
(d) all people in classroom 100 whose ages are more than 200.

Each of the phrases (a), (b), and (c) would describe a certain set, the set of all individuals who are described by the phrase. Phrase (d) is of the same nature as the others in that it is descriptive; the only difference is that there aren't any individuals who satisfy the description (at least so far as our experience is concerned). If phrases (a), (b), and (c) can be used to describe sets, would it not seem just as reasonable to use (d) to describe a set? If phrase (d) is used to describe a set, then the set will not have any members. A set which does not have any members is called the *null set*, or the *empty set;* the set described by (d) is the null set. This may seem strange at first, but there are several reasons which make it advisable to introduce the concept of null set. If we did not permit the null set, then it would be necessary to know whether or not there were any elements which satisfy a certain descriptive phrase before the phrase could be used to describe a set. This would cause unnecessary confusion. An example of this will appear in the next section. Other reasons for introducing the null set follow.

We denote the null set by Φ (the Greek letter phi, pronounced "fee" or "fie," depending on the particular "school" of Greek language in which one is trained). Consider the set $A = \{x, y, z\}$. Since Φ does not have any ele-

membership of any set is N, there will be 2^N subsets! N is no of elements in set.

ments, then the statement "each element of Φ is contained in A" is true. Hence Φ is considered a subset of A; actually, Φ is a subset of each and every ordinary set. Strange? But read on to see how useful this concept is! Now all the subsets of A can be listed:

$$\Phi, \quad \{x\}, \quad \{y\}, \quad \{z\}, \quad \{x, y\}, \quad \{x, z\}, \quad \{y, z\}, \quad \{x, y, z\}.$$

See Problem 5 of the next problem set for a consequence of this idea.

Suppose that a number is defined for the null set; call it zero and use 0 as its symbol; then

$$n(\Phi) = 0.$$

Is $0 = 1$? If so, then $n(\Phi) = n(S_1)$, and consequently Φ would match S_1. This last result is impossible, so $0 \neq 1$. Is $0 < 1$ or $1 < 0$? Now, Φ matches a proper subset of S_1 so that

$$n(\Phi) < n(S_1), \quad \text{or} \quad 0 < 1.$$

The null set has served a purpose; it has led to the introduction of zero and an important relationship between 0 and 1.

The set $\{0\}$ is not the empty set, since it does contain an element, the element 0.

PROBLEM SET 2–5

1. Write all the subsets of $\{$red, white$\}$.

2. Given $A = \{x, y, z, w\}$, write the following:
   (a) a subset, B, such that $n(B) = 3$.
   (b) a proper subset which contains y.
   (c) all the subsets not containing either x or z.

3. Prove the following:
   (a) $n\{u, v\} < n\{$red, white, green, yellow$\}$ (b) $4 < 6$
   (c) $5 < 9$ (d) $8 > 4$

4. (a) Write sixteen subsets of S_4. (b) Are there other subsets of S_4?

5. When forming a subset of $\{x, y\}$ the element x is either "put in" the subset or "left out" of the subset. The same is true of element y.
   (a) In how many ways can x be "handled" when forming a subset?
   (b) Suppose x is "handled" in a certain fashion, say it is "put in"; in how many ways could y be "handled"?
   (c) In how many ways could both x and y be "handled"? How many subsets are there?
   (d) Does one of the ways counted in part (c) yield the null set? If so, which one?

(e) Could this simple counting procedure have been used if the null set had not been permitted?

6. (a) Find the number of subsets of S_4.
   (b) Find the number of subsets of S_5.
   (c) To find the number of subsets of a given set, which is easier, the method of Problem 4 or the method of Problem 5?

7. Show that $0 < 3$.

8. Show that $0 < n$, where n represents any counting number.

2-6 ORDINAL AND CARDINAL CONCEPTS

It has been shown from the definitions of "number" and "less than" that the natural numbers can be placed in a definite order:

$$1 < 2 < 3 < 4 < 5 < \cdots$$

or, omitting the "less than" signs,

$$1, \quad 2, \quad 3, \quad 4, \quad 5, \ldots.$$

These numbers continue indefinitely in a precise pattern. They continue indefinitely because, once the numbers $1, 2, 3, \ldots, n$ are found, it is always possible to find another number, $n + 1$.

The word "count" is used in two ways: first, to name these numbers in the order stated above; second, to count the elements of a particular set. In the latter case each element of the set is paired with a finger (if the set has few members) and a number is named at each pairing, i.e., one, two, three, etc., until all elements of the set have been paired. This can be generalized by not using fingers but, rather, pairing each element with a_1, then a_2, then a_3, etc., until eventually the given set is matched with an S set. If the set matches S_6, it is said that there are 6 elements in the set; the set has been counted and the result of the count is 6. Thus, the numbers 1, 2, 3, etc., are used for counting. It is for this reason that these numbers are called *counting numbers*, as well as natural numbers.

Zero is not usually used for counting. However, it is used in conjunction with counting numbers. Hence it will be convenient to refer to the set

$$0, \quad 1, \quad 2, \quad 3, \quad 4, \ldots,$$

as the set of *whole numbers*.

The set $\{1, 2, 3\}$ matches the set $\{a_1, a_2, a_3\}$, so that $n\{1, 2, 3\} = n\{a_1, a_2, a_3\} = n(S_3) = 3$. Hence the set $\{1, 2, 3\}$ could be used in place of $\{a_1, a_2, a_3\}$. A similar statement could be made for every S set. Henceforth, in any matching procedure, we may use the simpler notation just described. For example, when reference is made to S_3, either $\{1, 2, 3\}$ or $\{a_1, a_2, a_3\}$ will be meant, whichever we choose to use.

The statement "a certain book contains 124 pages" means that the set of pages has been matched with S_{124}. In a sense, this gives an indication of the size of the book. When the number 124 is used in this way, it is being used in a *cardinal* sense. However, when "page 124" is mentioned, there is no thought of size; rather we are thinking of this page as being a certain one in a particular order: page 1, page 2, page 3, etc. Here the number 124 is being used in an *ordinal* sense. Hence the natural numbers are used to convey two different meanings, a "cardinal" meaning and an "ordinal" meaning.

Quite often it is difficult to tell whether natural numbers are being used in a cardinal or an ordinal sense. For example, suppose we obtain a count of a particular set A by intoning "one," "two," "three," "four." During the "intoning" stage each number is being used in an ordinal sense, denoting the first element, second element, etc. At the last step, the number 4 is used in an ordinal sense; yet when we then say "the set has four elements," "four" is being used in a cardinal sense, denoting "size." Certainly the suffixes "st," "nd," and "th" found in first, second, and fifth denote ordinal meaning.

PROBLEM SET 2–6

1. State whether each number appearing below is used in a cardinal sense or an ordinal sense.
   (a) "Thirty days hath September."
   (b) University classes begin on September 30.
   (c) Of the four boys, John is number four when ranked according to height.
   (d) The cost is fifty cents.
   (e) There are 240 payments in my mortgage plan, and I have just made payment number 58.
   (f) His address is 724 W. 56th St.
   (g) On his 21st birthday he will be twenty-one years old.
   (h) He has a five-dollar bill.
   (i) This is a 12-inch rule.
   (j) I am taking English 102.
   (k) The fourth class on his schedule meets in room 322.
   (l) There are five classes on my schedule.

2–7 CONCLUSION

The set concept has been used here to obtain quite precise notions of number. In actuality this concept can be and has been used very broadly. We can think of a set of experiments, a set of chemical elements having a certain property, a set of plants having a certain characteristic, e.g., a family, and a subset of this family called a "genus," etc.

Every academic discipline passes through several stages of development. An early stage is always the descriptive stage, where ideas are talked about, discussed, worked over; usually there is no great precision at this stage. As ideas become clarified there is a tendency to separate things into sets; these things may be plants, people, mental characteristics, diseases, thoughts, words, etc. Through such classification, greater insight is obtained as to interrelationships which may exist among members or collections of members.

SUGGESTED READING

ALLENDOERFER, C. B., and C. O. OAKLEY, *Principles of Mathematics*. New York: McGraw-Hill, 1955. Chapter 5.

JOHNSON, D., and W. GLENN. *Sets, Sentences, and Operations*. St. Louis: Webster, 1960.

JOHNSON, R., L. LENDSEY, and W. SLESNICK, *Modern Algebra, First Course*. Reading, Massachusetts: Addison-Wesley, 1961. Chapter 6.

KEMENY, JOHN, F. L. SNELL, and G. THOMPSON. *Introduction to Finite Mathematics*. Englewood Cliffs, New Jersey: Prentice Hall, 1957. Chapter 2.

MATHEMATICAL ASSOCIATION OF AMERICA. CUP: *Elementary Mathematics of Sets with Applications*. Tulane University, New Orleans. Chapter 1.

SWAIN, R., *Understanding Arithmetic*. New York: Rinehart, 1957. Chapter 2.

Can you tell how m - subsets if you are given elements Sets in a set? Subsets empty sets

CHAPTER 3

Operations and Their Properties

3–1 UNION OF SETS

If you were asked to explain how to add 2 and 3, you would probably take a set of 2 objects, say marbles, and another set of 3 objects and then "put together" the two sets; that is, you would form a single set from the two selected sets. This is a good intuitive approach. Intuition is usually a necessary component of successful thought processes, but it should be followed up with a precise thought sequence. Let us make the approach precise and logical.

Given the two sets $A = \{r, s\}$ and $B = \{x, y, z\}$, we can form a new set, $C = \{r, s, x, y, z\}$. This set C is called the *union* of A and B, and this union is denoted by $A \cup B$. Note that every element which appears in either A or B also appears in C, and no other elements appear in C.

Definition. *Set union.* The union of two sets X and Y is the set of all elements, without repetition, which belong to either X or Y.

To say that an element appears in either X or Y will include the possibility that the element may appear in both X and Y.

According to this definition the union of $X = \{a, b, c\}$ and $Y = \{a, r, s\}$ is $X \cup Y = \{a, b, c, r, s\}$. Each element in either X or Y appears in $X \cup Y$, and each element in $X \cup Y$ appeared in either X or Y, or possibly both. The element a was common to X and Y, yet it is written just once in the union.

If Mary is an only child and she has a husband, a son, and a daughter, then her immediate family is the union of two family units:

{Mary's immediate family}
$= \{$Mary, her mother, her father$\}$
$\cup \{$Mary, her husband, her son, her daughter$\}$
$= \{$Mary, her mother, her father, her husband, her son, her daughter$\}$.

34

The symbol "$+$" is sometimes used to denote union. Such use may cause confusion, however, since this symbol is also used to denote an operation of arithmetic. Hence this symbol will not be used here.

3–2 ADDITION OF NUMBERS

Let us return to the discussion at the beginning of the last section. Would it have been suitable to use sets $\{a_1, a_2\}$ and $\{a_1, b, c\}$, where a_1, a_2, b, and c represent the marbles in the two sets? When these sets are "swept together," would the result be a set which would illustrate the sum of 2 and 3? These sets would not be suitable to illustrate this sum, since there are only four marbles in the resulting set; this situation arose by reason of the common element, a_1, in the two sets. We should have used sets which did not have a common element.

Two sets which do not have any elements in common are said to be *disjoint*. Sets $\{a_1, a_2\}$ and $\{a_1, b, c\}$ are not disjoint; sets $\{a_1, a_2\}$ and $\{b, c, d\}$ are disjoint if no two of a_1, a_2, b, c, and d are alike.

Since any number x equals $n(X)$, for some set X, then we can state the following.

Definition. *Sum of numbers.* If $x = n(X)$ and $y = n(Y)$ then

$$x + y = n(X \cup Y), \quad \text{if } X \text{ and } Y \text{ are disjoint.}$$

The sum of two numbers is a number. For instance,

$$n\{a, b\} + n\{r, s, t\} = n\{a, b, r, s, t\}, \quad \text{disjointed}$$

$$n\{\text{Mary, John}\} + n\{\text{apple, orange}\} = n\{\text{Mary, John, apple, orange}\}.$$

This sum of x and y may be obtained by *adding* x and y; hence the operation of addition of numbers has been defined.

How can this definition be used in what would seem to be a more "down-to-earth" situation? Suppose it is desired to find $2 + 3$. Now,

$$2 = n\{a, b\} \quad \text{and} \quad 3 = n\{r, s, t\}.$$

Hence

$$2 + 3 = n\{a, b\} + n\{r, s, t\} = n\{a, b, r, s, t\},$$

where the last line follows from the preceding definition and the fact that the sets $\{a, b\}$ and $\{r, s, t\}$ are disjoint. Since $\{a, b, r, s, t\}$ matches S_5, then $n\{a, b, r, s, t\} = n(S_5)$; in turn $n(S_5) = 5$. As a result, it has been shown that $2 + 3 = 5$.

Would it not have been more natural to use S_2 instead of $\{a, b\}$ and S_3 instead of $\{r, s, t\}$ in the preceding problem? Then we would have

$$2 + 3 = n(S_2) + n(S_3).$$

Can the definition of addition be used here? No, since the sets $S_2 = \{1, 2\}$ and $S_3 = \{1, 2, 3\}$ are not disjoint. This difficulty can be overcome readily by introducing a new set which matches S_3 and is disjoint from S_2. We could return to the use of $\{r, s, t\}$, but it is easier if the set $\{3, 4, 5\}$ is used. Since $\{3, 4, 5\}$ matches S_3, then $n\{3, 4, 5\} = n(S_3)$; hence

$$n(S_2) + n(S_3) = n(S_2) + n\{3, 4, 5\}.$$

Since S_2 and $\{3, 4, 5\}$ are disjoint, the definition can *now* be applied, and we have

$$n(S_2) + n\{3, 4, 5\} = n(S_2 \cup \{3, 4, 5\})$$
$$= n\{1, 2, 3, 4, 5\} = n(S_5).$$

When the results of all these steps are combined, the final result is

$$2 + 3 = 5,$$

since $n(S_5) = 5$.

ILLUSTRATIVE EXAMPLE. Find $3 + 4$.

Solution. Since $3 = n(S_3)$ and $4 = n(S_4)$, then

$$3 + 4 = n(S_3) + n(S_4).$$

Since S_3 and S_4 are not disjoint, it is necessary to introduce a new set, say $C = \{4, 5, 6, 7\}$. The sets C and S_4 match, so that $n(C) = n(S_4)$; hence

$$
\begin{aligned}
3 + 4 &= n(S_3) + n(C) \\
&= n(S_3 \cup C) && \text{(by the definition of addition,} \\
& && \text{since } S_3 \text{ and } C \text{ are disjoint)} \\
&= n\{1, 2, 3, 4, 5, 6, 7\} && \text{(forming union of } S_3 \text{ and } C) \\
&= n(S_7) \\
&= 7.
\end{aligned}
$$

DISCUSSION EXERCISES

In these exercises, the symbol X represents any given set which matches some S set.

1. Show that $X \cup \Phi = X$.

2. Are X and Φ disjoint?

3. Is $n(X) + n(\Phi) = n(X \cup \Phi)$? Why?

4. Is $n(X) = n(X \cup \Phi)$? Why?

5. Exercises 1 through 4 should yield $n(X) + n(\Phi) = n(X)$. Let $x = n(X)$. Is x a set or a number? Fill in the following blank: $n(\Phi) = \underline{0}$.

6. Use x and the symbol placed in the above blank to write the equation $n(X) + n(\Phi) = n(X)$ in another form.

The result that you obtained in Problem 6 should be

$$x + 0 = x;$$

since X was any set, then x is any natural number. Show that the preceding results are true when $X = \Phi$. Consequently, $x + 0 = x$ when $x = 0$. In a problem of the following set you are asked to show that $0 + x = x$, for any whole number x. This discussion yields the following property.

Property of zero.

$$x + 0 = x \quad \text{and} \quad 0 + x = x, \quad \text{for } x \text{ any whole number.}$$

This commonly used property has been proved using previously introduced concepts and definitions.

Zero is often called the *identity element for addition*, since when it is added to a specific number the result is that same number.

PROBLEM SET 3–2

1. Find the union of each pair of sets below, and state whether or not they are disjoint. (Assume that different letters represent different things.)
   (a) $\{a, b, c, d\}$ and $\{x, r, z\}$
   (b) $\{a, b, c, d\}$ and $\{x, c, d, z\}$
   (c) {ball, bat, dog} and {house, bat, rabbit}
   (d) $\{2, 5, 7, 10, 11\}$ and $\{1, 2, 3, 7, 10\}$

2. If two sets are disjoint, can their union be found? Give an example.

3. If two sets are not disjoint, can their union be found? Give an example.

4. Write a set A such that A and $\{a, r, c, z\}$ are disjoint.

5. In each of the following, write a set which matches A and is disjoint from A.
   (a) $A = \{\text{cat, rabbit, dog}\}$
   (b) $A = \{c, h, m, r, s\}$
   (c) $A = \{1, 2, 3, 4\}$
   (d) $A = \{1, 2, 3, 4, 5, 6, 7\}$

← less

≤ equal

6. For each of the following pairs of sets show whether or not $n(A) + n(B)$ is equal to $n(A \cup B)$; state why or why not.
    (a) $A = \{1, 2, 3, 4\}$ and $B = \{10, 12, 16, 17, 18\}$
    (b) $A = \{1, 2, 3, 4\}$ and $B = \{7, 5, 3, 8\}$
    (c) $A = \{3, 4, 2, 7\}$ and $B = \{9, 4, 6\}$
    (d) $A = \{3, 2, 5, 8\}$ and $B = \{4, 6, 1, 7\}$

7. Explain in detail how each of the following sums may be found.
    (a) $5 + 2$ (b) $3 + 7$ (c) $4 + 6$
    (d) $6 + 8$ (e) $7 + 5$ (f) $2 + 4$

8. Find each of the following.
    (a) $7 + 0$ (b) $16 + 0$ (c) $0 + 9$
    (d) $0 + 0$ (e) $0 + 8$

9. Show, using set ideas, that $0 + x = \emptyset$ for any whole number x.

10. Let $A = \{$all women in your class$\}$, $B = \{$all light-haired women in your class$\}$, and $D = \{$all dark-haired women in your class$\}$.
    (a) Which of the following is true: $B \cup D = A$, $B \cup D \subset A$, or $B \cup D \subseteq A$?
    (b) If all the women are classified as either light-haired or dark-haired, would $A = B \cup D$?
    (c) Show that $n(B) \leq n(A)$. (The symbol "$\leq$" means "is less than or is equal to.")   as long as B and D are disjoint .
    (d) Under what conditions would $n(A) = n(B) + n(D)$?

11. Let $A = \{$all members of your class who take English$\}$ and $B = \{$all members of your class who take history$\}$.
    (a) Is $A \cup B = \{$all members of your class who take either English or history$\}$?
    (b) Is $n(A \cup B) = n(A) + n(B)$? If not, state the conditions under which it would be true.   not disjoint
    (c) If $n(A) = 5$ and $n(B) = 7$, find the smallest possible value of $n(A \cup B)$ and the largest possible value of $n(A \cup B)$.

3–3 COMMUTATIVE AND ASSOCIATIVE PROPERTIES OF ADDITION

Every child must learn the results of the addition combinations $1 + 1$, $1 + 2, \ldots, 9 + 9$ very early in his arithmetic experience. All too often this is accomplished by rote or through constant drill, rather than through the development of patterns. Stressing intuitive concepts, such as "breaking up" a set of 8 objects in various ways (e.g., $2 + 6$, $3 + 5$, $4 + 4$) should assist in this process. Actually, by manipulating sets of objects in this way, we would be using set ideas without using set language. What could be more natural?

We may have learned $2 + 3$ and $3 + 2$ as two distinct results. Would it not have saved us time and effort if very early we had been introduced to the idea that the results of $2 + 3$ and $3 + 2$ are the same? Why are they the same? Let $C = \{3, 4, 5\}$. Then

$$2 + 3 = n(S_2) + n(S_3) = n(S_2) + n(C) \quad \text{(why?)}$$
$$= n(S_2 \cup C) \quad \text{(why?)}$$
$$= n\{1, 2, 3, 4, 5\}$$

and

$$3 + 2 = n(S_3) + n(S_2) = n(C) + n(S_2)$$
$$= n(C \cup S_2)$$
$$= n\{3, 4, 5, 1, 2\}.$$

Since $\{1, 2, 3, 4, 5\} = \{3, 4, 5, 1, 2\}$, then $n\{1, 2, 3, 4, 5\} = n\{3, 4, 5, 1, 2\}$. Hence $2 + 3 = 3 + 2$.

The above demonstration is based on the fact that the order in which elements appear in a set is not material, that is, $S_2 \cup C = C \cup S_2$. This fact stems from the definition of union; when $X \cup Y$ is found, it does not matter what order is used in writing the elements, that is, $X \cup Y = Y \cup X$. Hence

$$n(X \cup Y) = n(Y \cup X), \quad \text{for all } X \text{ and } Y.$$

Let x and y be numbers; now, there are sets X and Y such that $x = n(X)$ and $y = n(Y)$. Unless X and Y are disjoint, $n(X \cup Y)$ cannot be written as $n(X) + n(Y)$. It has been shown, in specific examples, how Y may be replaced by a new set, Z, which matches Y, such that X and Z are disjoint; now $y = n(Z)$. Accordingly, since X and Y were chosen, the initial choice might just as well have been made such that X and Y were disjoint. Assume that this has been done. Then, from the above equation,

$$n(X) + n(Y) = n(Y) + n(X),$$

so that

$$x + y - y + x.$$

This is the

Commutative Property of addition.

$$x + y = y + x, \quad \text{for all whole numbers } x \text{ and } y.$$

The commutative property of addition (abbreviated C_a) holds even when x or y (or both) is zero, since the definition of union holds even when X or Y is the null set.

Most people use this property without realizing it when they add a column of "figures" down and then check by adding up. More about this later!

The addition of numbers is a *binary* operation; that is, two numbers are involved in the addition process, one number being added to the other, for example, $5 + 7$. How then would three numbers, say 2, 4, and 7, be added? One way would be to write $(2 + 4) + 7$. First, 2 and 4 are added (the parentheses indicate this); then to that result 7 is added. Are there any other ways? For the present let us restrict attention to situations where the order is not changed, the numbers always being written in the order 2, 4, then 7. Another way to add these numbers would be to write $2 + (4 + 7)$. The above are the only ways to add these numbers if addition is considered as a binary operation and if the order is kept the same. Are the sums $(2 + 4) + 7$ and $2 + (4 + 7)$ equal or are they different? The easiest way to answer this question is to perform the additions; let us obtain the answer by using sets, since this procedure leads to general results. Let

$$A = \{3, 4, 5, 6\} \quad \text{and} \quad B = \{7, 8, 9, 10, 11, 12, 13\};$$

then

$$
\begin{aligned}
(2 + 4) + 7 &= [n(S_2) + n(S_4)] + n(S_7) \\
&= [n(S_2) + n(A)] + n(B) &&\text{(why?)} \\
&= n(S_2 \cup A) + n(B) &&\text{(why?)} \\
&= n(S_6) + n(B) &&\text{(since } S_2 \cup A = S_6) \\
&= n(S_6 \cup B) &&\text{(why?)} \\
&= n(S_{13}).
\end{aligned}
$$

(The brackets, [ ], have the same effect as parentheses; they merely hold together the elements inside them.) Also,

$$
\begin{aligned}
2 + (4 + 7) &= n(S_2) + [n(S_4) + n(S_7)] \\
&= n(S_2) + [n(A) + n(B)] &&\text{(why?)} \\
&= n(S_2) + n(A \cup B) &&\text{(why?)} \\
&= n(S_2) + n\{3, 4, 5, 6, 7, 8, 9, 10, 11, 12, 13\} \\
&= n(S_2 \cup \{3, 4, 5, 6, 7, 8, 9, 10, 11, 12, 13\}) \\
&= n(S_{13}).
\end{aligned}
$$

Hence $(2 + 4) + 7 = 2 + (4 + 7)$. Either of these can be, and will be, used to express the meaning of $2 + 4 + 7$.

A proof of a similar result for the general numbers r, s, and t follows (a more general proof is outlined in Problem 11 of this section). Let

$$r = n(A), \quad \text{where } A = \{a_1, a_2, a_3, \ldots, a_r\},$$

$$s = n(B), \quad \text{where } B = \{b_1, b_2, b_3, \ldots, b_s\},$$

$$t = n(C), \quad \text{where } C = \{c_1, c_2, c_3, \ldots, c_t\},$$

where sets A, B, and C have no common elements, i.e., they are disjoint in pairs. Now

$$(A \cup B) \cup C = \{a_1, a_2, a_3, \ldots, a_r, b_1, b_2, b_3, \ldots, b_s\} \cup C$$
$$= \{a_1, a_2, a_3, \ldots, a_r, b_1, b_2, b_3, \ldots, b_s, c_1, c_2, c_3, \ldots, c_t\}$$

and

$$A \cup (B \cup C) = A \cup \{b_1, b_2, b_3, \ldots, b_s, c_1, c_2, c_3, \ldots, c_t\}$$
$$= \{a_1, a_2, a_3, \ldots, a_r, b_1, b_2, b_3, \ldots, b_s, c_1, c_2, c_3, \ldots, c_t\}.$$

Since $(A \cup B) \cup C$ and $A \cup (B \cup C)$ have the same elements, they are the same sets, so that

$$(A \cup B) \cup C = A \cup (B \cup C).$$

Since the above sets are the same, they must have the same number associated with them, so that

$$n[(A \cup B) \cup C] = n[A \cup (B \cup C)].$$

Now,

$$n[(A \cup B) \cup C] = n(A \cup B) + n(C),$$

since C and $A \cup B$ are disjoint. Then

$$n(A \cup B) + n(C) = [n(A) + n(B)] + n(C),$$

since A and B are disjoint, so that

$$n[(A \cup B) \cup C] = (r + s) + t.$$

Also,

$$n[A \cup (B \cup C)] = n(A) + n(B \cup C)$$
$$= n(A) + [n(B) + n(C)]$$
$$= r + (s + t).$$

Accordingly,

$$(r + s) + t = r + (s + t),$$

for all natural numbers. Prove this statement for whole numbers.

Associative property of addition.

$$(r + s) + t = r + (s + t), \qquad \text{for all whole numbers } r, s, \text{ and } t.$$

The name of this property (abbreviated A_a) can be easily remembered if we note that it merely states that when three numbers are added, they can be associated in any manner to obtain the same results. On the left side of the above statement, r and s are added first; on the right side, s and t are added first.

This property can be used to give meaning to the sum of three numbers:

$$3 + 4 + 5 \quad \text{means either} \quad (3 + 4) + 5 \quad \text{or} \quad 3 + (4 + 5),$$
$$r + s + t \quad \text{means either} \quad (r + s) + t \quad \text{or} \quad r + (s + t).$$

It is seen that the result is the same no matter which way the addition is performed.

How is this property used? Add, first up and then down, the column of numbers shown at the right. The first result is $(9 + 8) + 7$; the second is $(7 + 8) + 9$. Since the order is different in these two expressions, something must be involved other than the associative property. Let us see:

$$7$$
$$8$$
$$\underline{9}$$

$$(9 + 8) + 7 = 7 + (9 + 8) \quad \text{[by } C_a, \text{ treating } (9 + 8) \text{ as a single number]}$$
$$= 7 + (8 + 9) \quad \text{(by } C_a\text{)}$$
$$= (7 + 8) + 9 \quad \text{(by } A_a\text{)}.$$

Both the commutative and the associative properties had to be used.

What could $13 + 14 + 7 + 16$ mean? One meaning is $(13 + 14) + (7 + 16)$, which would yield $27 + 23 = 50$. Also,

$$(13 + 14) + (7 + 16) = 13 + [14 + (7 + 16)],$$

where $7 + 16$ is treated as a single number. Then

$$(13 + 14) + (7 + 16) = 13 + [(7 + 16) + 14]$$
$$= [13 + (7 + 16)] + 14$$
$$= [(13 + 7) + 16] + 14$$
$$= (13 + 7) + (16 + 14).$$

This example shows how numbers which are to be added may be rearranged in any order and in any association by using the commutative and associative properties, respectively. This rearrangement serves many purposes, one of which can be seen from the last arrangement above. The numbers $13 + 7 = 20$ and $16 + 14 = 30$ are multiples of 10; these additions together with the addition of 20 and 10 are slightly easier and faster than would be the following:

$$[(13 + 14) + 7] + 16 = [27 + 7] + 16$$
$$= 34 + 16$$
$$= 50.$$

PROBLEM SET 3-3

1. Show, by using fundamental definitions, that (a) $3 + 4 = 4 + 3$ and (b) $5 + 8 = 8 + 5$.

2. Suppose that x means "put a sock on your foot," y means "put a shoe on your foot," and $+$ means "and then perform the act."
   (a) Describe $x + y$.
   (b) Describe $y + x$.
   (c) Is the effect the same? Is $x + y = y + x$?
   (d) Is "and then perform the act" commutative for acts x and y?

3. If x means "run a mile" and y means "walk a mile" and $+$ has the same meaning as in Problem 2, is $x + y = y + x$?

4. If x means "paint a pile of lumber" and y means "build a closed box out of the lumber" and $+$ has the meaning of Problem 2, is $x + y = y + x$?

5. Draw a row of six small circles and show how to use your drawing to illustrate $4 + 2 = 2 + 4$.

6. If you work through several examples like Problem 5, would you ever prove the commutative law of addition for whole numbers? Why or why not?

7. Use the circles of Problem 5 to illustrate that $(1 + 2) + 3 = 1 + (2 + 3)$.

8. Show, by using definitions, that (a) $(3 + 2) + 4 = 3 + (2 + 4)$, (b) $(5 + 3) + 3 = 5 + (3 + 3)$.

9. Show, by using suitable properties, that the following equations hold. Justify each step by referring to a property.
   (a) $(3 + 4) + (2 + 5) = (2 + 4) + (3 + 5)$
   (b) $5 + [6 + (7 + 8)] = (8 + 6) + (5 + 7)$
   (c) $[r + (s + t)] + (u + v) = (u + r) + [v + (t + s)]$

10. Arrange the numbers 5, 6, 7, and 8 in a column. Show that the result should be the same whether addition is performed "up" or "down." Do not complete the additions, such as using 11 in place of $5 + 6$.

11. Fill in the blanks in the following proof of the associative property of addition. Let r be any element of $X \cup (Y \cup Z)$.
    (a) The element r belongs either to X or $(Y \cup Z)$.
    (b) If r is an element of X, show that it is an element of $X \cup Y$ and hence of $(X \cup Y) \cup Z$.
    (c) If r is not an element of X, then by reason of part (a) it must be an element of ____ and hence either an element of ____ or ____. Show that, as a result, r is an element of $(X \cup Y) \cup Z$.
    (d) Draw a conclusion from parts (a), (b), and (c).
    (e) Show, in a similar fashion, that if s is an element of $(X \cup Y) \cup Z$, it is also an element of $X \cup (Y \cup Z)$.
    (f) Why do parts (d) and (e) complete the proof?

The proof of the associative property given in the textual material is valid only for sets which match S sets; such sets are called *finite* sets. The proof outlined in the preceding Problem 11 is valid for any type of set whether finite or not. A set which is not finite is called an *infinite* set; little use will be made of this concept for the present.

3-4 MULTIPLICATION OF NUMBERS

Ordinarily, multiplication is thought of as a continued addition, for example, 3×4 would mean $4 + 4 + 4$ or the sum of three 4's. This addition could be handled as follows:

$$4 + 4 + 4 = n(S_4) + n(S_4) + n(S_4)$$
$$= n(S_4) + n\{5, 6, 7, 8\} + n\{9, 10, 11, 12\}$$
$$= n(S_{12}).$$

If this idea were used for such general problems as the proof of the commutative property, the notation would become unwieldy. Note that the primary step was to use $\{5, 6, 7, 8\}$ in place of one of the sets S_4 and $\{9, 10, 11, 12\}$ in place of the third set S_4, so that any two of the three sets S_4, $\{5, 6, 7, 8\}$, and $\{9, 10, 11, 12\}$ would be disjoint. Note also that the number of S_4's is the same as the number of elements in S_3. We will use these same ideas in another fashion, which may seem more complicated at first but which will become clear after a little experience.

In the following discussion let us use $S_3 = \{a_1, a_2, a_3\}$ and $S_4 = \{b_1, b_2, b_3, b_4\}$. We form three new sets, one corresponding to each of the elements of S_3, as shown below:

$\{(a_1, b_1), (a_1, b_2), (a_1, b_3), (a_1, b_4)\}$,   corresponding to a_1;

$\{(a_2, b_1), (a_2, b_2), (a_2, b_3), (a_2, b_4)\}$,   corresponding to a_2;

$\{(a_3, b_1), (a_3, b_2), (a_3, b_3), (a_3, b_4)\}$,   corresponding to a_3.

Note that:

(1) In each new set the elements are pairs. For example, (a_1, b_2) is an element of the first set, (a_2, b_3) is an element of the second, and (a_3, b_1) is an element of the third.

(2) Each new set matches S_4.

(3) Every possible pair is formed by coupling an element of S_3 with an element of S_4, the element of S_3 being written first.

(4) Any two of the three new sets are disjoint; this is accomplished by using a_1 in each element of the first set, a_2 in each element of the second, and a_3 in each element of the third.

The union of the above three sets may be formed; this union is called the *cross product* of S_3 and S_4 and is written $S_3 \times S_4$.

Definition. *Set cross product.* The cross product of sets X and Y is the set of all pairs which can be formed by coupling an element of X with an element of Y, the element of X being written first.

For the above example, the cross product is

$$S_3 \times S_4 = \{(a_1, b_1), (a_1, b_2), (a_1, b_3), (a_1, b_4)$$
$$(a_2, b_1), (a_2, b_2), (a_2, b_3), (a_2, b_4)$$
$$(a_3, b_1), (a_3, b_2), (a_3, b_3), (a_3, b_4)\}.$$

The elements are arranged in rows only to display the manner of formation more clearly. Be certain that you see the similarity between $S_3 \times S_4$ and the union of the three sets used in the determination of $4 + 4 + 4$. The use of subscript notation calls for lengthy expressions; hence we write the above cross product in the abbreviated form

$$S_3 \times S_4 = \{1, 2, 3\} \times \{1, 2, 3, 4\}$$
$$= \{(1, 1), (1, 2), (1, 3), (1, 4)$$
$$(2, 1), (2, 2), (2, 3), (2, 4)$$
$$(3, 1), (3, 2), (3, 3), (3, 4)\}.$$

This notation, however, should not be used until the concept of cross product is thoroughly understood.

ILLUSTRATIVE EXAMPLE 1. Find $\{2, 5, 3, 6\} \times \{4, 8\}$.

Solution.
$$\{2, 5, 3, 6\} \times \{4, 8\} = \{(2, 4), (2, 8)$$
$$(5, 4), (5, 8)$$
$$(3, 4), (3, 8)$$
$$(6, 4), (6, 8)\}.$$

The product of two numbers, x and y, can now be defined by using the concept of cross product, this definition evolving smoothly and naturally from intuitive ideas.

Definition. *Product of numbers.* If $x = n(X)$ and $y = n(Y)$, then the product of x and y is $n(X \times Y)$, that is,

$$x \cdot y = n(X) \cdot n(Y) = n(X \times Y).$$

Note that the product of the number x and the number y is also a number, which is denoted by $x \cdot y$ or xy. The product xy results from the *multiplication* of x by y.

ILLUSTRATIVE EXAMPLE 2. Find $4 \cdot 2$.

Solution. The results of Illustrative Example 1 may be used to give

$$4 \cdot 2 = n\{2, 5, 3, 6\} \cdot n\{4, 8\} = n[\{2, 5, 3, 6\} \times \{4, 8\}] = n(S_8),$$

since $\{2, 5, 3, 6\} \times \{4, 8\}$ matches S_8 (see Illustrative Example 1).

ILLUSTRATIVE EXAMPLE 3. Find $3 \cdot 4$.

Solution. With the natural choice of sets S_3 and S_4, we have

$$3 \cdot 4 = n(S_3) \cdot n(S_4) = n(S_3 \times S_4).$$

The set $S_3 \times S_4$, which was obtained immediately preceding Illustrative Example 1, matches S_{12}. Hence

$$3 \cdot 4 = n(S_{12}) = 12.$$

Again note the similarity between the above ideas and basic intuitive notions. For the example $3 \cdot 4$, the intuitive notion would be to take three sets, each containing four elements, and "put them together"; i.e., from the sets

we intuitively proceed to

 from first set,
from second set,
from third set.

There are as many sets of $\square$'s as there are elements in a set A such that $3 = n(A)$. The seemingly complicated notation of cross product merely yields a means of identifying where specific elements in the combined set came from, whether from the first set, the second set, or the third set.

The $\square$'s in the above illustration can be given distinguishing marks so that we will be talking about sets of distinct elements.

PROBLEM SET 3-4

1. (a) Use sets of $\square$'s to illustrate how you would demonstrate that $2 \cdot 5 = 10$.
   (b) Write the set $S_2 \times S_5$ and describe the similarity between the construction of this set and the handling of sets in part (a).
   (c) Using the set in (b), show that $2 \cdot 5 = 10$.

2. Fill in the blanks where indicated, or state whether the sentence given is true (T), false (F), or meaningless (M).

(a) $S_6 \times S_8$ is a _____ *set*

(b) $n(S_6) \cdot n(S_8)$ is a _____

(c) $S_3 \times S_5 = 7$ *meaningless*

(d) $n(S_2) \cdot n(S_3) = S_2 \times S_3$ F

(e) $S_3 \times S_2 = S_6$ F *matches*

(f) $n(S_2) \cdot n(S_3) = n(S_6)$ *True*

3. (a) Construct $S_4 \times S_2$ and show that it matches S_8. (b) Construct $S_3 \times S_5$ and show that it matches S_{15}.

4. (a) Use 3(a) to show that $4 \cdot 2 = 8$. (b) Use 3(b) to show that $3 \cdot 5 = 15$.

5. Show that the following are true.

(a) $4 \cdot 1 = 4$ (b) $6 \cdot 2 = 12$ (c) $3 \cdot 3 = 9$ (d) $2 \cdot 4 = 8$

6. (a) Is $n(A \times B) = n(A) \cdot n(B)$ true for all sets A and B? Why?

(b) Is $n(A \cup B) = n(A) + n(B)$ true for all sets A and B? If not, explain why.

3-5 COMMUTATIVE AND ASSOCIATIVE PROPERTIES OF MULTIPLICATION

Just as he did for addition, the young child must learn the results of the basic multiplication combinations from $1 \cdot 1$ to $9 \cdot 9$. Need the child learn both $2 \cdot 4$ and $4 \cdot 2$, for example? That the results of these combinations are the same is not obvious; moreover, most children have difficulty making the transition from considering $4 \cdot 2$ and $2 \cdot 4$ as distinct ideas to considering them as two forms of basically the same multiplication.

Let us construct both $S_2 \times S_4$ and $S_4 \times S_2$, writing the elements in columns for clarity.

$S_2 \times S_4$
{(1, 1)
(1, 2)
(1, 3)
(1, 4)
(2, 1)
(2, 2)
(2, 3)
(2, 4)}

$S_4 \times S_2$
{(1, 1)
(1, 2)
(2, 1)
(2, 2)
(3, 1)
(3, 2)
(4, 1)
(4, 2)}

To each element in the first column there is a corresponding element in the second column (examples are shown by the arrows). As a matter of fact $S_2 \times S_4$ and $S_4 \times S_2$ match. Hence

$$n(S_2 \times S_4) = n(S_4 \times S_2).$$

But $n(S_2 \times S_4) = n(S_2) \cdot n(S_4)$, and $n(S_4 \times S_2) = n(S_4) \cdot n(S_2)$. Hence

$$n(S_2) \cdot n(S_4) = n(S_4) \cdot n(S_2),$$

so that
$$2 \cdot 4 = 4 \cdot 2.$$

This example illustrates the following property.

Commutative property of multiplication.

$$r \cdot s = s \cdot r, \qquad \text{for all whole numbers } r \text{ and } s.$$

The proof of this property (abbreviated C_m) for any counting numbers r and s follows immediately by applying the procedure used above for the special case of 2 and 4; the case where either r or s is zero is discussed in the next section. Let us use the notation $r = n(A)$, where $A = \{a_1, a_2, a_3, \ldots, a_r\}$, and $s = n(B)$, where $B = \{b_1, b_2, b_3, \ldots, b_s\}$. Then,

$$A \times B = \{\text{all couples like } (a_1, b_1), (a_1, b_4), (a_3, b_1), (a_4, b_5)\},$$

and

$$B \times A = \{\text{all couples like } (b_1, a_1), (b_1, a_3), (b_5, a_4), (b_2, a_3)\}.$$

Each couple in $A \times B$ can be "tied to" a couple in $B \times A$, for example,

$$(a_1, b_1) \qquad \text{to} \qquad (b_1, a_1),$$
$$(a_3, b_1) \qquad \text{to} \qquad (b_1, a_3),$$
$$(a_6, b_4) \qquad \text{to} \qquad (b_4, a_6).$$

In this manner it can be shown that $A \times B$ matches $B \times A$; this is only one of several ways in which the matching may be indicated. Hence

$$n(A \times B) = n(B \times A) \qquad \text{(why?)},$$
$$n(A) \cdot n(B) = n(B) \cdot n(A) \qquad \text{(why?)},$$
$$r \cdot s = s \cdot r.$$

Now consider whether or not $2 \cdot (3 \cdot 4)$ is equal to $(2 \cdot 3) \cdot 4$. For $2 \cdot (3 \cdot 4)$, form $S_3 \times S_4$ and then $S_2 \times (S_3 \times S_4)$. The cross products needed in this problem are shown in Table 3–1. Corresponding elements in the two sets of that table can be "tied together," for example,

$$[1, (1, 3)] \qquad \text{with} \qquad [(1, 1), 3],$$
$$[2, (3, 4)] \qquad \text{with} \qquad [(2, 3), 4],$$
$$[2, (1, 2)] \qquad \text{with} \qquad [(2, 1), 2].$$

Table 3–1

$S_2 \times (S_3 \times S_4)$		$(S_2 \times S_3) \times S_4$	
{[1, (1, 1)],	[2, (1, 1)],	{[(1, 1), 1],	[(1, 1), 3],
[1, (1, 2)],	[2, (1, 2)],	[(1, 2), 1],	[(1, 2), 3],
[1, (1, 3)],	[2, (1, 3)],	[(1, 3), 1],	[(1, 3), 3],
[1, (1, 4)],	[2, (1, 4)],	[(2, 1), 1],	[(2, 1), 3],
[1, (2, 1)],	[2, (2, 1)],	[(2, 2), 1],	[(2, 2), 3],
[1, (2, 2)],	[2, (2, 2)],	[(2, 3), 1],	[(2, 3), 3],
[1, (2, 3)],	[2, (2, 3)],	[(1, 1), 2],	[(1, 1), 4],
[1, (2, 4)],	[2, (2, 4)],	[(1, 2), 2],	[(1, 2), 4],
[1, (3, 1)],	[2, (3, 1)],	[(1, 3), 2],	[(1, 3), 4],
[1, (3, 2)],	[2, (3, 2)],	[(2, 1), 2],	[(2, 1), 4],
[1, (3, 3)],	[2, (3, 3)],	[(2, 2), 2],	[(2, 2), 4],
[1, (3, 4)],	[2, (3, 4)]}	[(2, 3), 2],	[(2, 3), 4]}

In this manner it can be shown that $S_2 \times (S_3 \times S_4)$ matches $(S_2 \times S_3) \times S_4$; hence

$$n[S_2 \times (S_3 \times S_4)] = n[(S_2 \times S_3) \times S_4],$$

so that

$$n(S_2) \cdot n(S_3 \times S_4) = n(S_2 \times S_3) \cdot n(S_4) \quad \text{(why?)},$$

$$n(S_2) \cdot [n(S_3) \cdot n(S_4)] = [n(S_2) \cdot n(S_3)] \cdot n(S_4),$$

$$2 \cdot (3 \cdot 4) = (2 \cdot 3) \cdot 4.$$

This last equation is a special case of the following property (abbreviated A_m).

Associative property of multiplication.

$$r \cdot (s \cdot t) = (r \cdot s) \cdot t, \quad \text{for any whole numbers } r, s, \text{ and } t.$$

The preceding equation may also be written $r(st) = (rs)t$.

The case where one of r, s, and t is zero is discussed in the next section. If r, s, and t are natural numbers, use $r = n(A)$, where $A = \{a_1, a_2, a_3, \ldots, a_r\}$; $s = n(B)$, where $B = \{b_1, b_2, b_3, \ldots, b_s\}$; and $t = n(C)$, where $C = \{c_1, c_2, c_3, \ldots, c_t\}$. Just as in the special case above, the sets $A \times (B \times C)$ and $(A \times B) \times C$ can be formed; some particular elements of each set are, respectively,

$$[a_1, (b_1, c_1)] \quad \text{and} \quad [(a_1, b_1), c_1],$$

$$[a_3, (b_2, c_7)] \quad \text{and} \quad [(a_3, b_2), c_7].$$

Actually, these will be corresponding elements in the "string-tying" operation of showing that the sets $A \times (B \times C)$ and $(A \times B) \times C$ match.

Hence,

$$n[A \times (B \times C)] = n[(A \times B) \times C],$$

$$n(A) \cdot n(B \times C) = n(A \times B) \cdot n(C),$$

$$n(A) \cdot [n(B) \cdot n(C)] = [n(A) \cdot n(B)] \cdot n(C),$$

$$r \cdot (s \cdot t) = (r \cdot s) \cdot t.$$

ILLUSTRATIVE EXAMPLE. Show that $4(17 \cdot 5) = 17(4 \cdot 5)$. (Note that the sign " $\cdot$ " has been omitted in two places above; where no confusion can result, this sign is omitted for the sake of brevity.)

Solution.

$$\begin{aligned} 4(17 \cdot 5) &= (4 \cdot 17)5 & \text{(by } A_m) \\ &= (17 \cdot 4)5 & \text{(by } C_m) \\ &= 17(4 \cdot 5) & \text{(by } A_m). \end{aligned}$$

Which computation is easier,

$$4(17 \cdot 5) = 4(85) = 340$$

or

$$17(4 \cdot 5) = 17(20) = 340?$$

Most people would feel that the second is easier. The commutative and associative properties of multiplication justify such rearrangements.

The idea of multiplication as successive addition seems to have been lost; we shall return to it in Problem Set 3–7.

3–6 SPECIAL PROPERTIES

Why is $r \cdot 1 = r$, for all natural numbers r? We have $1 = n(S_1)$. If we let $r = n(A)$, where $A = \{a_1, a_2, a_3, \ldots, a_r\}$, then

$$A \times S_1 = \{(a_1, 1), (a_2, 1), (a_3, 1), \ldots, (a_r, 1)\}.$$

Show that $A \times S_1$ matches A. As a consequence of this matching,

$$n(A \times S_1) = n(A),$$

$$n(A) \cdot n(S_1) = n(A),$$

$$r \cdot 1 = r.$$

It can be shown, without using the commutative property, that $1 \cdot r = r$, for any natural number r. (You will be asked to do this in Problem 3 of this section.) These results comprise what is often called the "property of one."

Property of one. The number "one" satisfies the equations

$$r \cdot 1 = r \quad \text{and} \quad 1 \cdot r = r, \quad \text{for } r \text{ any whole number.}$$

The case where $r = 0$ is treated in a later paragraph of this section. One is often called the *identity element for multiplication*. Note that one plays the same role in multiplication that zero plays in addition.

More use can be made of this property than most people realize; for example, you will see it used later in connection with the division of fractions.

The null set, Φ, was introduced in Chapter 2 and it was shown that for this set $n(\Phi) = 0$. Does $A \times \Phi$ have meaning, where A is a set? Each element of $A \times \Phi$ is a pair (a, b), where a belongs to A and b belongs to Φ. Since Φ is empty, no elements b exist, and consequently no elements (a, b) exist. Accordingly, $A \times \Phi$ is the empty set, or the null set. Similarly, $\Phi \times A$ is Φ, so that

$$A \times \Phi = \Phi = \Phi \times A.$$

Hence

$$n(A \times \Phi) = n(\Phi),$$

$$n(A) \cdot n(\Phi) = n(\Phi),$$

$$n(A) \cdot 0 = 0.$$

This holds for any set A, even if $A = \Phi$; hence

$$r \cdot 0 = 0, \quad \text{for any whole number } r.$$

Likewise, from $\Phi \times A = \Phi$ it follows that

$$0 \cdot r = 0, \quad \text{for any whole number } r.$$

These results can be stated in a single property.

Multiplication property of zero.

$$r \cdot 0 = 0 = 0 \cdot r, \quad \text{for } r \text{ any whole number.}$$

The multiplication property of zero shows that $r \cdot s = s \cdot r$, when either r or s is zero. Hence the commutative property of multiplication holds for all whole numbers.

That the associative property of multiplication holds when one or more of r, s, and t is zero can be shown by treating several cases, such as

$$(r \cdot s) \cdot 0 = 0 \quad \text{and} \quad r \cdot (s \cdot 0) = r \cdot 0 = 0,$$

with the result that

$$(r \cdot s) \cdot 0 = r \cdot (s \cdot 0).$$

PROBLEM SET 3–6

1. Show that the following equations are true.

    (a) $(r \cdot 0) \cdot t = r \cdot (0 \cdot t)$ (b) $(0 \cdot s) \cdot t = 0 \cdot (s \cdot t)$

    (c) $(0 \cdot 0) \cdot t = 0 \cdot (0 \cdot t)$

2. Without performing the operations indicated, show that the following are true. Indicate the properties used at each step.

    (a) $4 \cdot [3 \cdot (7 \cdot 8)] = (7 \cdot 4) \cdot (8 \cdot 3)$

    (b) $[(5 \cdot 8) \cdot 6]9 = 6 \cdot [8 \cdot (9 \cdot 5)]$

    (c) $(4 \cdot 2) \cdot (5 \cdot 7) \cdot 8 = (2 \cdot 7) \cdot 4 \cdot (8 \cdot 5)$

    (d) $(5 + 3 \cdot 2) + 8 = [(2 \cdot 3) + 8] + 5$ — note book

3. Without using the commutative property, show that $1 \cdot r = r$ for all whole numbers r.

4. Show that:

    (a) If $r \neq 0$ and $t \neq 0$, then $S_r \times S_t \neq \Phi$. (The symbol "$\neq$" means "is not equal to.")

    (b) If $r \neq 0$ and $t \neq 0$, then $r \cdot t \neq 0$.

    (c) If $r \cdot t = 0$, then $r = 0$ or $t = 0$. [Show clearly how the argument is based on part (b).]

    (d) Where in your mathematical experience have you used the result of part (c)?

5. On the basis of properties and operations discussed thus far, how could it be shown that $5(7 + 4) = (5 \cdot 7) + (5 \cdot 4)$? Indicate the steps.

3–7 DISTRIBUTIVE PROPERTY

Subtraction & division not a — not a —

Thus far, with the exception of Problem 5 above, the operations of addition and multiplication have been kept separate, in the sense that no problem has been considered in which both operations appear. In Problem 5 it was necessary to actually perform the operations indicated. Could we have worked this problem in another way? Yes, by using the following property, which has far-reaching consequences in mathematics.

Distributive property.

    $t \cdot (r + s) = t \cdot r + t \cdot s,$ for r, s, and t any whole numbers.

In a sense, this property (abbreviated D_+) permits a multiplication of $r + s$ by t to be carried out by distributing it first "over" r and then "over" s. If it is desired to obtain $7(6 + 9)$, this could be worked in either of two ways,

$$7(6 + 9) = 7 \cdot 15 = 105$$

or

$$7(6 + 9) = 7 \cdot 6 + 7 \cdot 9 = 42 + 63 = 105.$$

Applications of this property in arithmetic will be more meaningful as a result of the discussions in the next chapter. In algebra this property forms the basis of factoring. For instance, when $tr + ts$ is written as $t(r + s)$, it is called "removing the common factor t"; the procedure is legitimate because of the distributive property.

ILLUSTRATIVE EXAMPLE. Without performing the operations indicated, show that

$$2(7 + 9) + 7 \cdot 5 = 7(2 + 5) + 9 \cdot 2.$$

Solution. Now,

$$
\begin{aligned}
2(7 + 9) + 7 \cdot 5 &= (2 \cdot 7 + 2 \cdot 9) + 7 \cdot 5 && \text{(by } D_+) \\
&= 2 \cdot 7 + (2 \cdot 9 + 7 \cdot 5) && \text{(by } A_a) \\
&= 2 \cdot 7 + (7 \cdot 5 + 2 \cdot 9) && \text{(by } C_a) \\
&= (2 \cdot 7 + 7 \cdot 5) + 2 \cdot 9 && \text{(by } A_a) \\
&= (7 \cdot 2 + 7 \cdot 5) + 9 \cdot 2 && \text{(by } C_m \text{, twice)} \\
&= 7(2 + 5) + 9 \cdot 2 && \text{(by } D_+).
\end{aligned}
$$

Note the following:

(1) Only one property is applied at each step of the above procedure; this is not necessary, but it does enable one to see exactly what is being done.

(2) There is a reason why each step is performed. The first step is carried out because we want to couple the "2" with the "7" and then with the "9" separately rather than together, as it was in $2(7 + 9)$. The second and third steps are performed because it is desired to have $7 \cdot 5$ "next to" $2 \cdot 7$. The fourth step is performed so as to couple $7 \cdot 5$ with $2 \cdot 7$; the fifth so as to have 7 stand first, as it does in $7 \cdot 5$.

(3) The reason that each of these steps is desirable can be seen by keeping the required result in mind.

(4) If you work this problem you might well use different steps; that is quite legitimate so long as each step can be justified.

Before proving the distributive property, let us demonstrate its validity. To see that $3 \cdot (4 + 5) = 3 \cdot 4 + 3 \cdot 5$, take a set of nine circles; the set corresponding to $3(4 + 5) = 3 \cdot 9$ would be obtained by placing three of the nine-element sets side by side:

```
O O O    O O O    O O O

O O O    O O O    O O O

O O O    O O O    O O O
```

The circles could be given distinguishing marks so that no two circles would be alike; we would then have a set of distinct elements. This set would be the union of the two sets below, which correspond to $3 \cdot 4$ and $3 \cdot 5$:

$$3 \times 4 \quad + \quad 3 \times 5$$

○ ○ ○ ○   ○ ○ ○ ○ ○
○ ○ ○ ○   ○ ○ ○ ○ ○
○ ○ ○ ○   ○ ○ ○ ○ ○

As might be expected, this demonstration leads directly to a proof of the distributive property.

For reasons of notational simplification, let us write AB in place of $A \times B$, where A and B are sets; thus AB is a set, the cross product of A and B. Now $A \cup B$ is a set; hence $C(A \cup B)$ is a cross product.

As a first step it is desired to prove that

$$C(A \cup B) = CA \cup CB.$$

This equation will be true if it can be shown that each element of $C(A \cup B)$ is an element of $CA \cup CB$ and, conversely, that each element of $CA \cup CB$ is an element of $C(A \cup B)$. Introduce the notation $A = \{a_1, a_2, a_3, \ldots, a_r\}$, $B = \{b_1, b_2, b_3, \ldots, b_s\}$, and $C = \{c_1, c_2, c_3, \ldots, c_t\}$, where the a's, b's, and c's are distinct elements. It now follows that

$$A \cup B = \{a_1, a_2, a_3, \ldots, a_r, b_1, b_2, b_3, \ldots, b_s\},$$

so that

$$C(A \cup B) = \{\text{all pairs similar to } (c_2, a_4), (c_5, a_2), \text{ etc.}$$

$$\text{or } (c_2, b_3), (c_3, b_4), \text{ etc.}\}.$$

Any element such as (c_2, a_4) or (c_5, a_2) is an element of CA (why?) and hence an element of $CA \cup CB$, the union of CA and CB. Likewise, any element such as (c_2, b_3) or (c_3, b_4) is an element of CB and hence of $CA \cup CB$ (why?). Accordingly, each element of $C(A \cup B)$ is an element of $CA \cup CB$. Now prove the converse of this. Each element of $CA \cup CB$ belongs either to CA or to CB (why?). If the element in question belongs to CA, it must be similar to (c_2, a_6) and consequently belongs to $C(A \cup B)$ (see the above notation for elements of this set). Likewise, if the element in question belongs to CB, it must be similar to (c_1, b_4) and hence belong to $C(A \cup B)$ (why?). This shows that each element of $CA \cup CB$ belongs to $C(A \cup B)$. Then, by the second sentence of this paragraph we can now conclude that

$$C(A \cup B) = CA \cup CB.$$

The proof of the last result concerning sets is somewhat tedious. From this point, however, to the desired result concerning numbers, the proof is straightforward. First,

$$n[C(A \cup B)] = n(CA \cup CB) \qquad \text{(why?)}.$$

Now,

$$n[C(A \cup B)] = n(C) \cdot n(A \cup B) \qquad \text{(why?)}$$
$$= n(C)[n(A) + n(B)],$$

since A and B were chosen disjoint; also

$$n(CA \cup CB) = n(CA) + n(CB),$$

since CA and CB are disjoint because A and B are disjoint. Thus

$$n(CA \cup CB) = n(C) \cdot n(A) + n(C) \cdot n(B).$$

Combining the results of the last five equations, we obtain

$$n(C) \cdot [n(A) + n(B)] = n(C) \cdot n(A) + n(C) \cdot n(B),$$

or, using notation which comes from the definitions of A, B, and C, we have

$$t \cdot (r + s) = t \cdot r + t \cdot s.$$

PROBLEM SET 3-7

1. By using sets of $\square$'s illustrate why (a) $4 \cdot 3 + 4 \cdot 5 = 4(3 + 5)$ and (b) $2(6 + 5) = 2 \cdot 6 + 2 \cdot 5$.

2. Show, using properties proved previously, that $(r + s) \cdot t = r \cdot t + s \cdot t$.

3. State in words the meaning of the following expressions. [For example, $(4 + 7)5$ means "4 and 7 are added; then the result is multiplied by 5."]
   (a) $4(6 + 5)$ (b) $9(3 + 11)$ (c) $4 \cdot 6 + 4 \cdot 5$
   (d) $9 \cdot 3 + 9 \cdot 11$ (e) $2 + 3(6 + 8)$ (f) $8(11 + 2) + 12$
   (g) $[(11 + 5)7]12$ (h) $(2 + 3)6 + 7(4 + 9)$

4. Show that the following statements are true, without performing the operations indicated. Justify each step.
   (a) $(5 \cdot 3 + 7 \cdot 5) + 3 \cdot 9 = 3(5 + 9) + 5 \cdot 7$
   (b) $5(1 + 6) + 6 \cdot 11 = (11 + 5)6 + 5$
   (c) $5 \cdot 10 + (4 \cdot 10 + 3 \cdot 10) = [(5 + 4) + 3]10$
   (d) $(2 \cdot 100 + 3 \cdot 10) + (6 \cdot 100 + 7 \cdot 10) = (2 + 6) \cdot 100 + (3 + 7) \cdot 10$
   (e) $(2 \cdot 7^2 + 4 \cdot 7) + (3 \cdot 7^2 + 5 \cdot 7) = (2 + 3) \cdot 7^2 + (4 + 5)7$
   (f) $(4 + 7) \cdot (5 + 8) = (4 \cdot 5 + 4 \cdot 8) + (7 \cdot 5 + 7 \cdot 8)$

multiplication

5. (a) Is $3 \cdot (4 \cdot 5) = (3 \cdot 4) \cdot (3 \cdot 5)$? — *all false*
   (b) Is $3(4 + 5) = 3 \cdot 4 + 3 \cdot 5$? — *true* *multi + add*
   (c) Why is one of parts (a) and (b) right and the other wrong?

6. (a) Why is $4 + 4 = 1 \cdot 4 + 1 \cdot 4$?
   (b) Why is $1 \cdot 4 + 1 \cdot 4 = (1 + 1)4$?
   (c) Complete the demonstration that $4 + 4 = 2 \cdot 4$.

7. Stating the properties used, show that (a) $4 + 4 + 4 = 3 \cdot 4$, and
   (b) $7 + 7 + 7 + 7 + 7 = 5 \cdot 7$.

8. What previously introduced ideas do the results of Problem 7 illustrate?

3–8 SUBTRACTION

Read

Intuitively, subtraction is usually associated with the notion of "take away"; the expression "5 take away 3" may be illustrated by starting with a set of 5 objects and then removing (taking away) a subset consisting of 3 of the objects, for example, 5 marbles take away 3 marbles. This intuitive concept forms the basis of a more precise approach to subtraction.

Suppose that a set A is given, say $A = \{$John, Henry, Mabel, George, Ruth$\}$; then $B = \{$Henry, Mabel, Ruth$\}$ is a subset of A, that is, $B \subseteq A$ (in this case it is true that $B \subset A$). Define the set $C = \{$John, George$\}$. Intuitively, C is the set of remaining elements when B is "taken away" from A. Since

$$n(A) = 5, \qquad n(B) = 3, \qquad n(C) = 2,$$

then, again intuitively,

$$n(C) = n(A) - n(B).$$

To be more precise, we will now define set subtraction.

Definition. *Set subtraction.* If A and B are sets such that B is a subset of A, that is, $B \subseteq A$, then $A - B$ is the set of all elements of A which are not in B.

The set $A - B$ is the set of elements of A which remain when B is "removed" from A. This definition is somewhat more restrictive than that usually given in mathematics; however, it is sufficient for present needs.

ILLUSTRATIVE EXAMPLE 1.   Given $A = \{2, 5, 11, 15, 14, 3, 8\}$, $B = \{5, 14, 11, 8\}$, and $C = \{3, 14\}$, find, if possible, $A - B$, $A - C$, and $B - C$.

Solution. From the definition,

$$A - B = \{2, 15, 3\},$$
$$A - C = \{2, 5, 11, 15, 8\}.$$

Now C is not a subset of B (why?); hence $B - C$ does not exist, according to the definition.

Now it is possible to define number subtraction.

Definition. *Number subtraction.* If $r = n(A)$ and $s = n(B)$, where $B \subseteq A$, then

$$r - s = n(A) - n(B) = n(A - B).$$

ILLUSTRATIVE EXAMPLE 2. Find $6 - 2$.

Solution. Now $6 = n(S_6)$, $2 = n(S_2)$, and $S_2 \subseteq S_6$; hence $S_6 - S_2$ has meaning, and

$$n(S_6) - n(S_2) = n(S_6 - S_2).$$

Also, the set $S_6 - S_2 = \{3, 4, 5, 6\}$ matches S_4; accordingly,

$$6 - 2 = n(S_6 - S_2) = n(S_4) = 4.$$

In our early years, we learned the results of subtraction combinations such as $9 - 3$, $5 - 4$, and $8 - 5$. However, if the subtraction concept is linked to the addition concept, as will be done later, it would not be necessary to learn the subtraction combinations.

Before proceeding, work through some of the early problems at the end of this section.

DISCUSSION EXERCISES

1. Does $A - \Phi$ have meaning? Why?
2. Find $A - \Phi$.
3. Find $r - 0$, where r is a whole number.
4. Does the result of Exercise 3 hold for $r = 0$?
5. (a) Under what conditions is $n(B) = n(A)$?
   (b) Why is $4 < 6$?
   (c) Under what conditions is $n(B) < n(A)$?
   (d) Under what conditions is $s < r$?

The notation $r > s$ was defined to mean the same as $s < r$ (the symbol ">" is read "is greater than"). Since $4 < 6$ it follows that $6 > 4$.

6. Show that (a) if $r > s$, then $r - s$ has meaning; (b) if $r = s$, then $r - s$ has meaning.

7. Combine the two statements of Exercise 6 into a single statement.

8. Even though it is known that $6 > 4$, show that it would not be wrong to state that $6 \geq 4$, where "$\geq$" means "greater than or equal to."

9. Show why $4 - 6$ does not have meaning for the set of whole numbers.

10. Is subtraction commutative?

11. Take A and B as sets where $B \subseteq A$ and $C = A - B$.
    (a) Show, both by example and in general, that C and B are disjoint.
    (b) Show that $B \cup C = A$.
    (c) Find $n(A)$ in terms of $n(B)$ and $n(C)$.

12. For sets A and B of Exercise 11 let $r = n(A)$ and $s = n(B)$.
    (a) Find $n(C)$ without using the relationship which you obtained in 11(c).
    (b) Show that $s + (r - s) = r$.

The preceding sequence of exercises actually contains the proof of the following property.

Subtraction property. If $r \geq s$, then

$$s + (r - s) = r.$$

The subtraction property, abbreviated (Sub), states that

$r - s$ is the number which, when added to s, yields r.

For example, $7 - 4$ is the number which, when added to 4, yields 7, and $9 - 3$ is the number which, when added to 3, yields 9.

When we wish to find $7 - 4$, we try to think of a number which when added to 4 yields 7, i.e., we ask ourselves

$$4 + ? = 7.$$

Since addition combinations are learned first and come readily to mind, some people prefer this mode of subtraction.

The first method of subtraction discussed will be termed the *take-away* method, because of the intuitive concept inherent in the procedure. In this method we must actually learn subtraction combinations. The second method of subtraction will be termed the *add-on* procedure, since it is performed by finding what should be "added on" to one number to produce another number.

It has been shown that commutativity does not hold for subtraction. Associativity, which is somewhat more complicated when applied to subtraction, will be discussed in the next chapter. Distributivity for subtraction appears in Problem 12 of Problem Set 3–8.

Subtraction is said to be the *inverse operation* of addition. The relationship between the two operations can be thought of as follows:

In addition we "do," e.g., we add 7 to 2 to obtain 9.

In subtraction we "undo," e.g., we take 7 from 9 to obtain 2 or we take 2 from 9 to obtain 7.

PROBLEM SET 3–8   Read

1. By using sets of circles to represent marbles, describe the following subtractions intuitively: (a) $8 - 5$, (b) $7 - 2$.

2. Perform the following operations. If an operation cannot be performed, state why.
   - (a) {rat, boy, book, cat} − {boy, rat, cat} − subset
   - (b) {4, 3, 15, 25, 49, 74, 83} − {25, 4, 74, 15, 49}
   - (c) {1, 2, 8, 3, 5} − {8, 2, 7} no meaning
   - (d) {6 ≤ even numbers ≤ 20} − {10 ≤ even numbers ≤ 16}
   - (e) {4 ≤ odd numbers < 12} − {6 ≤ odd numbers < 7} empty set

3. (a) Is $S_8 - S_5 = S_3$? Why?
   (b) Is $n(S_8) - n(S_5) = n(S_3)$? Show why.

4. Use set ideas to find the following.
(a) $9 - 6$	(b) $12 - 4$	(c) $8 - 1$
(d) $10 - 3$	(e) $4 - 4$	(f) $6 - 6$

5. Fill in the blanks in the following problems. inverse
(a) $6 + 3 = 9$	(b) $3 + \_\_ = 11$	(c) $1 + 6 = 7$
(d) $2 + 6 = 8$	(e) $3 + 7 = 10$	(f) $4 + 8 = 12$

6. Change the following from "take-away" to "add-on" form, or vice versa, as the case may be. $9 = 5 + 4$
8−6 (a) $6 + 2 = 8$	(b) $7 + 4 = 11$	(c) $9 - 5 = 4$
(d) $10 - 6 = 4$	(e) $11 + 13 = 24$	(f) $20 - 11 = 9$

7. Show by using set ideas that $r - r = 0$, for any whole number r.

8. Why is $3 - 8$ meaningless in terms of present concepts?

9. Given $A = \{x, y, z, u, v\}$, $B = \{z, u\}$, and $C = \{r, s\}$; perform the indicated operations.
   (a) $A - B$ (h) $C(A - B)$ (c) CA and CB (d) $CA - CB$

10. From the results of Problem 9, is $C(A - B) = CA - CB$? Why?

11. Given r and s as whole numbers such that $r \geq s$, show, using set ideas, that there is a number u such that $s + u = r$.

12. For the following, use the notation of Problem 11 and let

$$B = \{b_1, b_2, b_3, \ldots, b_s\},$$
$$A = \{b_1, b_2, \ldots, b_s, a_1, a_2, a_3, \ldots, a_u\},$$
$$C = \{c_1, c_2, c_3, \ldots, c_t\}.$$

(a) Construct $A - B$.

(b) Find $n(A - B)$.

(c) Construct $C(A - B)$, CA, and CB.

(d) Is $C(A - B) = CA - CB$? Why?

(e) Show that $n(A) = r$.

(f) Show that $t(r - s) = tr - ts$.

(g) State the distributive property as it is applied to subtraction. This property will be denoted by D_-.

3–9 DIVISION

In mathematics it is always permissible and usually advisable to "build" on what is already known, i.e., to describe a new concept in terms of known concepts. In the previous section this procedure was not followed. To describe subtraction, we introduced the new concept of set subtraction, and this new concept was used to describe subtraction of numbers. Then it was proved that $r - s$ is the number which, when added to s, yields r, that is, $s + (r - s) = r$. This property itself could have been used as the definition of subtraction, i.e., we could have defined $r - s$ as "that number, if it exists, which when added to s yields r." If this had been done, we would have defined subtraction of numbers in terms of addition of numbers, so that the new concept would have been defined in terms of known concepts. We will use this approach to define division.

It is said that 12 is divisible by 4 because there exists a number 3 such that $12 = 3 \cdot 4$. The number 3 is the result of dividing 12 by 4, that is, $12 \div 4 = 3$. Likewise, $18 \div 6$ is 3, since $18 = 3 \cdot 6$, and $14 \div 7$ is 2, since $14 = 2 \cdot 7$. In general, the definition of division is as follows.

Definition. *Division of numbers.* If r and s are whole numbers, $s \neq 0$, such that there exists a whole number x for which $r = x \cdot s$, then r is divisible by s (or s divides r). That is,

$$r \div s = x, \quad \text{if} \quad r = x \cdot s.$$

In practice, division combinations are usually learned by working with *multiples*. For instance, combinations involving divisibility by 4 are learned by working with the multiples of 4, such as

$$4 = 1 \cdot 4, \quad 8 = 2 \cdot 4, \quad 12 = 3 \cdot 4, \quad 16 = 4 \cdot 4.$$

How can we tell directly whether or not 8 is divisible by 4 without having to consider several multiples of 4? Intuitively, we could start with a set of 8 objects, say □'s, and try to separate that set into subsets of 4 each. This would illustrate that

$$8 = 4 + 4 \quad \text{or} \quad 8 = 2 \cdot 4.$$

We could then conclude that
$$8 \div 4 = 2.$$

Suppose we had started with 12 □'s. We would first separate 4 □'s, which would amount to removing a subset from the original set. This should remind us of set subtraction; the procedure illustrates that $12 - 4 = 8$. We then remove another subset of 4 □'s, which illustrates that $(12 - 4) - 4 = 4$. According to the "add-on" property of subtraction this equation becomes

$$12 - 4 = 4 + 4, \quad \text{and then} \quad 12 = 4 + (4 + 4).$$

By Problem 7 of Problem Set 3–7, this last equation becomes $12 = 3 \cdot 4$. We now see that the result of dividing 12 by 4 can be found by continued subtraction of 4 from 12, the result being the number of 4's subtracted. In the same manner, to find $24 \div 6$ the number 6 could be subtracted time after time until eventually

$$\{[(24 - 6) - 6] - 6\} - 6 = 0;$$

then, by the property Sub,

$$[(24 - 6) - 6] - 6 = 0 + 6 = 6,$$
$$(24 - 6) - 6 = 6 + 6,$$
$$24 - 6 = 6 + (6 + 6),$$
$$24 = 6 + [6 + (6 + 6)]$$
$$= 6 + 6 + 6 + 6$$
$$= 4 \cdot 6.$$

If we were asked to divide 156 by 12, we probably would not have a division combination in mind which would give the result. However, we could find the result by continued subtraction. If this procedure seems onerous, reserve judgment until the next chapter.

Just as subtraction can be considered as "undoing" addition, so division can be thought of as "undoing" multiplication. For this reason, division is considered the inverse operation to multiplication.

There is no whole number x such that $32 = x \cdot 6$; hence $32 \div 6$ does not exist for whole numbers. (How could this be shown?) Yet it is common practice to say "divide 32 by 6." If you are confused, there is little wonder! Let us try to divide 32 by 6, using continued subtraction, until there results a number < 6. This would yield

$$[\{[(32 - 6) - 6] - 6\} - 6] - 6 = 2,$$

from which, by using the Sub property of subtraction, we obtain

$$32 = (6 + 6 + 6 + 6 + 6) + 2$$
$$= 5 \cdot 6 + 2.$$

When 32 is divided by 6 the number 5 is called the *quotient* and 2 the *remainder*. Obtaining this quotient and this remainder is what is meant by "divide 32 by 6."

If the same procedure were applied to divide 30 by 6, the result would be $30 = 5 \cdot 6 + 0$ or $30 = 5 \cdot 6$. The last equation indicates that 30 is divisible by 6, since the remainder is zero. This exemplifies the following statement: if x and y are counting numbers, y can be divided by x so as to obtain a remainder $< x$; if the remainder is zero, then y is divisible by x. These ideas will be discussed in greater detail in Chapter 5.

Is there a remainder when you attempt to divide 35 by 7? Yes, the remainder is zero! When someone says "there is no remainder," he is saying that zero is not anything. But zero *is* something; it is a number just as useful as 1 or 2 or 7.

We will now answer two somewhat troublesome questions. First, does $0 \div s$ have meaning? If $0 \div s = x$, then $0 = s \cdot x$ by the definition of division.

(a) When $s \neq 0$, then $0 = s \cdot x$ requires that x be zero (see Problem 4 of Problem Set 3–6); moreover, $0 = s \cdot 0$. Hence $0 \div s = 0$, when $s \neq 0$. For example, $0 \div 6 = 0$, since $0 = 6 \cdot 0$.

(b) When $s = 0$, then $0 = 0 \cdot x$ holds for any whole number x. Thus $0 \div 0$ could not have a unique result, and since an operation must yield a unique result, $0 \div 0$ is meaningless.

The second question is whether or not $r \div 0$ has meaning. If it has meaning, then $r = 0 \cdot x$; but then r must be zero. The case $0 \div 0$ was considered above and shown to be meaningless. Hence,

$$r \div 0 \quad \text{is impossible for } r \neq 0,$$

$$0 \div 0 \quad \text{is meaningless,}$$

and

$$0 \div s = 0, \quad \text{for any counting number } s.$$

A similar discussion for fractions appears in Section 7–11.

PROBLEM SET 3-9

1. Change the following statements to the inverse form. (For example, the inverse form of $30 \div 5 = 6$ is $30 = 5 \cdot 6$.)
   (a) $42 \div 6 = 7$ (b) $55 \div 11 = 5$ (c) $4 \cdot 7 = 28$
   (d) $9 \cdot 5 = 45$ (e) $4 \cdot 8 = 32$ (f) $26 \div 13 = 2$

2. Show, by continued subtraction, that the following are true. [For example, $21 - 7 = 14$, so that $(21 - 7) - 7 = 7$, and $21 - 7 = 7 + 7$, and $21 = 7 + (7 + 7) = 3 \cdot 7$.]
   (a) $18 = 2 \cdot 9$ (b) $21 = 3 \cdot 7$ (c) $20 = 4 \cdot 5$
   (d) $17 = 3 \cdot 5 + 2$ (e) $24 = 3 \cdot 7 + 3$ (f) $19 = 2 \cdot 7 + 5$

3. (a) Is $6 \div 3$ equal to $3 \div 6$? Why? *no answer*
   (b) Is division of numbers commutative? State why precisely. *division*

4. (a) Is $(54 \div 6) \div 3$ equal to $54 \div (6 \div 3)$? *yes*
   (b) Is division of numbers associative? *no*

subtraction not   not Commutative
comm - not ass,   not associative

3-10 SUMMARY

What, in this mass of detail, is most important? Broadly speaking, we now see how the structure of the system of whole numbers develops from a few basic definitions, and how the manipulations which are performed with numbers are based on these definitions and the resulting properties. Finally, by using these properties, we should be able to determine when a manipulation is being performed correctly.

Some of the properties of whole numbers which have been developed thus far are listed below.

Multiplication + addition study both Comm + ass,

C_a: $x + y = y + x$.
A_a: $x + (y + z) = (x + y) + z$.
C_m: $xy = yx$.
A_m: $x(yz) = (xy)z$.
D_+: $x(y + z) = xy + xz$, $(y + z)x = yx + zx$.
$P_{0,a}$: $x + 0 = x = 0 + x$.
P_1: $x \cdot 1 = x = 1 \cdot x$.
$P_{0,m}$: $x \cdot 0 = 0 = 0 \cdot x$.
Sub: $x - y = z$ means $x = y + z$.
D_-: $x(y - z) = xy - xz$, if $y \geq z$.

The above properties hold for all whole numbers. The abbreviations for the properties will be used in ensuing discussions when reasons are stated for taking certain steps.

CHAPTER 4

Computations: The Application of Properties

As young children many of us had the urge to investigate, to question. But these natural inclinations were often thwarted by having to learn arithmetic on the basis of "do it because it works" or "do it because you are told to." We can attempt to overcome such frustrations, as well as fear and dislike of mathematics, by thoroughly investigating the "inner workings" of mathematics and the reasons why things interact as they do. This is why so much time is being, and will be, spent on an analysis of the properties of numbers and their applications.

It is amazing how few people understand a "long division" computation. This, and other basic computations, will be analyzed in this chapter, particularly as they apply to the Hindu-Arabic system of numerals. First, the basic principles of that system will be discussed more thoroughly.

4–1 HINDU-ARABIC NUMERATION SYSTEM *also decimal system*

The symbols (numerals) 0, 1, 2, 3, . . . introduced in Chapter 2 are, of course, part and parcel of the Hindu-Arabic system of numeration. As larger sets were used, more numerals were needed. Suppose that $R = $ {all fingers on a "normal" man's hands}, $S = $ {all elements of R, □}, $T = $ {all elements of R, □, △}, and $U = $ {all elements of R, □, △, ◻}. New symbols can be introduced for the numbers of these sets; for instance, $n(R) = *$, $n(S) = \theta$, $n(T) = \dagger$, $n(U) = \P$. But for further sets, still more symbols would be needed. This horribly cumbersome symbolism (as cumbersome as that of the Greeks) can be simplified materially by noting that $* = * + 0$, $\theta = * + 1$, $\dagger = * + 2$, $\P = * + 3$, etc. That is, if $*$ is used as a symbol for a basic number, or *unit*, then $n(S)$, $n(T)$, and $n(U)$ can be related to it as follows:

$$n(S) = * + 1, \quad n(T) = * + 2, \quad n(U) = * + 3.$$

Hence an agreement is made to write

$$n(R) = 10, \quad \text{meaning } 1 \cdot * + 0,$$

$$n(S) = 11, \quad \text{meaning } 1 \cdot * + 1,$$

$$n(T) = 12, \quad \text{meaning } 1 \cdot * + 2, \text{ etc.}$$

Continuation of this procedure leads to the set $V = \{\text{all fingers and toes of a "normal" man}\}$, and since V matches $S_2 \times R$, we have

$$n(V) = n(S_2) \cdot n(R) = 2 \cdot * = 2 \cdot * + 0.$$

Hence $n(V)$ would be written 20. Since $n\{\text{elements of } V, \square\} = n(V) + 1 = 2 \cdot * + 1$, it is agreed to write this 21. What would 22 mean?

This procedure can be continued until we reach a set W such that $n(W) = 99$. Now consider $X = \{\text{elements of } W, \square\}$. Suppose we desire to introduce no new symbols, i.e., we want to use no symbols other than $0, 1, 2, \ldots, 9$ in writing $n(X)$. We could use X as a new basic set, call the number $n(X)$ "hundred," and write it 100, since $n(X) = 1 \cdot n(X) + 0 \cdot * + 0 \cdot 1$. The number of the next "larger" set would then be written 101. We have introduced a new unit, the "hundred" unit. Continuing with "larger" sets, we eventually obtain a set Y such that $n(Y)$ is written 999. Again we are faced with the problem of "running out of digits" when using three of them. We must introduce another new unit, the "thousand" unit. This procedure continues indefinitely. Since $* - 10$ and $n(X) = 100$, we will now use the more usual notation, for example, $22 = 2 \cdot 10 + 2$ and $346 = 3 \cdot 100 + 4 \cdot 10 + 6$.

The numbers ten, hundred, thousand, etc. are units in the sense that other numbers are being expressed in terms of them.

If the elements of X and also of $S_{10} \times S_{10}$ were displayed, it could be shown that these two sets match. Accordingly,

$$n(X) = n(S_{10} \times S_{10})$$
$$= n(S_{10}) \cdot n(S_{10}),$$
$$100 = 10 \cdot 10.$$

Similarly, $\{\text{elements of } Y, \square\}$ will match $S_{10} \times S_{100}$, so that

$$n\{\text{elements of } Y, \square\} = n(S_{10} \times S_{100})$$
$$= n(S_{10}) \cdot n(S_{100}),$$
$$1000 = 10 \cdot 100.$$

Continuation of this procedure yields

$$\text{each unit} = 10 \cdot (\text{previous unit}).$$

Since ten is the basic unit size and other units are related to it, this is a base-ten system, often called the *decimal* system.

The procedures described above are merely the introduction of the "position" concept into our notation, whereby only the basic symbols 0, 1, 2, 3, . . . , 9 are used and numbers ten or larger are indicated by placing these symbols in particular positions. In the number 547, the 4 refers to tens and the 5 to hundreds. We say that the 4 is the "tens digit" and the 5 is the "hundreds digit." This system of notation depends heavily on the use of a symbol for zero. Indeed, such a system could not have been developed before the concept of zero was known and a symbol introduced to represent it. Thus, in the Hindu-Arabic system of notation, every numeral has a form like

$$a_5 \cdot 10000 + a_4 \cdot 1000 + a_3 \cdot 100 + a_2 \cdot 10 + a_1,$$

where the a_i's are the digits and each is one of 0, 1, 2, 3, . . . , 9. These digits are themselves numerals.

In a numeral such as 634, the digit 4 will be called the "ones" digit, since it counts the number of 1's. Many people refer to this digit as the units digit, so that care must be taken not to confuse this usage with our use of "unit" as the number of a basic set. A number which has three digits in its Hindu-Arabic numeral will be referred to as a three-digit number.

In the remaining portion of this chapter modes of procedure for performing the operations of addition, multiplication, subtraction, and division will be considered *for numbers whose numerals are written in the Hindu-Arabic, or decimal, system.*

4–2   ADDITION OF NATURAL NUMBERS

In Chapter 3 we added numbers such as 10 and 2 by using disjoint sets, matching of sets, and the definition of addition of numbers. How can $13 + 24$ be performed without using set ideas? Writing each numeral in a form which expresses its meaning, we have

$$
\begin{aligned}
13 + 24 &= (1 \cdot 10 + 3) + (2 \cdot 10 + 4) \\
&= (1 \cdot 10 + 2 \cdot 10) + (3 + 4) &&\text{(by } A_a \text{ and } C_a) \\
&= (1 + 2)10 + (3 + 4) &&\text{(by } D_+) \\
&= 3 \cdot 10 + 7 &&\text{(addition combinations)} \\
&= 37.
\end{aligned}
$$

This example indicates that when two-digit numbers are to be added, the meaning of the notation should be considered. By the associative and commutative properties of addition, we can "collect" the tens parts and the ones parts separately. Then by applying the distributive law, we can reduce the problem to one of applying basic addition combinations (e.g., the $1 + 2$ and $3 + 4$ in the above display). If more than two digits are involved, is anything new needed? Let us try to add 234 and 153:

$234 + 153$

$= (2 \cdot 100 + 3 \cdot 10 + 4) + (1 \cdot 100 + 5 \cdot 10 + 3)$ — *Expanded notation*

$= (2 \cdot 100 + 1 \cdot 100) + (3 \cdot 10 + 5 \cdot 10) + (4 + 3)$ — (by A_a and C_a)

$= (2 + 1)100 + (3 + 5)10 + (4 + 3)$ (by D_+)

$= 3 \cdot 100 + 8 \cdot 10 + 7 = 387.$ *positional notation*

Hence, three-digit numbers can be added in the same way as two-digit numbers, the only difference being that the application of the properties A_a and C_a is more involved (work through all the details in the above display). In fact, this method may be used for adding three or more numbers with any number of digits.

Now try $64 + 78$. After three steps, we have

$$64 + 78 = (6 + 7)10 + (4 + 8),$$

but neither $6 + 7$ nor $4 + 8$ is a single digit. This difficulty is easy to overcome; since $6 + 7 = 1 \cdot 10 + 3$ and $4 + 8 = 1 \cdot 10 + 2$, then

$64 + 78 = (1 \cdot 10 + 3)10 + (1 \cdot 10 + 2)$

$= [(1 \cdot 10)10 + 3 \cdot 10] + (1 \cdot 10 + 2)$ (by D_+)

$= (1 \cdot 10)10 + (3 + 1)10 + 2$ (by A_a and D_+)

$= 1 \cdot (10 \cdot 10) + 4 \cdot 10 + 2$ (by A_m)

$= 1 \cdot 100 + 4 \cdot 10 + 2.$

It was stated earlier that there were two stages of mathematical procedure: a learning stage, when everything must be done in great detail, and a manipulative stage, where reasons can be omitted and several detailed steps can be performed simultaneously. This second stage must not be attempted until the ideas used in the first are thoroughly understood.

After we have worked several problems of the types discussed previously, we should be ready to perform additions in a somewhat more formal fashion, i.e., by the "usual" procedure. Consider $348 + 549 + 627$. Of course, it is usual to write these numbers in a column instead of in a row. That is, to abbreviate

	3 hundreds +	4 tens +	8 ones
(+)	5 hundreds +	4 tens +	9 ones
(+)	6 hundreds +	2 tens +	7 ones
	14 hundreds +	10 tens +	24 ones

we write

3	4	8
5	4	9
6	2	7
14	10	24

hundreds   tens   ones

This column addition can be justified by the horizontal addition used earlier in this section. For instance, use of properties A_a, C_a, and D_+ showed that the tens terms should be grouped together and the tens digits added to give the number of tens. Since $24 = 2 \cdot 10 + 4$, $10(10) = (1 \cdot 10 + 0)10 = 1 \cdot 100 + 0 \cdot 10$ and $14(100) = (1 \cdot 10 + 4)100 = 1 \cdot 1000 + 4 \cdot 100$, the bottom line of the above display can be replaced by

$$
\begin{array}{c}
2\;4 \\
1\;0 \\
1\;4
\end{array}
$$

This arrangement was justified previously by using A_a and D_+. Adding the digits in these last columns yields the result. The complete procedure is shown in the display at the right. Usually this procedure is abbreviated further by "carrying." For example, when the digits in the right-hand column have been added, the "2" in 24 is recognized as meaning 2 tens; hence 2 is added in the tens column. If this "2" is written, it is usually placed at the top of the tens column.

$$
\begin{array}{r}
3\;4\;8 \\
5\;4\;9 \\
6\;2\;7 \\
\hline
2\;4 \\
1\;0 \\
1\;4 \\
\hline
1\;5\;2\;4
\end{array}
$$

Note that if "carrying" is not used, it is just as easy and just as correct to proceed from left to right as it is to proceed from right to left. In this instance, time can be saved by using a form of "backward carrying," such as that used in the display at the left. Note how certain digits have been crossed out, so that only the digits in the answer remain.

$$
\begin{array}{r}
3\;4\;8 \\
5\;4\;9 \\
6\;2\;7 \\
\hline
1\;4 \\
5\;0 \\
2\;4 \\
\hline
\end{array}
$$

In practice, it is desirable to add in the simplest fashion possible, so long as the method is completely understood. Accuracy will be promoted by understanding.

PROBLEM SET 4–2

1. Perform each of the following additions by three methods: (1) horizontal procedure, such as that used in the examples $234 + 153$ and $64 + 78$ (give reasons for each step); (2) column procedure, right to left; (3) column procedure, left to right.

    (a) $987 + 763 + 495$
    (c) $59 + 47 + 68 + 74$
    (e) $435 + 62 + 1014$
    (g) $5480 + 6007 + 159$

    (b) $4863 + 7928 + 683$
    (d) $62345 + 97216$
    (f) $31458 + 6271 + 13 + 287$
    (h) $683 + 114 + 8073$

2. How can the answers to Problem 1 be checked? By what properties can your checking procedure be justified?

3. Without actually performing the additions, determine in each of the following whether or not the results would be the same. Justify your answers.
(a) $38 + 79$ and $78 + 39$ — *same digits* – $C_a + a_a$
(b) $342 + 687 + 519$ and $642 + 589 + 317$ – $C_a + a_a$
(c) $483 + 527 + 946$ and $526 + 487 + 943$ – $C_a + a_a$

4. Perform the following additions in the base indicated. Work each problem both horizontally and vertically.
(a) $634 + 565$ (base seven)   (b) $39T4 + E98T$ (base twelve)
(c) $101101 + 1101101$ (base two)

5. Were the properties A_a, C_a, D_+, and A_m used in performing the additions of Problem 4? If so, give an example of each.

6. Is XXVI + XVIII equal to XVIII + XXVI? Why? *yes*

7. Is the commutative property of addition a property of numbers or does its truth or falsity depend on the notation used? Explain.

8. Answer the question of Problem 7 for A_a, C_m, A_m, and D_+.

4–3 EXPONENTS

The number 347 can be written as $3 \cdot 100 + 4 \cdot 10 + 7$; likewise 428359 can be written

$$4 \cdot 100000 + 2 \cdot 10000 + 8 \cdot 1000 + 3 \cdot 100 + 5 \cdot 10 + 9.$$

Let us see if this cumbersome notation can be simplified. Each unit was introduced as 10 times the previous unit, that is, $10 = 10 \cdot 1$, $100 = 10 \cdot 10$, $1000 = 10 \cdot 100$, etc. Hence

$$100 = 10 \cdot 10,$$
$$1000 = 10 \cdot 100 = 10 \cdot 10 \cdot 10,$$
$$10{,}000 = 10(1000) = 10 \cdot 10 \cdot 10 \cdot 10,$$
$$100{,}000 = 10(10000) = 10 \cdot 10 \cdot 10 \cdot 10 \cdot 10.$$

In the product $10 \cdot 10$, each 10 is called a *factor;* likewise, in $2 \cdot 3 \cdot 4$ the 2, 3, and 4 are factors. Suppose 10^2 is defined as $10 \cdot 10$, 10^3 as $10 \cdot 10 \cdot 10$, 10^k as $10 \cdot 10 \cdot 10 \cdots$ to k factors. Then

$$100 = 10^2, \qquad 1000 = 10^3, \qquad 10{,}000 = 10^4, \qquad 100{,}000 = 10^5$$

would yield the abbreviated notation

$$428359 = 4 \cdot 10^5 + 2 \cdot 10^4 + 8 \cdot 10^3 + 3 \cdot 10^2 + 5 \cdot 10 + 9.$$

Let us now define this exponential notation in general.

Definition. *Exponential notation.* If k is a counting number, then x^k means $x \cdot x \cdot x \cdots$ to k factors, i.e., x^k is the product of k like factors x. The notation x^k is read "x to the kth *power*" or "x to the *power k.*"

Hence, $5^4 = 5 \cdot 5 \cdot 5 \cdot 5$, $7^6 = 7 \cdot 7 \cdot 7 \cdot 7 \cdot 7 \cdot 7$, $a^4 = a \cdot a \cdot a \cdot a$, etc.

Now let us use this notation to find the product of 5^3 and 5^4:

$$
\begin{aligned}
5^3 \cdot 5^4 &= (5 \cdot 5 \cdot 5)(5 \cdot 5 \cdot 5 \cdot 5) \\
&= 5 \cdot 5 \cdot 5 \cdot 5 \cdot 5 \cdot 5 \cdot 5 \quad \text{(by extension of A}_\text{m}\text{)} \\
&= 5 \cdot 5 \cdot 5 \cdots \text{to 7 factors} \\
&= 5^7 \\
&= 5^{3+4}.
\end{aligned}
$$

Would the following be true: $4^2 \cdot 4^3 = 4^{2+3}$, $8^4 \cdot 8^5 = 8^{4+5}$, $a^2 \cdot a^3 = a^{2+3}$, $b^4 \cdot b^7 = b^{4+7}$? This type of thought sequence and the preceding definition should yield the following property immediately.

Multiplication property for exponential notation. If k and m are counting numbers, then

$$
x^k \cdot x^t = x^{k+t}.
$$

Could the above property (abbreviated E_m) be used to simplify $5^3 \cdot 4^2$? It could not, because the factors in 5^3 are fives, while those in 4^2 are fours; in the statement of E_m the factors of both x^k and x^m are x's, that is, they are alike. In a number written in exponential form, such as x^k, the k is called the *exponent* and the x is called the *base*. With this terminology, we can express E_m in words:

The product of two numbers in exponential form with the *same base* equals a new number in exponential form with the same base, the new exponent being the sum of the original exponents.

If you learn E_m in word form, you will find it much easier to apply correctly.

Be careful not to explain 5^6 as "5 multiplied by itself 6 times," since this might be interpreted as $5(5 \cdot 5 \cdot 5 \cdot 5 \cdot 5)$, and such is not the meaning of 5^6. Explain 5^6 as "5 times 5 times 5, etc., to six factors."

PROBLEM SET 4-3

1. Write each of the following in a form which will show its meaning.
    (a) 7^5 (b) 12^6 (c) 8^4 (d) x^6 (e) x^8 (f) r^5

Read

2. Write the following numbers in *expanded form*, using exponential notation. (For example, $307 = 3 \cdot 10^2 + 0 \cdot 10 + 7$.)

(a) 62,349   (b) 148,602   (c) 6,459,027
(d) 82,051,487   (e) 2,008   (f) 400,305

3. Write each of the following products as a single number in exponential form.

(a) $5^6 \cdot 5^{13} = 5^{19}$?   (b) $12^7 \cdot 12^6$

(c) $4^{15} \cdot 4^{32}$ $4 + ?$ 30 (d) $(8^{127} \cdot 8^{345})8^{21}$

(e) $x^7 \cdot (x^{18} \cdot x^5)$ X (f) $y^{10} \cdot y^{15}$

(g) $r^{52} \cdot (r^{16} \cdot r^{11})$ (h) $(t^{14} \cdot t^{27})(t^5 \cdot t^{17})$

(i) $x^a \cdot x^b = x^{a+b}$ $(s+t) + (u+w)$ (j) $(x^r \cdot x^s)x^t$

(k) $(y^s \cdot y^t)(y^u \cdot y^w)$ (l) $s^u(s^w \cdot s^a)$ $S^{u+(w+a)}$

4. Is $x^a \cdot x^b$ equal to $x^b \cdot x^a$, where x, a, and b are counting numbers? Why or why not? Cm

5. Can E_m be used to simplify $5^2 + 5^3$? Why or why not? *cannot because it is addition*

6. Show that $4^3(4^2 + 4^5) = 4^5 + 4^8$. – Dm

7. Show that $x^a(x^b + x^c) = x^{a+b} + x^{a+c}$ Dm

8. The notation x^1 is defined as x. Em x^k if $x^1 = x$

(a) Show how this definition agrees with the definition of x^k, for $k = 1$, if the meaning of "factor" is broadened.

(b) Using this definition, show that Property E_m holds for $k = 1$. $x^2 x = x^1$

4–4   MULTIPLICATION OF NATURAL NUMBERS

The units used in the decimal system could be considered as forming a scale:

ten-thousands	thousands	hundreds	tens	ones
10000	1000	100	10	1

Each unit (reading from right to left) is one place higher in the scale than the preceding unit; the hundreds unit is two places higher than the ones unit; the ten-thousands unit is three places higher than the tens unit.

Now consider 10(426):

$$
\begin{aligned}
10(426) &= 10(4 \cdot 10^2 + 2 \cdot 10 + 6) \\
&= 10(4 \cdot 10^2) + 10(2 \cdot 10) + 10 \cdot 6 &&\text{(by } D_+) \\
&= 4(10 \cdot 10^2) + 2(10 \cdot 10) + 6 \cdot 10 &&\text{(by } A_m \text{ and } C_m) \\
&= 4 \cdot 10^3 + 2 \cdot 10^2 + 6 \cdot 10 &&\text{(by } E_m) \\
&= 4 \cdot 10^3 + 2 \cdot 10^2 + 6 \cdot 10 + 0 \cdot 1 \\
&= 4260.
\end{aligned}
$$

truly

In 4260 each of the original digits (of 426) is now the digit for a unit one place higher in the scale than previously, and the ones digit is zero. In general:

If a number is multiplied by 10^k each of the original digits becomes associated with a unit which is k places higher in the scale than formerly, and each of the last k digits in the product is zero.

By this method, perform 7638×10^3 and 4259×10^4. Isn't this statement a precise formulation of the usual rule about "adding" a certain number of zeros? Although the statement of the usual rule is much shorter, it is rarely completely understood.

Now we are ready to consider the general problem of multiplication. First, we will multiply 624 by a one-digit number, say by 7.

$$
\begin{aligned}
7 \cdot 624 &= 7(6 \cdot 10^2 + 2 \cdot 10 + 4) & &\text{— E N} \\
&= 7(6 \cdot 10^2) + 7(2 \cdot 10) + 7 \cdot 4 & &\text{(by } D_+) \\
&= (7 \cdot 6)10^2 + (7 \cdot 2)10 + 7 \cdot 4 & &\text{(by } A'_m) \\
&= 42 \cdot 10^2 + 14 \cdot 10 + 28 & &\text{— multiplication fact} \\
&= (4 \cdot 10 + 2)10^2 + (1 \cdot 10 + 4)10 + (2 \cdot 10 + 8) & &\text{E, notation} \\
&= [(4 \cdot 10)10^2 + 2 \cdot 10^2] + [(1 \cdot 10)10 + 4 \cdot 10] + (2 \cdot 10 + 8) & & \\
& & &\text{(by } D_+) \text{ twice} \\
&= 4 \cdot 10^3 + (2 \cdot 10^2 + 1 \cdot 10^2) + (4 \cdot 10 + 2 \cdot 10) + 8 & & \\
& & &\text{(by } A_m, A_a, \text{ and } E_m) \\
&= 4 \cdot 10^3 + (2 + 1)10^2 + (4 + 2)10 + 8 & &\text{(by } D_+) \text{ twice} \\
&= 4 \cdot 10^3 + 3 \cdot 10^2 + 6 \cdot 10 + 8 & &\text{— basic facts of addition} \\
&= 4368. \quad \text{positional Notation} & &
\end{aligned}
$$

So, application of the same old properties does the job! This horizontal procedure can be replaced by a vertical procedure which is better suited to actual practice. As a first step we obtain

6	2	4
		(×) 7
42	14	28

where the 2 means $2 \cdot 10$, so that we actually perform $7(2 \cdot 10) = (7 \cdot 2)10$; hence the number 14 appears in the tens column. In the horizontal method we saw that the 28, the 14(10), and the 42(10²) must be added to give the final result. Therefore, as shown in the discussion of addition, the vertical procedure may be written in a better form, as shown at the left below. Here the concept of "carrying" can, and should be, used, but only after one becomes thoroughly conversant with the reasons why. When the numbers carried are not written down, the form is that shown at the right below.

$$
\begin{array}{r}
6\ 2\ 4 \\
(\times)\ 7 \\
\hline
2\ 8 \\
1\ 4 \\
4\ 2 \\
\hline
4\ 3\ 6\ 8
\end{array}
\qquad\qquad
\begin{array}{r}
6\ 2\ 4 \\
(\times)\ 7 \\
\hline
4\ 3\ 6\ 8
\end{array}
$$

Now consider a multiplication where the multiplier has two or more digits, say 37. We obtain

$$
\begin{aligned}
37 \times 624 &= (3 \cdot 10 + 7)624 \\
&= (3 \cdot 624)10 + 7 \cdot 624 \qquad \text{(by } D_+, A_m, \text{ and } C_m).
\end{aligned}
$$

Now the products $3 \cdot 624$ and $7 \cdot 624$ involve multiplying by one-digit numbers; hence, they can be obtained by the method discussed above. Thus,

$$
(3 \cdot 624)10 = 1872 \cdot 10 = 18720;
$$

accordingly,

$$
37 \times 624 = 18720 + 4368.
$$

Since additions are easier to perform when the numbers are written under each other, the above expression may be written as shown at the right. It must be realized that the "3" in 37 represents $3 \cdot 10$; hence the multiplication of $3 \cdot 624$ by 10 gives rise to the zero in the fourth row.

$$
\begin{array}{r}
624 \\
(\times)\ 37 \\
\hline
4368 \\
18720 \\
\hline
23088
\end{array}
$$

If the multiplier has three digits, such as in the example

$$
\begin{aligned}
637 \times 624 &= (6 \cdot 10^2 + 3 \cdot 10 + 7)624 \\
&= (6 \cdot 624)10^2 + (3 \cdot 624)10 + 7 \cdot 624,
\end{aligned}
$$

we will have to add a third term, which has two zeros on the right (see display at the right); many persons leave out the zeros on the right end of rows four and five. (How can this be justified?) This should be avoided until the whole procedure has been mastered; retaining the zeros may well increase understanding and prevent mistakes.

$$
\begin{array}{r}
624 \\
(\times)\ 637 \\
\hline
4368 \\
18720 \\
374400 \\
\hline
397488
\end{array}
$$

ILLUSTRATIVE EXAMPLE. Show, using both horizontal and vertical procedures, how to multiply 76 by 49.

Solution.

$$49 \times 76 = (4 \cdot 10 + 9)76 = (4 \cdot 10)76 + 9 \cdot 76 \quad - \text{EX}$$
$$= (4 \cdot 76)10 + 9 \cdot 76 \quad A - C$$
$$= [4(7 \cdot 10 + 6)] \cdot 10 + 9(7 \cdot 10 + 6) \quad D$$
$$= [4 \cdot 7 \cdot 10 + 4 \cdot 6]10 + (9 \cdot 7 \cdot 10 + 9 \cdot 6) \quad A\,A \qquad \overset{E}{M}$$
$$= [(4 \cdot 7)10^2 + (4 \cdot 6)10] + [(9 \cdot 7)10 + 9 \cdot 6].$$

	7 6	76
	(×) 4 9	(×) 49
$9 \cdot 6$:	54	54
$(9 \cdot 7) \cdot 10$:	63	630
$(4 \cdot 6) \cdot 10$:	24	240
$(4 \cdot 7) \cdot 10^2$:	28	2800
		3724

PROBLEM SET 4-4

1. The number 7345 is to be multiplied by 1000.
   (a) What is the effect on each digit of 7345? *all changed 3 powers of 10*
   (b) Name the unit with which each digit of 7345 is associated in the result
       (e.g., 5 becomes the ___?___ digit). - *moved 3 places → 5 in 1000*
   (c) Which digits in the result are zero? *100 - 10 - 0*

2. Repeat Problem 1 for 796×10^5.

3. Repeat Problem 1 for 1345×10^4.

4. Use both horizontal and vertical procedures to explain how to multiply the following.

   (a) 8×724 (b) 6×395 (c) 5×1438
   (d) 9×2876 (e) 27×453 (f) 65×1428
   (g) 97×604 (h) 432×763

5. Devise a procedure for multiplying 48 by 60 which would be simpler than the usual two-digit by two-digit procedure. Justify each step.

6. Explain how to multiply the following in a simpler than usual fashion.

   (a) 436×80 (b) 1427×600 (c) 3415×4000
   (d) 3410×400 (e) 5600×73000 (f) 6010×2030

7. (a) If you were going to learn how to multiply, using Roman numerals, what would be the first step? Illustrate.
   (b) Multiply XVII by V. Justify each step by using a horizontal procedure.
   (c) Multiply CLXXVI by X and CCLXV by L.
   (d) Multiply XXVII by VI. Justify each step by a horizontal procedure.
   (e) Multiply DCCXVI by XV and MCCLXXV by CV.
   (f) Does the Roman numeral system lend itself to "easy" multiplication?

8. Using the horizontal procedure, develop a method for multiplying the following in the numeral systems indicated: (a) 34(seven) × 256(seven), (b) 93(twelve) × 4T2(twelve).

9. Carry out the following multiplications in the numeral systems indicated.

   (a) 503(seven) × 362(seven)   (b) 473(eight) × 215(eight)
   (c) 3T8(twelve) × ETT(twelve)   (d) 43E(twelve) × 97E(twelve)
   (e) 342(five) × 403(five)   (f) 1011(two) × 1001(two)
   (g) 1101(two) × 10101(two)   (h) 1110(two) × 101(two)

4-5 PROPERTIES OF EQUALITY AND PARENTHESES

Equality has three fundamental properties, which may seem trivial at first glance. Some of these properties have already been used though not pointed out.

Fundamental properties of equality.

Reflexive: $x = x$.
Symmetric: if $x = y$, then $y = x$.
Transitive: if $x = y$ and $y = z$, then $x = z$.

An example of the use of the reflexive property will appear in the next paragraph; the transitive property will be exemplified later in this section. The symmetric property enables us to use an equality "in either direction"; as an example, the associative property of addition could be used to write

$$r + (s + t) \quad \text{in place of} \quad (r + s) + t$$

or

$$(r + s) + t \quad \text{in place of} \quad r + (s + t).$$

Also, all too often a student of algebra will recognize that

$$(a + b)^2 \quad \text{is equal to} \quad a^2 + 2ab + b^2,$$

but will fail to recognize that

$$a^2 + 2ab + b^2 \quad \text{is equal to} \quad (a + b)^2.$$

Where were the symmetric and transitive properties used on page 55? Watch for the use of these properties in later work.

We have been using $x = y$ to mean that x and y are symbols for the same number. For example, 12 and $3(6 - 2)$ are symbols for the same number. In that case, would it be reasonable to replace each by the other in a mathematical expression? For instance, if in the expression $12 + 35$ the 12 were to be replaced by $3(6 - 2)$, would it seem sensible to have

$12 + 35$ and $3(6 - 2) + 35$ represent the same number? Let us agree that such a replacement is reasonable; it will be one of the "ground rules" which we agree to use in our thought patterns. Now, since $x + z = x + z$, by the reflexive property of equality, then if $x = y$ it should follow that $x + z = y + z$. The last equation was obtained by replacing one of the x's by a y. This principle is stated formally in the following property.

Addition property of equality.

$$\text{If} \quad x = y, \quad \text{then} \quad x + z = y + z,$$

for all whole numbers x, y, and z.

Note how this property (designated by AP) is used in the proof of another important property, which follows.

Parentheses property PP$_1$. If x, y, and z are whole numbers such that $y \geq z$, then

$$(x + y) - z = x + (y - z).$$

To prove this property, we begin with the equation

$$(y - z) = y - z,$$

which, by the reflexive property, is known to be true. The parentheses have been inserted to indicate that the number on the left-hand side is to be treated as an entity. Applying the subtraction property (Section 3–8) to this last equation, we obtain

$$(y - z) + z = y,$$

which, by the property AP, yields

$$x + [(y - z) + z] = x + y.$$

Accordingly,

$$[x + (y - z)] + z = x + y \qquad \text{(by A}_a\text{)}$$

and

$$x + (y - z) = (x + y) - z \qquad \text{(by Sub)}.$$

The property PP$_1$ permits us to write

$$(7 + 5) - 3 \quad \text{in place of} \quad 7 + (5 - 3)$$

or, by the symmetric property of equality,

$$7 + (5 - 3) \quad \text{in place of} \quad (7 + 5) - 3.$$

Property PP$_1$ will be used extensively in the next section.

There is another parentheses property similar to that above.

Parentheses property PP$_2$. If x, y, and z are whole numbers such that $x \geq y + z$, then

$$x - (y + z) = (x - y) - z.$$

To prove this property, let $x - (y + z) = a$. Then

$$x = (y + z) + a \qquad \text{(by Sub)}$$
$$x = y + (z + a) \qquad \text{(by A}_\text{a}\text{)}$$
$$x - y = z + a \qquad \text{(why?)}$$
$$(x - y) - z = a \qquad \text{(why?).}$$

Since both $x - (y + z)$ and $(x - y) - z$ equal a, then $x - (y + z) = (x - y) - z$.

Note that both PP$_1$ and PP$_2$ are similar to the associative property of addition.

The transitive property of equality was used in the proof of PP$_2$. From the first line of the proof, $x = (y + z) + a$. But $(y + z) + a = y + (z + a)$ by A$_\text{a}$. Hence $x = y + (z + a)$, by the transitive property of equality. These steps are frequently combined without comment, as was done in the preceding proof.

ILLUSTRATIVE EXAMPLE. Show that $(12 + 14) - (5 + 8) = (12 - 5) + (14 - 8)$ without actually performing the indicated additions and subtractions.

Solution. Applying the property PP$_1$ with $x = 12$, $y = 14$, and $z = (5 + 8)$, we obtain

$$(12 + 14) - (5 + 8) = 12 + [14 - (5 + 8)].$$

Thus,

$$(12 + 14) - (5 + 8) = 12 + [14 - (8 + 5)] \qquad \text{(by C}_\text{a}\text{)}$$
$$= 12 + [(14 - 8) - 5] \qquad \text{(by PP}_2\text{)}$$
$$= [12 + (14 - 8)] - 5 \qquad \text{(by PP}_1 \text{ with } x = 12,$$
$$y = (14 - 8), \text{ and}$$
$$z = 5)$$
$$= [(14 - 8) + 12] - 5 \qquad \text{(by C}_\text{a}\text{)}$$
$$= (14 - 8) + (12 - 5) \qquad \text{(by PP}_1\text{)}$$
$$= (12 - 5) + (14 - 8) \qquad \text{(by C}_\text{a}\text{).}$$

This type of manipulation is basic in subtraction.

For ready reference the new properties are listed below.

AP: if $x = y$, then $x + z = y + z$.

PP_1: $(x + y) - z = x + (y - z)$,   if $y \geq z$.

PP_2: $(x - y) - z = x - (y + z)$,   if $x \geq y + z$.

PROBLEM SET 4–5

1. Without performing the additions and subtractions indicated, show that the following are true. Justify each step.
   (a) $(8 + 9) - (5 + 3) = (8 - 5) + (9 - 3)$
   (b) $(10 + 7) - (6 + 2) = (10 - 2) + (7 - 6)$

2. Show that if $a \geq c$ and $b \geq d$, then $(a + b) - (c + d) = (a - c) + (b - d)$, where a, b, c, and d are whole numbers.

3. In the proof of PP_2 there appear equations $x - (y + z) = a$ and $(x - y) - z = a$. Show how properties of equality are used to obtain the final conclusion.

4–6   SUBTRACTION FOR NATURAL NUMBERS

The basic idea of subtraction was discussed in Chapter 3. Two procedures were presented there for handling subtraction combinations: the "take-away" method, where the results of combinations such as $7 - 3$ and $9 - 2$ are learned and used in that form, and the "add-on" method, by which a question such as $7 - 3 = ?$ is transformed to the question $3 + ? = 7$. It is probable that most people prefer to use the first of these methods. However, many people use the second method with equal facility.

How should one proceed to handle problems like $27 - 5$ and $68 - 45$? We write

$$27 - 5 = (2 \cdot 10 + 7) - 5$$
$$= 2 \cdot 10 + (7 - 5) \quad \text{(by } PP_1)$$

and

$$68 - 45 = (6 \cdot 10 + 8) - (4 \cdot 10 + 5)$$
$$= (6 \cdot 10 - 4 \cdot 10) + (8 - 5).$$

This last expression is obtained by applying the procedure of the last illustrative example or the result of Problem 2, Problem Set 4–4. Thus

$$68 - 45 = (6 - 4)10 + (8 - 5) \quad \text{(by } D_-).$$

These examples indicate that in subtraction corresponding digits can, and should, be grouped together. This is the justification for writing the left-hand display below, then saying $8 - 5 = 3$ and $(6 - 4)$ tens $= 2$ tens, and combining these to obtain the right-hand display.

$$
\begin{array}{r}
6\ 8 \\
(-)\,4\ 5 \\
\hline
\end{array}
\qquad\qquad
\begin{array}{r}
6\ 8 \\
(-)\,4\ 5 \\
\hline
2\ 3
\end{array}
$$

More digits in the numbers involved would merely result in further terms of the same type. The following form indicates exactly what steps are taken (digits of the answer are in boldface type).

$$
\begin{array}{r}
②\ ① \\
6\ \ 8 \\
(-)\,4\ \ 5 \\
\hline
2\ \ 3
\end{array}
\qquad
\begin{array}{l}
①\quad 8 - 5 = \mathbf{3} \\
②\quad (6 - 4)10 = \mathbf{2}\cdot 10
\end{array}
$$

The "take-away" procedure was used above. If the "add-on" procedure is used, then

$$
\begin{array}{r}
②\ ① \\
6\ \ 8 \\
(-)\,4\ \ 5 \\
\hline
2\ \ 3
\end{array}
\qquad
\begin{array}{l}
①\quad 5 + \mathbf{3} = 8 \\
②\quad (4 + \mathbf{2})10 = 6\cdot 10
\end{array}
$$

In the above problem, $8 \geq 5$ and $6 \geq 4$, so the procedure was straightforward. Suppose that it is desired to perform $63 - 48$. In this case $(6 - 4)10 + (3 - 8)$ cannot be performed in a straightforward manner because the statement $3 \geq 8$ is not true. However, by using D_+ and A_a and by grouping digits, we obtain

$$
\begin{aligned}
(6\cdot 10 + 3) - (4\cdot 10 + 8) &= (5\cdot 10 + 1\cdot 10 + 3) - (4\cdot 10 + 8) \\
&= (5\cdot 10 + 13) - (4\cdot 10 + 8) \\
&= (5 - 4)10 + (13 - 8).
\end{aligned}
$$

Now the subtraction can proceed as before, since $13 \geq 8$. Actually, a tens unit has been "borrowed" to use with the ones; for this reason, the procedure is called the "borrow method." This borrow method can be combined with either the "take-away" or the "add-on" method, as exemplified below.

Borrow, take-away:

$$
\begin{array}{r}
②\ ① \\
^{5}\!\not{6}\ \ 3 \\
(-)\,4\ \ 8 \\
\hline
1\ \ 5
\end{array}
\qquad
\begin{array}{l}
①\quad 6\cdot 10 - 1\cdot 10 = \mathbf{5}\cdot 10 \\
 10 + 3 \ \ \ \ \ \ = \mathbf{13} \\
 13 - 8 \ \ \ \ \ \ = \mathbf{5} \\
②\quad 5\cdot 10 - 4\cdot 10 = \mathbf{1}\cdot 10
\end{array}
$$

Borrow, add-on:

$$
\begin{array}{r}
\overset{②}{}\overset{①}{} \\
5\!\!\!\!\overset{}{6} . 3 \\
(-)\;4\;\;8 \\
\hline
1\;\;5
\end{array}
\qquad
\begin{array}{ll}
① & 6 \cdot 10 - 1 \cdot 10 = \mathbf{5} \cdot 10 \\
 & 10 + 3 = \mathbf{13} \\
 & 8 + 5 = 13 \\
② & (4 + \mathbf{1}) \cdot 10 = \mathbf{5} \cdot 10
\end{array}
$$

The boldface numerals are for numbers which are used in a later step or which appear in the answer.

Some people don't like to borrow; it is against their principles! Let us see if they can be made happy! If $x \geq y$, then

$$
\begin{aligned}
(x + 10) - (y + 10) &= (x - y) + (10 - 10) \\
&= (x - y) + 0 \\
&= x - y,
\end{aligned}
$$

so that ten may be added to each term of a difference, $x - y$, without changing the number. Hence

$$
\begin{aligned}
63 - 48 &= (63 + 10) - (48 + 10) \\
&= (6 \cdot 10 + 3 + 10) - (4 \cdot 10 + 8 + 10) \\
&= (6 \cdot 10 + 13) - [(4 + 1)10 + 8] \\
&= (6 \cdot 10 + 13) - (5 \cdot 10 + 8) \\
&= (6 - 5)10 + (13 - 8).
\end{aligned}
$$

The ten which has been added to 3 to get 13 has been "counterbalanced" by subtracting another ten, i.e., by subtracting a total of 5 tens instead of 4 tens. (Note that we have reached the point where we do not give justification for *each* step, but only for those which seem most important at the moment.) This method of subtraction will be called the "carry method" since the "counterbalancing" ten is "carried" into the 4 tens to yield 5 tens. In the above problem, 10 was added to each of the numbers, 63 and 48, involved in the subtraction; for that reason the "carry method" is sometimes called the "equal additions method." In vertical form, these procedures could be displayed as follows.

Carry, take-away:

$$
\begin{array}{r}
\overset{②}{}\overset{①}{} \\
6\;\;3 \\
(-)\overset{5}{4}\;\;8 \\
\hline
1\;\;5
\end{array}
\qquad
\begin{array}{ll}
① & 3 + 10 = \mathbf{13} \\
 & 13 - 8 = 5 \\
② & 4 \cdot 10 + 1 \cdot 10 = \mathbf{5} \cdot 10 \\
 & 6 \cdot 10 - 5 \cdot 10 = (6 - 5)10 \\
 & = \mathbf{1} \cdot 10
\end{array}
$$

Carry, add-on: *on equal addition, take away*

$$\begin{array}{cc} ② & ① \\ 6 & 3 \end{array}$$
$$(-) \overset{5}{\cancel{4}}\; 8$$
$$\overline{1\; .5}$$

① $3 + 10 = 13$
  $8 + 5 = 13$

② $4 \cdot 10 + 1 \cdot 10 = 5 \cdot 10$
  $(5 + 1)10 = 6 \cdot 10$

ILLUSTRATIVE EXAMPLE. Use the "carry, add-on" method to perform $5367 - 2899$.

Solution.

$$\begin{array}{cccc} ④ & ③ & ② & ① \\ 5 & 3 & 6 & 7 \end{array}$$
$$(-)2\overset{3}{}\; 8\overset{9}{}\; 9\overset{0}{}\; 9$$
$$\overline{2\quad 4\quad 6\quad 8}$$

① $7 + 10 = 17$
  $9 + 8 = 17$

② $9 \cdot 10 + 1 \cdot 10 = 10 \cdot 10 = 1 \cdot 100 + 0 \cdot 10$
  $0 \cdot 10 + 6 \cdot 10 = 6 \cdot 10$

③ $8 \cdot 10^2 + 1 \cdot 10^2 = 9 \cdot 10^2$
  $3 \cdot 10^2 + 10 \cdot 10^2 = 13 \cdot 10^2$
  $(9 + 4)10^2 = 13 \cdot 10^2$

④ $2 \cdot 10^3 + 1 \cdot 10^3 = 3 \cdot 10^3$
  $(3 + 2)10^3 = 5 \cdot 10^3$

Note the double "carry" resulting from step ①. The $1 \cdot 10$ carried to step ② yields $10 \cdot 10$; thus $1 \cdot 100$ is carried to the hundreds column in step ③.

Which of the four methods of subtraction is preferable? The authors believe that there is little difference from an arithmetic standpoint. Psychologically, the answer probably depends on which method you use most often, by which method you were trained. We should be ready to cope with any of these procedures, since we will encounter people who use them.

PROBLEM SET 4–6

1. Use the horizontal procedure to show how the following subtractions should be carried out. Where necessary, use the "borrow" method.
   (a) $78 - 54$ (b) $73 - 54$ (c) $682 - 498$
   (d) $940 - 678$ (e) $724 - 357$ (f) $1467 - 984$

2. Repeat Problem 1, using the "carry" method where necessary. *use carry method*

3. Perform each of the following subtractions, using all four methods.
   (a) $95 - 43$ (b) $95 - 68$ (c) $563 - 379$ (d) $821 - 607$

4. Prove that if $x \geq y$, then $(x + z) - (y + z) = x - y$.

5. Prove that $(x + y + z) - (a + b + c) = (x - a) + (y - b) + (z - c)$, assuming that necessary inequalities are satisfied. [*Hint:* Use A_a on each term and then PP_1.]

6. An individual performs $8734 - 6972$, obtaining 1672 as the result.
   (a) How can he check the accuracy of his work?
   (b) Check it. Is the result correct?

7. Perform the following subtractions, using any method you wish. Check the result of your work.
   (a) $89413 - 7968$ (b) $41305 - 29768$
   (c) $40301 - 28986$ (d) $80030 - 48977$

8. Use expanded notation to explain a method of working the following problems.
   (a) 546(seven) $-$ 234(seven) (b) 612(seven) $-$ 455(seven)
   (c) 96T(twelve) $-$ 438(twelve) (d) 814(twelve) $-$ 6T9(twelve)

9. Perform the following subtractions in the numeral systems indicated.
   (a) 403(five) $-$ 244(five) (b) TEE(twelve) $-$ 93T(twelve)
   (c) 102(three) $-$ 21(three) (d) 1101(two) $-$ 1011(two)
   (e) 1101(three) $-$ 1011(three) (f) 6004(seven) $-$ 4656(seven)

4–7 DIVISION FOR NATURAL NUMBERS

So-called "long division" seems to be a "bête noire," probably because the basic ideas are hidden under a mass of contractions. Both a simplified version and the usual version of this procedure are based on the concepts discussed in the previous chapter.

Consider the division of 104 by 23; this can be carried out by continued subtraction:

$$104 - 23 = 81,$$
$$(104 - 23) - 23 = 58,$$
$$[(104 - 23) - 23] - 23 = 35,$$
$$\{[(104 - 23) - 23] - 23\} - 23 = 12,$$

the subtraction ceasing when a number is obtained which is less than 23. Hence,

$$[(104 - 23) - 23] - 23 = 23 + 12,$$
$$(104 - 23) - 23 = 23 + (23 + 12) = (23 + 23) + 12$$
$$= (1 + 1)23 + 12 = 2 \cdot 23 + 12,$$
$$104 - 23 = 23 + (2 \cdot 23 + 12) = (23 + 2 \cdot 23) + 12$$
$$= (1 + 2)23 + 12 = 3 \cdot 23 + 12,$$
$$104 = 23 + (3 \cdot 23 + 12) = (1 + 3)23 + 12$$
$$= 4 \cdot 23 + 12.$$

$$
\begin{array}{r|l}
104 & \\
(-)\ \ 23 & 1 \\
\hline
81 & \\
(-)\ \ 23 & 1 \\
\hline
58 & \\
(-)\ \ 23 & 1 \\
\hline
35 & \\
(-)\ \ 23 & 1 \\
\hline
12 &
\end{array}
$$

This mass of numbers can readily be written in the form shown at the left. In this setup, the digit 1 appears on the right each time the number 23 is subtracted. An individual performing subtractions of this nature will soon realize that the procedure can be shortened by subtracting a multiple of 23 instead of 23 itself. He might then obtain the following display at the left, which is explained by the equations to the right.

$$
\begin{array}{r|l}
104 & \\
(-)\ \ 46 & 2 \\
\hline
58 & \\
(-)\ \ 46 & 2 \\
\hline
12 &
\end{array}
$$

$$(104 - 2\cdot 23) - 2\cdot 23 = 12,$$
$$104 - 2\cdot 23 = 2\cdot 23 + 12,$$
$$104 = 2\cdot 23 + (2\cdot 23 + 12)$$
$$= (2\cdot 23 + 2\cdot 23) + 12$$
$$= (2 + 2)23 + 12$$
$$= 4\cdot 23 + 12.$$

Each number which appears on the right-hand side of the vertical line denotes the number of 23's in the multiple of 23 which is being subtracted. The quotient of the division procedure is the sum of the numbers on the right-hand side of the vertical line; the remainder is the final difference obtained.

Consider the problem $2795 \div 23$. What multiple of 23 should or could be subtracted? The answer is, any multiple which is not larger than 2795. Certainly products such as

$$10 \times 23 \qquad \text{and} \qquad 100 \times 23$$

are very easy to find. Suppose, at each step, we decide to use the largest possible of these basic multiples; the display at the left would result (the *divisor* is placed at the left of the *dividend* for ready reference). The quotient is $100 + 10 + 10 + 1 = 121$ and the remainder is 12.

$$
\begin{array}{r r|l}
23) & 2795 & \\
(-) & 2300 & 100 \\
\hline
& 495 & \\
(-) & 230 & 10 \\
\hline
& 265 & \\
(-) & 230 & 10 \\
\hline
& 35 & \\
(-) & 23 & 1 \\
\hline
& 12 &
\end{array}
$$

This procedure could be shortened somewhat by combining steps 2 and 3, that is, by subtracting $20\cdot 23$ instead of subtracting $10\cdot 23$ twice. However, time is often lost in searching for a "better" multiple.

With a little practice, this procedure can be carried through as rapidly as the usual procedure. Moreover, it has two advantages: (1) it is readily understood, and (2) it does not matter whether or not the "best" multiple is being subtracted; if it is not the "best," the procedure is merely prolonged somewhat.

PROBLEM SET 4-7

1. In each of the following perform the division by continued subtraction of multiples of the divisor. Set up the work in horizontal form, indicating how both the quotient and remainder are determined.

    (a) $672 \div 43$ (b) $8495 \div 621$ (c) $2614 \div 75$ (d) $4863 \div 247$

2. In each of the following divisions, state the most advisable basic multiple to use at the first step. [In part (a) both 490 and 4900 are basic multiples.]

    (a) $7321 \div 49$ (4900) (b) $832154 \div 62$ 10000
    (c) $45827 \div 628$ 10 (d) $97105 \div 4006$ 10

3. Perform the divisions of Problem 2 using only basic multiples as the numbers to be subtracted.

4. For the division $9935 \div 32$, (a) find the best basic multiple to use in step one, and (b) write those multiples of this basic multiple which it would be possible to use in step one.

5. If x and y are counting numbers, $x > y$, how does one know when to stop the subtraction procedure in the problem $x \div y$? *when x is less t...*

6. Perform the following divisions. At each step use a basic multiple or some multiple of it; do not try to get the best multiple but be satisfied with a "good" multiple.

    (a) $9104 \div 87$ (b) $34201 \div 98$ (c) $60105 \div 27$
    (d) $8342 \div 93$ (e) $604873 \div 653$ (f) $73214 \div 804$

7. If 17 is divided by 5, the quotient is 3 and the remainder is 2; then

$$17 = 3 \cdot 5 + 2.$$

    (a) Divide 134 by 11, then write an equation connecting the dividend, divisor, quotient, and remainder.
    (b) Given that x divided by y yields a quotient q and remainder r, write an equation connecting x, y, q, and r. $q \cdot y + r = x$
    (c) Describe a method for checking a division problem.

8. Check the results obtained in Problem 6.

4-8 INEQUALITY PROPERTIES

Certain inequality properties are needed for a treatment of the "best multiple" procedure. In the earlier discussion of "less than" it was stated that if $x = n(A)$ and $y = n(B)$, where A and B are sets, then $x < y$ if A matches a proper subset of B. Hence $3 < 7$, since S_3 matches a proper subset of S_7. Then $7 - 3$ was defined and it was shown that if $7 - 3 = c$, then $7 = 3 + c$. Now consider the converse problem: suppose that b is given as a number such that $7 = 3 + b$. Define a set B such that $b = n(B)$

Read

and so that B and S_3 are disjoint. Then, since $7 = n(S_7)$ and $3 = n(S_3)$,

$$n(S_7) = n(S_3) + n(B) = n(S_3 \cup B) \qquad \text{(why?)}.$$

Hence S_7 matches $S_3 \cup B$, that is, $\{1, 2, 3, 4, 5, 6, 7\}$ matches $\{1, 2, 3,$ elements of $B\}$. Accordingly, $\{$elements of $B\} = B$ matches $\{4, 5, 6, 7\}$, which is a proper subset of S_7; hence $n(B) < n(S_7)$, or $b < 7$. To summarize,

$$\text{if} \quad 3 + b = 7, \qquad \text{then} \qquad b < 7 \ (\text{or } 7 > b).$$

The general result is given in the following property.

Inequality property I_1. Let x, y, and z be counting numbers;

$$\text{if} \quad x + y = z, \qquad \text{then} \qquad y < z \ (\text{or } x < z).$$

The proof of this property is called for in Problem 1 of Problem Set 4–8. As a consequence of this property, since $4 + 11 = 15$, then $4 < 15$ and $11 < 15$; since $23 + 14 = 37$, then $23 < 37$. These numerical statements seem trivial; the real value of I_1 is in theoretical developments.

We will now state another inequality property.

Inequality property I_2. Let c be a counting number;

$$\text{if} \quad x < y, \qquad \text{then} \qquad c \cdot x < c \cdot y.$$

Let us prove this property. Since $x < y$, there is a counting number z such that $x + z = y$. Hence,

$$c(x + z) = c \cdot y \qquad \text{(see Problem 3, Problem Set 4–8)},$$

$$c \cdot x + c \cdot z = c \cdot y.$$

Since $c \cdot x$, $c \cdot y$, and $c \cdot z$ are counting numbers (why?), then, by I_1, $c \cdot x < c \cdot y$. For example, since $5 < 7$, then $4 \cdot 5 < 4 \cdot 7$; since $18 > 11$, then $32 \cdot 18 > 32 \cdot 11$.

There is another inequality property which is needed in the following work but which will not be proved at this stage.

Inequality property I_3. For a counting number c,

$$\text{if} \quad ca < cb, \qquad \text{then} \qquad a < b.$$

This property will be discussed in Chapter 8. Its only application prior to that time is to numerical problems involving "best multiples." Logically, the discussion of "best multiples" could be delayed until I_3 has been proved. However, it seems better to complete the discussion at this point.

PROBLEM SET 4–8

1. Prove the inequality property I_1.

2. Where was the property I_1 used in this section?

3. (a) Prove that if $r = s$, then $cr = cs$, for c, r, and s any natural numbers.
   (b) Where was the result of part (a) used in the proof of I_2?

4. Prove that if x and y are whole numbers such that $x < y$, then $x + c < y + c$, for any whole number c.

4–9 "BEST MULTIPLES" AND "USUAL" PROCEDURE

Now consider the problem of finding the "best multiple" to use at each step of the division procedure. Let us compute $6758 \div 7$, the steps being shown in the display below. Obviously, $1000 \cdot 7$ is too large a multiple; $100 \cdot 7 = 700$ is the best basic multiple to use in step one. The question is: What is the largest multiple of 700 which can be subtracted? Any multiple of 700 would have two zeros on the right, so that we need a number b such that $b \cdot 700$ would be ≤ 6700 (i.e., the digits 5 and 8 can be disregarded momentarily). Hence, $b \cdot 7$ should not be larger than 67, and therefore the largest possible value of b is 9. (How would you find this value of b?) Thus we want to subtract

$$9 \cdot 700 = 900 \cdot 7.$$

In the second step,

$$
\begin{array}{r r | r}
7) & 6758 & \\
(-) & 6300 & 900 \\
\hline
 & 458 & \\
(-) & 420 & 60 \\
\hline
 & 38 & \\
(-) & 35 & 5 \\
\hline
 & 3 & \\
\end{array}
$$

$10 \cdot 7 = 70$ is the basic multiple;
$c \cdot 70$ should be ≤ 450,
$c \cdot 7$ should be ≤ 45;
use $c = 6$,
i.e., subtract $6 \cdot 70 = 60 \cdot 7$.

It is recommended that, in practice, no further shortcuts be attempted and that subtraction of the "best multiple" be made optional with the individual. If an individual understands the procedure, he will gravitate quite naturally toward the use of a "best multiple." Let nature take its course! Accuracy is more important than speed!

Since the "usual" division procedure is taught so widely, we must understand it. To that end, the "best multiple" idea must be considered in detail. Let us work with $675 \div 74$. We want the largest possible number b such

Rearl

that $b \cdot 74 \leq 675$. Since this value of b may not be evident, we will simplify the problem by finding the largest possible number c such that $c \cdot 70 \leq 675$. That is, we will find a number c such that $c \cdot 70 \leq 670$ or $c \cdot 7 \leq 67$. Obviously, $c = 9$. Now $70 < 74$; thus $c \cdot 70 < c \cdot 74$, by I_2. We will represent the numbers in question on a line to facilitate discussion:

$$c \cdot 70 \qquad\qquad 675$$

The number $c \cdot 74$ lies to the right of $c \cdot 70$ and therefore *might* lie to the right of 675; hence c *might* be too large to use as the value of b. Now let us show that c cannot be too small. Suppose that c is too small; then $c + 1$ can be used as an appropriate value of b, that is, $(c + 1)74 \leq 675$. Since $70 < 74$, then $(c + 1)70 < (c + 1)74$. This last inequality, when combined with $(c + 1)74 \leq 675$, yields

$$(c + 1)70 < 675.$$

Hence c could not be the largest number for which $c \cdot 70 \leq 675$, contrary to its mode of choice. Accordingly, c *cannot* be too small, although it *may* be too large. In summary, to divide 675 by 74 we find a trial divisor by dividing 67 by 7 (actually $670 \div 70$); whether or not this trial divisor is too large is determined by a trial multiplication, $9 \cdot 74$ in this example.

The previous discussion can be applied directly to such a problem as $6758 \div 74$, which is worked out at the left. The first basic multiple of 74 to be used is $10 \cdot 74 = 740$ (why not use $100 \cdot 74 = 7400$?). We want to determine the largest number b such that $b \cdot 740 \leq 6758$. We will simplify this relation to $b \cdot 740 \leq 6750$, or $b \cdot 74 \leq 675$. The problem is now identical with that of the last paragraph: 9 is the trial multiplier and it works; also, $9 \cdot 740 = 90 \cdot 74$.

```
74) 6758 |
    6660 | 90
      98 |
      74 | 1
      24 |
```

If the divisor has three or more digits, the procedure is an extension of the above. For example, the division $22375 \div 748$ proceeds as follows: 7480 is the basic multiple; we need a number b such that

$$b \cdot 7480 \leq 22375,$$
$$b \cdot 7480 \leq 22370,$$
$$b \cdot 748 \leq 2237.$$

To simplify the arithmetic, we find a number c such that

$$c \cdot 700 \leq 2237,$$
$$c \cdot 700 \leq 2200,$$
$$c \cdot 7 \leq 22.$$

Hence, in the display at the left below, 3 is used first as a trial value of b.

Since this value turns out to be too large, it is decreased to $b = 2$. In the second step, $b \cdot 748 \le 7415$ leads to $c \cdot 700 \le 7400$, and then to $c \cdot 7 \le 74$. This inequality is satisfied by $c = 10$; however, b is a one-digit number, so its largest possible value is 9. This number 9 is tried, and it serves the purpose.

```
748)  22375
      22440    30
      14960    20
       7415
       6732     9
        683
```

It is both interesting and instructive to see how the form being used here can be modified to produce the "usual" form. To obtain this "usual" form, "best multiples" must be used at each step. To see this conversion, let us use a somewhat longer problem, $71583 \div 74$. The zeros which are crossed out in lines 2 and 4 have the effect of "bringing down" the digits immediately above them; the 3 in row 3 is not used until row 5. Hence if these digits are omitted from the display and if it is agreed that in step two the 8 of line one is "brought down" and in step three the 3 of line one is "brought down," everything needed is preserved. Moreover, the partial quotients, 900, 60, and 7, can be written above the top line. This produces the arrangement shown at the left below. Further, this display of partial quotients can be "telescoped" into one line, since at each step there will be fewer digits in the partial quotient than previously. Hence the final form is that shown on the right.

```
74)  71583
     66600    900
      4983
      4440     60
       543
       518      7
        25
```

```
         7
        60
       900
    74)71583
       666
       498
       444
       543
       518
        25
```

```
       967
    74)71583
       666
       498
       444
       543
       518
        25
```

10-100

It is the artificiality of this last display which makes it difficult to follow and to understand. No wonder so many people cannot perform long division with ease. Unease breeds inaccuracy!

Work the problem $59570 \div 74$ by the "usual" procedure. Why is the answer to this problem 805, rather than 85? This question can be answered readily if the form recommended here is used.

PROBLEM SET 4-9

1. Consider $8934 \div 27$.
   (a) Find the best basic multiple, g, to use in step one.
   (b) Show that if $b \cdot g$ is the best multiple of g to use in step one, then b must be the largest number which satisfies $b \cdot 27 \leq 89$.
   (c) Determine b; state the simplest way to do this.
   (d) Show why the value of b determined above indicates that $300 \cdot 27$ should be subtracted at step one.
   (e) Obtain a similar set of results for step two.

2. For each of the divisions below, use a procedure similar to that used in Problem 1.
   (a) $9374 \div 18$ (b) $8701 \div 43$ (c) $11233 \div 35$ (d) $16348 \div 54$

3. Consider $43759 \div 67$. In each step, use the "best multiple" of the basic multiple.
   (a) Show that the inequality to be satisfied in step one is $b \cdot 67 \leq 437$.
   (b) To find b, we first find a number c such that $c \cdot 60 \leq 437$; show that c must satisfy $c \cdot 6 \leq 43$.
   (c) Find c.
   (d) *Must* this value of c serve as a suitable value of b? Does it in this case?
   (e) What value of b does serve?

4. For each of the divisions below carry through a sequence of steps similar to those in Problem 3. Concern yourself on y with step one in the division process.
   (a) $67293 \div 83$ (b) $59406 \div 97$ (c) $34916 \div 74$ (d) $46293 \div 58$

5. Using the recommended format, perform the divisions indicated below.
   (a) $329574 \div 28$ (b) $94176 \div 37$ (c) $16273 \div 473$
   (d) $621498 \div 761$ (e) $40021 \div 897$ (f) $92013 \div 987$
   (g) $863425 \div 1489$ (h) $704189 \div 6248$

6. Suppose that when dividing 6732 by 47, an individual obtains a quotient of 142 and a remainder of 15. How could he check the accuracy of the result? Is the result correct? Why?

7. Check the results of the divisions in Problem 5.

8. Use expanded notation to show the following.
   (a) $436(\text{seven}) \times 10(\text{seven}) = 4360(\text{seven})$.
   (b) $81T(\text{twelve}) \times 10(\text{twelve}) = 81T0(\text{twelve})$.

9. Consider the problem $563(\text{seven}) \div 23(\text{seven})$.
   (a) What would be the basic multiple to be used in step one?
   (b) Perform the division by continued subtraction of basic multiples (there should be five steps).
   (c) Perform the division a second time, using multiples of the basic multiple.

10. Perform the indicated divisions (do not try to find the "best" multiple of the basic multiple).

(a) 603(seven) ÷ 31(seven)

(b) 465(seven) ÷ 35(seven)

(c) 121(three) ÷ 11(three)

(d) 432(five) ÷ 22(five)

(e) 6724(eight) ÷ 56(eight)

(f) 3948(twelve) ÷ 43(twelve)

(g) T936(twelve) ÷ 98(twelve)

(h) 97E1T(twelve) ÷ E4(twelve)

CHAPTER 5

Special Methods. Division Theorem

5–1 DOUBLING AND SUMMING

There is a simple multiplication procedure which is based on representing numbers in base two. Suppose that the number 31 is written in base two:

$$31 = 1 \cdot 2^4 + 1 \cdot 2^3 + 1 \cdot 2^2 + 1 \cdot 2 + 1.$$

Then

$$31 \times 48 = (2^4 + 2^3 + 2^2 + 2 + 1)48$$
$$= 2^4 \cdot 48 + 2^3 \cdot 48 + 2^2 \cdot 48 + 2 \cdot 48 + 48.$$

Now $2^2 \cdot 48 = 2(2 \cdot 48)$, so that if $2 \cdot 48$ is known, then $2^2 \cdot 48$ can be found by multiplying $2 \cdot 48$ by 2, that is, by doubling 96. Hence, the above sum can be found if we start with 48, double it, double that result, etc., the appropriate number of times, and then add these computed numbers. Hence this multiplication could be performed as shown at the left. Note that the only multiplication combinations needed are the $2 \cdot u$, for u from 0 to 9; there is less strain on the memory! Since

$$
\begin{aligned}
1 \times 48 &= 48 \\
2 \times 48 &= 96 \\
2^2 \times 48 &= 192 \\
2^3 \times 48 &= 384 \\
2^4 \times 48 &= 768 \\
\hline
&1488
\end{aligned}
$$

$$23 = 1 \cdot 2^4 + 0 \cdot 2^3 + 1 \cdot 2^2 + 1 \cdot 2 + 1,$$

then

$$23 \cdot 48 = (1 \cdot 2^4 + 0 \cdot 2^3 + 1 \cdot 2^2 + 1 \cdot 2 + 1)48$$
$$= 2^4 \cdot 48 + 0(2^3 \cdot 48) + 2^2 \cdot 48 + 2 \cdot 48 + 48.$$

Hence in this problem the term $384 = 2^3 \cdot 48$ would not be added in finding the total. How can a formal procedure be set up which will indicate when the doubling process is to stop and, also, which terms are to be added?

Suppose that the base two representation of n is given by

$$n = a \cdot 2^3 + b \cdot 2^2 + c \cdot 2 + d,$$

91

where a, b, c, and d are the digits of the base two representation, either 0 or 1 ($a \neq 0$). Since

$$n = 2(a \cdot 2^2 + b \cdot 2 + c) + d, \qquad \text{where} \quad 0 \leq d < 2,$$

then d is the remainder when n is divided by 2; the quotient is $a \cdot 2^2 + b \cdot 2 + c$. Since

$$a \cdot 2^2 + b \cdot 2 + c = 2(a \cdot 2 + b) + c, \qquad \text{where} \quad 0 \leq c < 2,$$

then c is the remainder when the preceding quotient is divided by 2. Continuing in this fashion, we have

$$a \cdot 2 + b = 2(a) + b, \qquad 0 \leq b < 2,$$

and

$$a = 2(0) + a, \qquad 0 \leq a < 2.$$

Thus, the digits of the base two representation of n are the remainders obtained when n is divided by 2, then the resulting quotient is divided by 2, etc., until a zero quotient is obtained. This procedure for finding the base two representation of a number is somewhat more direct than that used earlier in the book.

These ideas lead to a simple format for the multiplication procedure under consideration. The multiplier is treated as the n of the last paragraph; the successive quotients are written in a column, as below, with the corresponding remainder to the right; the first remainder is opposite the number being multiplied, in these cases 48. These remainders are the digits in the base two representation of n, the multiplier.

31 × 48			23 × 48		
15 : 1	48		11 : 1	48	
7 : 1	96		5 : 1	96	
3 : 1	192		2 : 1	192	
1 : 1	384		1 : 0	~~384~~	
0 : 1	768		0 : 1	768	
	1488			1104	

The last doubling appears opposite the zero quotient. The terms which are to be added may be determined on sight; those opposite a remainder 1 are added; those opposite a zero remainder, i.e., corresponding to a zero digit in the base two representation, are discarded.

The procedure just discussed is sometimes called "Russian multiplication," since it was used by many Russian peasants even during the first two decades of the twentieth century. It may also be called *doubling and summing*.

PROBLEM SET 5–1

1. Using the procedure of this section, write the following base ten numerals in the base two system.

   (a) 94   (b) 173   (c) 212   (d) 125

2. For each product below, express the first number in the base two system and use this expression to show how the multiplication can be performed by successive doubling.

   (a) 43 × 51   (b) 29 × 73   (c) 69 × 94   (d) 59 × 68

3. Perform the following by doubling and summing.

   (a) 89 × 126   (b) 49 × 75   (c) 101 × 210
   (d) 52 × 321   (e) 72 × 105   (f) 120 × 68

4. Using the procedure of doubling and summing, find the product of 25 and 62, first by doubling 62 and then by doubling 25.

   (a) Which is the shorter procedure? Why?
   (b) By C_m, you have a choice between these two methods; state how you choose the shorter.

5. In each of the following, state which number should be doubled when using the doubling and summing method.

   (a) 436 × 221   (b) 89 × 125   (c) 256 × 143   (d) 225 × 67

6. A number written in base seven has the form $n = a \cdot 7^4 + b \cdot 7^3 + c \cdot 7^2 + d \cdot 7 + e$, where a, b, c, d, and e are whole numbers ≤ 6 and $a \neq 0$. Show that these digits are the remainders when n is divided by 7, the resulting quotient is divided by 7, etc., for each successive quotient. When does the procedure terminate?

7. Carry through the procedure of Problem 6 for $a \cdot 6^3 + b \cdot 6^2 + c \cdot 6 + d$, in the base six numeral system.

8. Write the following base ten numerals in the base indicated.

   (a) 487, seven   (b) 3472, seven   (c) 742, six
   (d) 2703, six   (e) 2400, seven   (f) 1295, six

9. Investigate the "grating method" of multiplication. Refer to a book such as Swain: *Understanding Arithmetic*.

10. Investigate the "Napiers bones" method of multiplication. Refer to a book such as Mueller: *Arithmetic—Its Structure and Concepts*.

5–2   THE DIVISION THEOREM

Much can be gained by visualizing number operations on a number line. Draw a line and mark a point, O, on it; then choose a line segment of any length. On the line mark a segment OA equal in length to the chosen segment; place A to the right of O. Then mark a point B to the right of A, so that segment AB is equal in length to segment OA. This procedure can be continued indefinitely; the result is shown below.

$$O \quad A \quad B \quad C \quad D \cdots$$

Let us agree to associate each of the marked points with a number: 0 with O, 1 with A, 2 with B, etc. This yields a visual representation of the set of whole numbers:

$$0 \quad 1 \quad 2 \quad 3 \quad 4 \quad 5 \quad 6 \quad 7 \quad 8$$

For brevity, we will speak of "the point 1" instead of "the point A which corresponds to 1."

Addition can be illustrated by using the number line as follows: to find $3 + 4$, start at 3 and move 4 units to the right; the result is 7. Think through $3 + 5$ and $6 + 4$. To illustrate the subtraction $7 - 3$, start at 7 and move 3 units to the left; the result is 4. Think through $9 - 6$ and $12 - 4$.

Now consider the multiples of 3. Since $2 \cdot 3 = 3 + 3$, then $2 \cdot 3$ should be 3 units to the right of 3. Since $3 \cdot 3 = (2 + 1)3 = 2 \cdot 3 + 3$, then $3 \cdot 3$ should be 3 units to the right of $2 \cdot 3$. Likewise $4 \cdot 3$ would be 3 units to the right of $3 \cdot 3$. This could be continued indefinitely; any two consecutive points, which represent multiples of 3, would be 3 units apart. In the same fashion, we could mark on the line the multiples of 5, the multiples of 14, the multiples of 327, or the multiples of n, where n is any counting number.

Suppose that it is desired to think through the problem of dividing 19 by 5. Mark the multiples of 5 on a line (only a portion of the line is shown below.)

$$\cdots \quad 10 \qquad 15 \qquad 20 \cdots$$

Since 19 lies between two consecutive multiples of 5, $3 \cdot 5$ and $4 \cdot 5$, then $19 = 3 \cdot 5 + (\text{some number } r)$. This number r is the number of units from 15 to 19, and therefore it must be smaller than 5, the number of units between two consecutive multiples of five. Since 19 lies to the right of $3 \cdot 5$, then r must be greater than 0. Hence $r > 0$ and $r < 5$; this can be abbreviated to $0 < r < 5$.

If n is any counting number which is not a multiple of 5, then n must lie between two consecutive multiples of 5, say $k \cdot 5$ and $(k + 1) \cdot 5$. Hence $n = k \cdot 5 + r$, where r is some counting number such that $0 < r < 5$. Every counting number either is a multiple of 5 or lies between two consecutive multiples of 5. If it is a multiple of 5, it must have the form $k \cdot 5$, which could be written $k \cdot 5 + 0$. Otherwise, as illustrated previously, n would have the form $k \cdot 5 + r$, where $0 < r < 5$. These results can be collected in a single statement:

For n any counting number, $n = k \cdot 5 + r$, where $0 \leq r < 5$.

Note that the possibility of r being 0 has been included. Of course, the k and r are the quotient and remainder, respectively, when n is divided by 5. This result can be written in another form:

Any counting number n has one of the forms
$$k \cdot 5 + 0, \quad k \cdot 5 + 1, \quad k \cdot 5 + 2, \quad k \cdot 5 + 3, \quad k \cdot 5 + 4.$$

Similarly, if division by 7 is considered, every counting number n would have one of the forms $k \cdot 7 + 0$, $k \cdot 7 + 1$, $k \cdot 7 + 2$, $k \cdot 7 + 3$, $k \cdot 7 + 4$, $k \cdot 7 + 5$, $k \cdot 7 + 6$. That is, every counting number n must have the form
$$k \cdot 7 + r, \quad \text{where} \quad 0 \leq r < 7.$$

Now, since $0 = 0 \cdot 7 + 0$, then 0 has the form $k \cdot 7 + r$, where $0 \leq r < 7$. Hence, the above result is true for all whole numbers.

Let us generalize this result one step further. Consider division of n by b, where b is any counting number. Think of the multiples of b as being marked on the line; then n must be one of these multiples or lie between two consecutive multiples. Hence n must have the form $k \cdot b$ or $k \cdot b + r$, where $0 < r < b$, that is, n must have one of the forms
$$k \cdot b + 0, \quad k \cdot b + 1, \quad k \cdot b + 2, \ldots, k \cdot b + (b - 1).$$

This general result is given in the following theorem.

Division theorem. If n is any whole number and b is any counting number, then there exist whole numbers k and r such that
$$n = k \cdot b + r, \quad \text{where} \quad 0 \leq r < b.$$

The preceding discussion does not constitute a proof; the proof will be reserved for a later stage of mathematical experience (see Chapter 15).

The division theorem will prove useful. For instance, suppose it is desired to show that $P = n(n + 1)(n + 2)$ is divisible by 3, for any whole number n. Since we are interested in divisibility by 3, we can apply the division theorem for $b = 3$. Hence, no matter what n is, it must have one of the forms $k \cdot 3$, $k \cdot 3 + 1$, $k \cdot 3 + 2$ (henceforth, this will be written $3k$, $3k + 1$, $3k + 2$).
   (a) If $n = 3k$, then
$$P = n(n + 1)(n + 2) = 3k(3k + 1)(3k + 2) = 3[k(3k + 1)(3k + 2)].$$

Accordingly, $P = 3 \cdot$ (a whole number), and hence P is divisible by 3.

(b) If $n = 3k + 1$, then

$$P = n(n + 1)(n + 2) = (3k + 1)(3k + 2)(3k + 3)$$
$$= (3k + 1)(3k + 2)[3(k + 1)]$$
$$= 3[(3k + 1)(3k + 2)(k + 1)].$$

Again $P = 3 \cdot$ (a whole number); thus P is divisible by 3.

(c) If $n = 3k + 2$, then

$$P = (3k + 2)(3k + 3)(3k + 4) = 3[(3k + 2)(k + 1)(3k + 4)]$$
$$= 3 \cdot \text{(a whole number)},$$

and therefore P is divisible by 3.

It has now been shown that in each of the three possible cases P is divisible by 3. Now, n, $n + 1$, and $n + 2$ are consecutive whole numbers. Accordingly, we have proved the following statement:

The product of any three consecutive whole numbers is divisible by 3.

It follows that $2723 \cdot 2724 \cdot 2725$ is divisible by 3; note that there is no need to carry out division by 3 to show this, since it follows from the above result. Note also where properties D_+ and C_m were used in the previous proof.

Since

$$38 = 12 \cdot 3 + 2 = 3 \cdot 12 + 2 = 3 \cdot \text{(a whole number)} + 2,$$

then it will be said that 38 has the form $3k + 2$; this is the form of 38 with respect to divisibility by 3. Likewise, 46 would be of form $3k + 1$ and also of form $7k + 4$ or form $11k + 2$, etc.

The division theorem states the existence of a quotient, k, and a remainder, r, such that $0 \le r < b$, for n divided by b. Is this pair of whole numbers, k and r, unique, or could there be two or more such pairs? From the intuitive discussion leading up to the theorem, it appears that they are unique. This we will prove in the following exercises.

DISCUSSION EXERCISES

Let there be two such pairs as mentioned above, i.e., let $n = kb + r$, where $0 \le r < b$, and $n = tb + s$, where $0 \le s < b$.

1. Justify the assumption $s \ge r$.

2. From $kb + r = tb + s$, obtain $(k - t)b = s - r$. Justify each step.

3. Use the definition of "less than" to show that from $s \ge r$ it follows that $s - r \ge 0$.

4. Show that $s - r \le s$. [*Hint:* use sets.]

5. Show that from $s - r \le s$ and $s < b$ it follows that $s - r < b$.

6. Why can we conclude that $0 \le s - r < b$?

7. From the last equation in Exercise 2, $s - r$ is a multiple of b. How does this observation, coupled with the inequality in Exercise 6, permit the conclusion that $s - r$ must be zero?

8. Show how to argue that $s - r = 0$ implies that $s = r$.

9. Hence $(k - t)b$ must be a certain number; what is it?

10. From $(k - t)b = 0$, what must follow?

11. Why is b not zero?

12. Draw a conclusion from Exercises 10 and 11.

13. Can we conclude that both $s = r$ and $t = k$?

14. State the conclusion in words.

According to the result just proved, if two different methods are used to divide n by b, so that the remainder $<b$, then the remainders obtained must be equal and the quotients obtained must be equal. This idea was used in the preceding section: $n = a \cdot 2^3 + b \cdot 2^2 + c \cdot 2 + d$ was written in the form $2(a \cdot 2^2 + b \cdot 2 + c) + d = 2k + d$, where $0 \le d < 2$. It was then concluded that d must be the remainder when n is divided by 2, since this remainder is unique.

PROBLEM SET 5-2

1. Use a result proved in the text to show that the product of any four consecutive whole numbers is divisible by 3.

2. Show that $n(2n + 2)(4n + 2)$ is divisible by 3 for any whole number n.

3. (a) Prove that the product of any four consecutive whole numbers is divisible by 4.
   (b) Show that the product of any five consecutive whole numbers is divisible by 4 [use part (a)].
   (c) Would a product of six consecutive whole numbers be divisible by 4?
   (d) Would a product of t consecutive whole numbers, $t \ge 4$, be divisible by 4?

4. Write the division theorem for $b = 2$. Complete each of the following sentences by substituting a word for the blank.
   (a) Any whole number of the form $2k$ is called an _____ number.
   (b) Any whole number of the form $2k + 1$ is called an _____ number.
   (c) The division theorem implies that any whole number is either _____ or _____.

5. In a certain division problem where the divisor is 21, one person obtains a quotient of 112 and a remainder of 17; a second person obtains a quotient of 113 and a remainder of 11. Can both persons be correct? Why?

5-3 "CASTING OUT NINES"

The sum of the digits of the number 627 is $6 + 2 + 7$; for the number $a \cdot 10^4 + b \cdot 10^3 + c \cdot 10^2 + d \cdot 10 + e$ the sum of the digits is $a + b + c + d + e$.

DISCUSSION EXERCISES

1. Show that 10 has the form $9t + 1$.

2. Show, first directly and then by using Exercise 1, that 10^2 has the form $9s + 1$.

3. Use Exercises 1 and 2 to show that 10^3 has the form $9u + 1$.

4. Can you now conclude that any power of 10 has the form $9c + 1$? Why?

5. Assume that 10^k has the form $9v + 1$; use $10^{k+1} = 10^k \cdot 10$ to show that 10^{k+1} has the form $9w + 1$.

6. After working Exercises 1, 2, 3, and 5, would you feel content to draw the conclusion that any power of ten has the form $9z + 1$? Try to explain this.

It is hoped that in Exercise 4 you refused to draw the conclusion, because proving that a statement is true in special cases does not show that it is true in general. In Exercise 5 you showed that if the result is true in a certain case, then it is true for the "next" case. In a sense, this shows that the arguments used in Exercises 1, 2, and 3 can be continued to give a general result. This form of reasoning is called mathematical induction; it is used quite often to prove a general theorem.

It is quite possible to write

$$
\begin{aligned}
627 &= 6 \cdot 10^2 + 2 \cdot 10 + 7 \\
&= 6(99 + 1) + 2(9 + 1) + 7 \\
&= (6 \cdot 99 + 2 \cdot 9) + (6 + 2 + 7) \\
&= 9(6 \cdot 11 + 2) + (6 + 2 + 7),
\end{aligned}
$$

or, using the ideas developed in the preceding discussion exercises,

$$
\begin{aligned}
627 &= 6(9u + 1) + 2(9v + 1) + 7 \\
&= (6 \cdot 9u + 2 \cdot 9v) + (6 + 2 + 7) \\
&= 9(6u + 2v) + (6 + 2 + 7) \\
&= 9T + (6 + 2 + 7),
\end{aligned}
$$

where T is a whole number whose value we could find in this special case but which we are not interested in finding. Likewise,

$$a \cdot 10^4 + b \cdot 10^3 + c \cdot 10^2 + d \cdot 10 + e$$
$$= a(9x + 1) + b(9t + 1) + c(9s + 1) + d(9w + 1) + e$$
$$= 9(ax + bt + cs + dw) + (a + b + c + d + e)$$
$$= 9T + \text{(sum of the digits)},$$

where T is some whole number. Since this could be done for any whole number n, when it is written in decimal form, then

$$n = 9T + \text{(sum of digits)},$$

for T some whole number.

Let us try this for 67838:

$$67838 = 9T + (6 + 7 + 8 + 3 + 8)$$
$$= 9T + 32,$$

and

$$32 = 9y + (3 + 2)$$
$$= 9y + 5,$$

so that

$$67838 = 9T + (9y + 5)$$
$$= 9(T + y) + 5$$
$$= 9z + 5.$$

Now, $67838 = 9 \cdot z + 5$, where $0 \leq 5 < 9$, so that 5 must be the remainder, which is less than 9, on dividing 67838 by 9. The uniqueness of the remainder which is less than the divisor, as shown earlier, is the fact which produces this result. It certainly is much easier to find the remainder by this "sum of digits" method than by actual division.

In the above illustration the first "sum of digits" was itself a number, 32, having more than one digit; 32 was then expressed in terms of its "sum of digits." Actually, the procedure was continued until this "sum of digits" was a one-digit number <9. Let us show that this is always possible.

(a) If $n = 9T + \text{(sum of digits)}$, and n has two or more digits, then $T \geq 1$ and hence (sum of digits) $<n$.

(b) From part (a) this "sum of digits" decreases from step to step but is always a counting number.

(c) Since there are only a finite number of counting numbers between 1 and n, eventually the "sum of digits" must be less than 10.

(d) If the "sum of digits" is 9 at this stage, this term can be combined with the first term, for example,

$$648 = 9z + 18 = 9z + (9y + 9)$$
$$= 9(z + y) + 9 = 9(z + y + 1) + 0.$$

When n is divided by 9 so as to obtain a remainder <9, this remainder will be called the "nines remainder" and will be denoted by $R_9(n)$. Thus $R_9(67838) = 5$; in the computation of this number note where the step $R_9(n) = R_9$ (sum of digits) was used. Finding $R_9(n)$ by this procedure is called *casting out nines*, since, in effect, the multiple of 9 is discarded. "Casting out nines" can be used to check computations. We will illustrate this checking procedure by four examples.

ILLUSTRATIVE EXAMPLE 1. Perform $6728 + 9376$, and check your result by casting out nines.

Solution. Since $6728 = 9r + 5$ and $9376 = 9s + 7$, then

$$6728 + 9376 = 9(r + s) + (5 + 7)$$
$$= 9(r + s + 1) + 3.$$

Thus, R_9(sum) must be 3; the addition can be performed and R_9(computed sum) can be found. If this last number is not 3, then the computed sum is incorrect. For example,

	R_9		
6728	5	$6 + 7 + 2 + 8 = 23,$	$R_9(23) = 2 + 3 = 5,$
(+) 9376	7	$9 + 3 + 7 + 6 = 25,$	$R_9(25) = 2 + 5 = 7,$
16094	3	$R_9(5 + 7) = R_9(12) = 1 + 2 = 3.$	

$$R_9(16094) = R_9(1 + 6 + 0 + 9 + 4) = R_9(20) = 2 + 0 = 2.$$

The answer is incorrect since $R_9(16094) \neq 3$. The correct answer is 16104.

Suppose someone had obtained 16014 as an answer for the above problem; note that the digits 1 and 0 in the correct result have been transposed. Now $R_9(16014) = 3$, and R_9(answer) must be $R_9(5 + 7) = 3$; this example shows that when the nines remainders are the same, the answer may still be wrong. Hence:

When nines remainders are different, the answer is wrong.

When nines remainders are equal, the answer *may* be correct.

A check by casting out nines will not catch such errors as transposition of digits.

ILLUSTRATIVE EXAMPLE 2.   Perform $9372 - 6728$, and check your result by casting out nines.

Solution.

$$9372 - 6728 = (9r + 3) - (9s + 5)$$
$$= [9(r - 1) + 12] - (9s + 5)$$
$$= 9(r - 1 - s) + (12 - 5)$$
$$= 9(r - 1 - s) + 7.$$

Since $3 < 5$, it was necessary to "borrow" a 9 from $9r$ so that the result of subtracting "remainders" would be between 0 and 9.

$$
\begin{array}{rl}
 & R_9 \\
9372 & 3 \text{ (use 12)} \\
(-)\,6728 & 5 \\
\hline
2644 & 7
\end{array}
$$

$$R_9(2644) = 7$$

There is a "good chance" that the answer is correct; at least, no error is indicated.

ILLUSTRATIVE EXAMPLE 3.   Perform 671×48, and check your result by casting out nines.

Solution. Since

$$671 \times 48 = (9t + 5) \cdot (9r + 3)$$
$$- (9t + 5)9r + (9t \mid 5)3 \qquad\qquad (\text{by } D_+)$$
$$= (9t \cdot 9r + 5 \cdot 9r) + (9t \cdot 3 + 5 \cdot 3) \qquad (\text{by } D_+, \text{ twice})$$
$$= 9^2 tr + 45r + 27t + 5 \cdot 3,$$

then

$$R_9(671 \times 48) = R_9(5 \cdot 3) = R_9(15) = 1 + 5 = 6.$$

Thus, R_9(answer) must be 6 if the computation is correct.

$$
\begin{array}{rl}
 & R_9 \\
671 & 5 \qquad R_9(5 \cdot 3) = R_9(15) = 1 + 5 \\
(\times)\,48 & 3 \\
\hline
5368 & 6 \\
26840 & \qquad R_9(32208) = 6 \\
\hline
32208 &
\end{array}
$$

No error is indicated!

ILLUSTRATIVE EXAMPLE 4.   Divide 684 by 53, and check your result by casting out nines.

Solution. The quotient obtained is 12 and the remainder is 48. If these are correct, then

$$684 = 12 \cdot 53 + 48.$$

Now, from the previous illustrations, $R_9(12 \cdot 53 + 48)$ is found by computing

$$R_9(12) \cdot R_9(53) + R_9(48) = 3 \cdot 8 + 3 = 27,$$
$$R_9(27) = 0.$$

Since $R_9(684) = 0$, then no error is indicated; there is a good possibility that the answer is correct.

PROBLEM SET 5–3

1. For each of the following numbers, n, show that n has the form $9r +$ (sum of digits).
   (a) 4328   (b) 17629   (c) 5037   (d) 82164

2. Find $R_9(n)$ for each of the following.
   (a) $n = 67248$ (b) $n = 80372$ (c) $n = 1243$ (d) $n = 8679049$

3. Without performing the operations indicated, describe, by using equations, how to find $R_9(n)$ for each of the following.
   (a) $n = 763 + 482$ (b) $n = 8476 + 9205$ (c) $n = 743 - 528$
   (d) $n = 804 - 676$ (e) $n = 78 \cdot 845$ (f) $n = 684 \cdot 38$
   (g) $n = 85 \cdot 43 + 22$ (h) $n = 79 \cdot 143 + 64$

4. Use casting out nines to check the accuracy of the results indicated below.
   (a) $5472 + 8631 = 14103$ (b) $862 + 7438 = 8400$
   (c) $7621 - 3485 = 4146$ (d) $9143 - 6028 = 2315$
   (e) $54 \cdot 79 = 4276$ (f) $87 \cdot 142 = 12354$

5. Perform the following operations, and check your results by using casting out nines.
   (a) $7642 \div 87$ (b) $831042 \div 279$ (c) $7057 \cdot 424$
   (d) $3298 \cdot 4276$ (e) $83215 \div 149$ (f) $6842 \cdot 537$

5–4 "CASTING OUT ELEVENS"

The "elevens remainder" can be used for checking purposes just as was the nines remainder. First a short method of finding the elevens remainder is needed.

DISCUSSION EXERCISES

1. Show that 10^2 has the form $11r + 1$.

2. Show that 10^4 has the form $11s + 1$ [use $10^4 = (10^2)^2$].

3. What does "$2k$ is a general form for an even whole number" mean?

4. Write $10^{\text{even number}}$ in general form.

5. Assume that 10^{2k} has the form $11t + 1$, and then show that 10^{2k+2} has the form $11u + 1$ (use $10^{2k+2} = 10^{2k} \cdot 10^2$).

6. Draw a conclusion from Exercises (1) and (5).

7. Show that 10 has the form $11v - 1$.

8. Show that 10^3 has the form $11w - 1$.

9. Write $10^{\text{odd number}}$ in general form.

10. Assume that 10^{2k+1} has the form $11x - 1$, and then show that 10^{2k+3} has the form $11y - 1$ (use $10^{2k+3} = 10^{2k+1} \cdot 10^2$).

11. Draw a conclusion from Exercises (7) and (10).

From the above exercises, we should conclude that

$$10^{2k} \qquad \text{has the form} \qquad 11b + 1,$$
$$10^{2k+1} \qquad \text{has the form} \qquad 11c - 1.$$

These results can be applied to the powers of 10 in the following numeral:

$$
\begin{aligned}
435762 &= 4 \cdot 10^5 + 3 \cdot 10^4 + 5 \cdot 10^3 + 7 \cdot 10^2 + 6 \cdot 10 + 2 \\
&= 4(11r - 1) + 3(11s + 1) + 5(11t - 1) + 7(11u + 1) \\
&\qquad + 6(11v - 1) + 2 \\
&= (44r - 4) + (33s + 3) + (55t - 5) + (77u + 7) \\
&\qquad + (66v - 6) + 2 \qquad\qquad\qquad\qquad \text{(by } D_+) \\
&= [11(3s + 7u) + (3 + 7 + 2)] \\
&\qquad + [11(4r + 5t + 6v) - (4 + 5 + 6)] \\
&\qquad \text{(by } C_a, A_a, D_+, \text{ and an extension of Problem 2 of} \\
&\qquad \text{Problem Set 4–5)} \\
&= [11x + (3 + 7 + 2)] + [11y - (4 + 5 + 6)] \quad \text{(new notation)} \\
&= 11x + [\{11y + (3 + 7 + 2)\} - (4 + 5 + 6)] \\
&\qquad\qquad\qquad\qquad\qquad \text{(by } A_a, C_a, \text{ and } PP_1) \\
&= 11x + [\{11(y - 1) + (11 + 3 + 7 + 2)\} - (4 + 5 + 6)] \\
&= 11x + [11(y - 1) + \{(11 + 3 + 7 + 2) - (4 + 5 + 6)\}] \\
&\qquad\qquad\qquad\qquad\qquad\qquad\qquad \text{(by } PP_1) \\
&= 11[x + (y - 1)] + [(11 + 3 + 7 + 2) - (4 + 5 + 6)].
\end{aligned}
$$

In these manipulations an 11 had to be "borrowed" so that certain sub-tractions could be performed; in some problems this would not have been necessary. Accordingly, for $w = x + y - 1$,

$$435762 = 11w + (23 - 15)$$
$$= 11w + 8.$$

Since 8 is a number ≥ 0 and < 11, then it must be the remainder on dividing 435762 by 11, that is, $R_{11}(435762) = 8$.

The preceding manipulations illustrate the fact that a counting number, n, can be written as follows:

$n = 11w + [(\text{sum of odd-numbered digits}) - (\text{sum of even-numbered digits})]$,

where the digits are numbered from the right. In actuality, the "sum of odd-numbered digits" may have to be replaced by "sum of odd-numbered digits + a multiple of 11," as occurred in the preceding example. This difficulty can be overcome more readily after negative numbers have been introduced.

The elevens remainder is used for checking in exactly the same way as the nines remainder. If both a "nines check" and an "elevens check" are carried out and neither indicates an error, it is more probable that the computation is correct than if either check is used alone. It can be shown that an error due to transposition of digits will be caught by an "elevens check."

ILLUSTRATIVE EXAMPLE. Compute 8734×526, and check your result by both casting out nines and casting out elevens.

Solution.

	Nines	Elevens
8734	4	$11 - 11 = 0$
($\times$) 526	4	$11 - 2 = 9$
52404	$7 = R_9(4 \cdot 4)$	$0 = R_{11}(0 \cdot 9)$
174680		
3467000		
3694084		

$$R_9(3694084) = 7;$$

$$R_{11}(3694084) = R_{11}[(11 + 4 + 0 + 9 + 3) - (8 + 4 + 6)]$$
$$= R_{11}[(11 + 16) - 18] = R_{11}(9) = 9.$$

The nines check does not indicate an error; the elevens check does indicate an error; hence the computation is not correct. What type of error was made?

These "casting-out" methods are useful for checking purposes, but their real importance lies in applications to be made later.

PROBLEM SET 5–4

1. For each of the following numbers, n, show that n has the form $11x +$ (sum of odd-numbered digits) $-$ (sum of even-numbered digits).

   (a) 764897   (b) 382697549   (c) 432158761   (d) 410320507

2. Find the elevens remander for n by casting out elevens.

   (a) $n = 76325$ (b) $n = 9328756$
   (c) $n = 1304572$ (d) $n = 20389683$

3. Check the following computational results by casting out elevens.

   (a) $9143 - 6828 = 2325$ (b) $79 \times 54 = 4366$
   (c) $142 \times 87 = 12354$

4. Check, both by casting out nines and casting out elevens, the computation $4516 \times 7283 = 32892008$. Draw a conclusion. Now perform the multiplication. Does your conclusion agree with this result?

5. Perform the following operations and check the results.

   (a) $67245 + 81352$ (b) $81352 - 67245$ (c) 67245×51
   (d) $67245 \div 51$ (e) $294057 + 13209$ (f) $294057 - 13209$
   (g) 294057×682 (h) $13209 \div 227$

6. If an error is indicated by "casting out nines" is there any need to "cast out elevens?" Why?

If sum of digits is div. by 9 — 0

CHAPTER 6

Primes and Divisibility

Read

We do many things in life because of interest rather than utility. For example, most of the people who like to fish are drawn to the activity because of some almost inexplicable interest, while only a few fish for a living. In mathematics there are many ideas which are investigated because the investigator has a natural curiosity about them; it may turn out later that these investigations have important applications for someone. Einstein found use in his relativity theory for ideas which, when they were first discovered, seemed little more than curiosities to many people.

In this chapter many ideas will be discussed which do not have immediate application but which are interesting in themselves. Also, they lead to the "fundamental theorem of arithmetic" and the concept of least common multiple. The fundamental theorem is used by all of us repeatedly without our realizing it; the concept of least common multiple will be used in Chapter 7.

all natural no. are either prime or composite

6–1 PRIMES AND COMPOSITE NUMBERS

The classification of things, whether they be people, plants, or numbers, is an everyday occurrence; sometimes classification is a necessity, while at other times it is merely a convenience. Frequently a thing is classified according to its properties, so that it can be easily recognized. The counting numbers have already been classified into those which are even and those which are odd. Recall that a counting number is even if it is divisible by 2, that is, if it can be written in the form $2k$, where k is a counting number; all other counting numbers are odd. When 14 is written as $2 \cdot 7$, both 2 and 7 are called *factors* or *divisors* of 14; the number 2 is a factor of 14 because $14 = 2 \cdot$ (a counting number). Likewise, 3 is a factor of 12 because $12 = 3 \cdot$ (a counting number); both 4 and 5 are divisors of 20. In general,

$$d \text{ is a factor of } x, \quad \text{if} \quad x = d \cdot y,$$

where x, d, and y are counting numbers. For some counting numbers the only divisors are 1 and the number itself; examples of such counting num-

106

bers are 1, 2, 3, 5, 7, 11, 13, 17, etc.   The number 1 plays a special role in mathematics, by reason of the property of one.   The other members of this set are called *prime numbers,* or *primes.*   All other counting numbers are called *composite* numbers.   Accordingly, a composite number has divisors other than 1 and the number itself, examples being $12 = 2 \cdot 6$ and $9 = 3 \cdot 3$.

How can one find the primes?   There is a very simple, yet cumbersome, procedure called the "sieve of Eratosthenes."   Suppose the counting numbers in sequence are displayed in an array, which may contain as many numbers as one desires to write down (1 can be omitted).   Any number divisible by 2, except 2 itself, is composite and will be stricken from the array; any number divisible by 3, except 3 itself, is composite and will also be stricken from the array.   Continuation of this procedure will eliminate all composite numbers from the array and leave the primes.   For an array up to 100 this would yield

2, 3, 4, 5, 6, 7, 8, 9, 10, 11, 12, 13, 14, 15, 16,
17, 18, 19, 20, 21, 22, 23, 24, 25, 26, 27, 28, 29, 30, 31,
32, 33, 34, 35, 36, 37, 38, 39, 40, 41, 42, 43, 44, 45, 46,
47, 48, 49, 50, 51, 52, 53, 54, 55, 56, 57, 58, 59, 60, 61,
62, 63, 64, 65, 66, 67, 68, 69, 70, 71, 72, 73, 74, 75, 76,
77, 78, 79, 80, 81, 82, 83, 84, 85, 86, 87, 88, 89, 90, 91,
92, 93, 94, 95, 96, 97, 98, 99, 100.

The numbers remaining,

2, 3, 5, 7, 11, 13, 17, 19, 23, 29, 31, 37, 41,
43, 47, 53, 59, 61, 67, 71, 73, 79, 83, 89, 97,

are primes and are the only primes ≤ 100.

Perform the above procedure yourself and take careful note of the largest prime that it was necessary to use in striking out multiples of that prime. Did you find it necessary to strike out multiples of 11 (except 11 itself) or were they already stricken out in previous steps?   Consider multiples of 13 and 17 in the same fashion.   If your arithmetic was correct, 7 was the largest prime that it was necessary to use.   Was this pure chance, or is there some general property which can be used?

Suppose that *n* is some composite counting number ≤ 100.   Hence *n* must have at least two prime divisors; these may be different, as in $30 = 2 \cdot 3 \cdot 5$, or equal, as in $25 = 5 \cdot 5$.   Let the two primes be denoted by p and q, and assume that neither is ≤ 10.   Accordingly, $p > 10$ and $q > 10$.   Now,

$$p > 10 \quad \text{implies} \quad pq > 10q \quad \text{(by } I_2);$$
$$q > 10 \quad \text{implies} \quad 10q > 10 \cdot 10 \quad \text{(by } I_2).$$

These results imply that $pq > 10 \cdot 10$. Now $n \geq pq$, since n may have factors other than p and q. Then

$$n \geq pq \quad \text{and} \quad pq > 100 \qquad \text{imply} \qquad n > 100.$$

But $n \leq 100$, so that the inequality $n > 100$ cannot be true. Our assumption that neither p nor q is ≤ 10 has led to a contradiction. Can the assumption be true? Of course not! Thus one of p and q must be ≤ 10, that is, n must have a prime divisor ≤ 10. Since 7 is a prime and there are no primes between 7 and 10, including 10, then n must have a prime divisor ≤ 7. This is a special case of a general theorem.

Theorem 6–1. If n is a composite counting number, then n has a prime divisor $\leq \sqrt{n}$.

It will be assumed here that we understand the meaning of $\sqrt{n}$, i.e., that $(\sqrt{n})^2 = n$, and how to find it for a particular value of n, at least approximately. For example, $(\sqrt{153})^2 = 153$ and $12 < \sqrt{153} < 13$. Explain the meaning of this last "double" inequality.

The proof used for the example above is an indirect type of proof. We assume that the conclusion of the theorem is not true and then proceed by logical steps, hoping to obtain some statement which contradicts a "known" fact. If such a contradiction is obtained, the assumption must be false, and hence the theorem is true. Since n is composite, it has at least two prime divisors, p and q. Assume that neither of these divisors is $\leq \sqrt{n}$. Hence $p > \sqrt{n}$ and $q > \sqrt{n}$. Accordingly,

$$p \cdot q > \sqrt{n} \cdot \sqrt{n} = n.$$

But $n \geq pq$, since $n = p \cdot q \cdot$ (some counting number). Since these inequalities involving n contradict each other, the assumption must be false. Hence n must have a prime divisor $\leq \sqrt{n}$.

ILLUSTRATIVE EXAMPLE. In applying the sieve of Eratosthenes to find all primes ≤ 1000, what is the largest prime whose multiples must be stricken from the table?

Solution. By the last theorem, if n is a composite number it must have a prime divisor $\leq \sqrt{n}$. Since $n \leq 1000$, then $\sqrt{n} \leq \sqrt{1000}$. But $31 < \sqrt{1000} < 32$; hence n must have a prime divisor ≤ 31, since $\sqrt{n} \leq 31^+$, where 31^+ stands for a number larger than 31 but smaller than 32. The largest prime we need to use is 31.

Theorem 6–1 can be used in another way. Suppose that we want to determine whether a number, say 191, is prime or composite without going through the sieve of Eratosthenes. We could simply try primes one after another to see if any of them divides 191. When should we stop trying? If 191 is composite it must have a prime divisor $\leq \sqrt{191} = 13^+$. Therefore we should try all primes up to and including 13; note that none of them divides 191. What conclusion can be drawn? Can 191 be composite? State why 191 must be a prime.

PROBLEM SET 6-1

1. Determine all primes between 100 and 200. You may use the array in the text for the numbers from 2 to 100. What is the largest prime which need be used in the "striking-out" procedure?

2. Determine whether the following numbers are primes or composite numbers. In each case state your reasoning.
   (a) 209 – *Composite*   (b) 331   (c) 547
   (d) 631   (e) 667   (f) 1249

6-2 DETERMINING DIVISIBILITY

You can determine whether or not a number is divisible by 2 merely by "looking at" its decimal numeral. You look at the units digit and if it is 0, 2, 4, 6, or 8, you know that the number is even, i.e., it is divisible by 2. Why is this so? Are there other simple tests for divisibility?

To attack these questions it will be necessary to write a counting number in the following way:

$$4067 = 4 \cdot 10^3 + 0 \cdot 10^2 + 6 \cdot 10 + 7$$
$$= (4 \cdot 2^3 \cdot 5^3 + 0 \cdot 2^2 \cdot 5^2 + 6 \cdot 2 \cdot 5) + 7$$
$$= 2(4 \cdot 2^2 \cdot 5^3 + 0 \cdot 2 \cdot 5^2 + 6 \cdot 5) + 7$$
$$= 2 \cdot (\text{sum of terms, each a whole number}) + 7$$
$$= 2t + 7,$$

where t is the whole number in the above parentheses. This sequence of steps is based on the fact that 2 divides 10, and hence each term except the last term is divisible by 2.

Using decimal system notation, any counting number, n, can be represented as

$$n = a_k \cdot 10^k + a_{k-1} \cdot 10^{k-1} + \cdots + a_2 \cdot 10^2 + a_1 \cdot 10 + a_0.$$

Each term except the last is divisible by 2, since 10 is divisible by 2, so that

$$n = 2 \cdot (\text{sum of terms, each a whole number}) + a_0 = 2t + a_0,$$

where t is a whole number. Hence, if a_0 is divisible by 2, then $a_0 = 2r$, where r is a whole number, and $n = 2(t + r)$ so that n is divisible by 2. Likewise, if n is divisible by 2, then $n = 2s$; hence $2s = 2t + a_0$, so that $a_0 = 2(s - t)$. Hence a_0 is divisible by 2. This proves the first part of the following theorem.

Theorem 6–2. A counting number, n, is divisible by

   (a) 2, if and only if 2 divides the ones digit of n,

   (b) 4, if and only if 4 divides the number formed by using the last two digits of n,

   (c) 8, if and only if 8 divides the number formed by using the last three digits of n.

The phrase "if and only if" requires explanation. Prior to the statement of Theorem 6–2 two sentences were proved to be true:

(1) *If* 2 divides a_0, *then* 2 divides n.

(2) *If* 2 divides n, *then* 2 divides a_0.

Both sentences have the form "if . . . . . , then . . . . . ," the "if" part being the hypothesis and the "then" part being the conclusion. In sentence (2) the hypothesis and conclusion of (1) are interchanged; such a sentence is called the *converse* of (1). The phrase "if and only if" means that an "if . . . . . , then . . . . ." statement and its converse are both true. Accordingly, part (b) of Theorem 6–2 means that both of the following statements are true.

(3) *If* 4 divides n, *then* 4 divides the number formed by using the last two digits of n.

(4) *If* 4 divides the number formed by using the last two digits of n, *then* 4 divides n.

To prove part (b) of Theorem 6–2, note that 4 divides 10^2, so that 4 divides 10^3 and each higher power of 10. Hence 4 divides each term of n except the last two, so that

$$n = 4 \cdot (\text{sum of whole numbers}) + (a_1 \cdot 10 + a_0).$$

Now, $a_1 \cdot 10 + a_0$ is just a two-digit number; denote this number by A, and write $n = 4 \cdot b + A$. If $A = 4 \cdot r$, then $n = 4(b + r)$, so that 4 divides n; this proves sentence (4) of the last paragraph. If $n = 4s$, then

$$4s = 4b + A \quad \text{and} \quad A = 4(s - b),$$

so that 4 divides A; this proves sentence (3) of the last paragraph. Part (b) of Theorem 6–2 has now been proved.

Let us illustrate the above ideas for $n = 73562$. We have

$$
\begin{aligned}
n &= (7 \cdot 10^4 + 3 \cdot 10^3 + 5 \cdot 10^2) + 62 \\
&= (7 \cdot 2^4 \cdot 5^4 + 3 \cdot 2^3 \cdot 5^3 + 5 \cdot 2^2 \cdot 5^2) + 62 \\
&= 4(7 \cdot 2^2 \cdot 5^4 + 3 \cdot 2 \cdot 5^3 + 5 \cdot 5^2) + 62 \\
&= 4b + 62.
\end{aligned}
$$

There is no need to find b since we are only interested in the fact that 4 divides the sum of terms in the parentheses on the first line above. If n were divisible by 4, then $62 = n - 4b$ would have to be divisible by 4; but 4 does not divide 62. Hence 4 cannot divide $n = 73562$. Actually, there is an indirect proof here. This procedure is much shorter than actual division by 4.

The reader will be asked to prove part (c) and the following theorem in Problem Set 6–2.

Theorem 6–3. If n is a counting number, then n is divisible by
(a)   5,   if and only if 5 divides the ones digit of n;
(b)   25,   if and only if 25 divides the number formed by using the last two digits of n.

Does 25 divide 47650? It does, since 25 divides 50, the number formed by using the last two digits of 47650.

In Chapter 5 it was shown that any counting number, n, can be written as

$$n = 9T + \text{sum of digits}, \qquad \text{where } T \text{ is a whole number.}$$

This equation could be used, as above, to prove that n is divisible by 9 if and only if 9 divides the sum of digits. Also, since

$$n = 3(3T) + \text{sum of digits},$$

a similar result holds for divisibility by 3. This proves the following theorem.

Theorem 6–4. If n is a counting number, then n is divisible by
(a) 3, if and only if 3 divides the sum of digits;
(b) 9, if and only if 9 divides the sum of digits.

The discussion of "casting out elevens" in the preceding chapter leads directly to another theorem. That discussion yielded

$$n = 11T + [(a_0 + a_2 + \cdots) - (a_1 + a_3 + \cdots)],$$

where there are as many terms within the brackets as there are digits in n. Hence, the following theorem holds.

Theorem 6–5. If n is a counting number, then n is divisible by 11 if and only if the difference $(a_0 + a_2 + \cdots) - (a_1 + a_3 + \cdots)$ is divisible by 11.

In applying Theorem 6–5, $(a_0 + a_2 + \cdots)$ may be less than $(a_1 + a_3 + \cdots)$. In that case, we "borrow" a multiple of 11 from $11T$ so as to make

$$11r + a_0 + a_2 + \cdots \geq a_1 + a_3 + \cdots.$$

Other tests for divisibility can be found, but as a rule they are more complicated and hence quite impractical for elementary work. The preceding tests would have been of considerable assistance in Section 6–1. They also aid in determining the factors of a number, especially if the number is large.

ILLUSTRATIVE EXAMPLE. Write the number $n = 17199$ as a product of powers of primes, if it is composite.

Solution. That neither 2 nor 5 are divisors can be seen immediately by looking at the last digit. Since $1 + 7 + 1 + 9 + 9 = 27$ is divisible by 3, then 3 divides n. But 27 is divisible by 9, so that 9 divides n. By actual division, $n = 9 \cdot 1911$. From this point on it will be simpler to find the divisors of 1911. Need we try 2 or 5? Should we try 3? Yes, we should, since there may be more factors 3. Actually $1 + 9 + 1 + 1 = 12$, so that 1911 is divisible by 3; now $1911 = 3 \cdot 637$, and hence $n = 3^3 \cdot 637$.

Since there is a simple test for divisibility by 11, try this next instead of testing for divisibility by 7. But $7 + 6 - 3 = 10$ is not divisible by 11; hence 637 is not divisible by 11.

Henceforth, actual division is necessary:

$$637 = 7 \cdot 91 = 7(7 \cdot 13) = 7^2 \cdot 13.$$

Accordingly,

$$17199 = 3^3 \cdot 7^2 \cdot 13.$$

The proof of each theorem in this section uses the decimal system representation of a natural number n; accordingly, the theorems hold in the Hindu-Arabic numeration system. The number $n(A)$, where

$$A = \{\square, \triangle, a, *, b, o, c, u\},$$

is even in the sense that it is divisible by two, as can be shown by using set ideas. However, in base seven numerals $n(A)$ would be written 11(seven), and for this numeral Theorem 6–2(a) would not be true. Accordingly, Theorems 6–2 through 6–5 are properties of numerals, and not properties of numbers. This is in direct contrast with a property such as C_a, which is a property of numbers.

PROBLEM SET 6–2

1. Without actually dividing, determine whether or not each of the following numbers is divisible by the numbers stated. Show why in each case.
   (a) 3472 by 3, 4, 8, and 11
   (b) 162864 by 3, 9, 8, and 11
   (c) 970535 by 8, 9, and 11
   (d) 100354 by 4, 9, and 11

2. (a) If n is not divisible by 2, need it be tested for divisibility by 4?
   (b) If n is not divisible by 3, need it be tested for divisibility by 9?

3. Determine whether the following numbers are prime or composite. If a number is composite, find the prime factors and write the number as a product of powers of primes.
   (a) 1144
   (b) 11475
   (c) 4356
   (d) 3448
   (e) 21241
   (f) 9464

4. Prove that n is divisible by 8 if and only if the number formed by using the last three digits is divisible by 8.

5. Prove Theorem 6–3.

6. Show, by using an example, that Theorem 6–3(a) does not hold for numbers written in base seven.

7. Show, by using an example, that Theorem 6 4(a) docs not hold for base eight numerals.

8. Show that Theorem 6–2(a) holds for base twelve numerals.

9. Find and prove a theorem similar to Theorem 6–4(b) for base seven numerals.

10. The pair of primes, 3 and 5, is called a "prime pair," since they differ by 2. The pair 5 and 7 is also a "prime pair." (a) Find three more prime pairs. (b) Consult a reference work to find out what is known about how many such prime pairs there are.

11. The primes 3, 5, and 7 form a prime triple, since consecutive members differ by 2. Are there any more prime triples among the primes <200?

12. Let $N = (2 \cdot 3 \cdot 5 \cdot 7 \cdot 11 \cdots 97) + 1$, where the number in parentheses is the product of all primes up to and including 97.
   (a) Prove that 2 does not divide N. Prove that 3 does not divide N.
   (b) Prove that none of the primes from 2 up to 97 divides N.
   (c) Prove that N is larger than 97.

6–3   INFINITUDE OF PRIMES

How many primes are there? The answer to this question has been known for a long period of time; it is contained in the following theorem, the proof of which is usually ascribed to Euclid.

Theorem 6–6. There is no largest prime.

Read

Does this theorem imply that the number of primes is infinite? The statement of the theorem is what we mean when we say that the number of primes is infinite.

The proof of this theorem follows ideas discussed in Problem 12 of Problem Set 6–2. Suppose that there is a largest prime, which is denoted by p_r. We can then form the counting number

$$N = 1 + (2 \cdot 3 \cdot 5 \cdot 7 \cdots p_{r-1} \cdot p_r),$$

where the number in parentheses is the product of *all* primes up to and including p_r. Since N is either prime or composite, we must consider two cases.

Case I (N is a prime). Now, $N > 2 \cdot 3 \cdot 5 \cdots p_{r-1} \cdot p_r$ and $(2 \cdot 3 \cdot 5 \cdots p_{r-1})p_r \geq 1 \cdot p_r$, since $2 \cdot 3 \cdot 5 \cdots p_{r-1} \geq 1$. Hence, N is larger than p_r and is a prime, so that we now have a prime larger than p_r (in this case).

Case II (N is composite). Here N must be divisible by a prime, which we will denote by q, so that $N = q \cdot t$. From the definition of N, we write

$$N - (2 \cdot 3 \cdot 5 \cdots p_r) = 1.$$

Can q be 2? If it is 2, then the left-hand side of the equation becomes

$$2t - (2 \cdot 3 \cdot 5 \cdots p_r) = 2[t - (3 \cdot 5 \cdots p_r)].$$

Accordingly, the number 2 must divide the right-hand side, which is 1, but this is impossible. In similar fashion, $q = 3$ would yield an impossibility. In turn it can be shown that q cannot be any of $2, 3, 5, 7, \ldots, p_r$. Hence q must be a prime larger than p_r.

The assumption that there is a largest prime, p_r, has led in each case to the contradictory statement that there is a larger prime. Hence the assumption is false. There is no largest prime.

In several places, we have used an important property.

Property. If q divides each of two numbers, say x and y, then q divides their sum and their difference. $35 + 75 = 5K$

Let $x = q \cdot r$ and $y = q \cdot s$; then $75 - 35 = 5K$

$$x + y = qr + qs = q(r + s) \qquad \text{and} \qquad x - y = q(r - s).$$

Since r and s are whole numbers, then $r + s$ and $r - s$ are also whole numbers (assuming $r \geq s$). Accordingly, q does divide each of $x + y$ and $x - y$. This property will also be used in Section 6–5.

Read

6–4 SET INTERSECTION

The points on a line form a set. Two distinct lines, l_1 and l_2, which lie in the same plane but are not parallel, are said to intersect in a point. This point, say P, is the intersection of l_1 and l_2. Moreover, $\{P\}$ is the set of all points which lie on *both* l_1 and l_2. Considering l_1 and l_2 as sets and using set language, $\{P\}$ is the set of all points common to l_1 and l_2. The set $\{P\}$ is called the *intersection* of l_1 and l_2 and is denoted by $l_1 \cap l_2$.

Definition. *Set intersection.* The intersection of two sets A and B is the set of all elements common to A and B.

If $A = \{1, 3, 7, 8, 9\}$ and $B = \{4, 8, 9, 10\}$, then $A \cap B = \{8, 9\}$. Also, if $C = \{2, 4, 10, 12\}$, then $A \cap C = \Phi$, the empty set. Previously, the terminology "A and C are disjoint" has been used to describe the situation now described by $A \cap C = \Phi$.

PROBLEM SET 6–4

1. Find $A \cap B$ for each of the following pairs of sets.
   (a) $A = \{p, q, r, s\}$, $B = \{g, r, t, w\}$
   (b) $A = \{p, q, r, s\}$, $B = \{u, v\}$
   (c) $A = \{2 \le \text{counting numbers} < 10\}$, $B = \{\text{counting numbers} < 20\}$
   (d) $A = \{\text{primes} < 45\}$, $B = \{\text{primes} > 23\}$

2. Find $A \cap A$, for any set A.

6–5 GREATEST COMMON DIVISOR

The divisors (or factors) of 24 form a set $A = \{1, 2, 3, 4, 6, 8, 12, 24\}$; likewise, the set of divisors of 42 is $B = \{1, 2, 3, 6, 7, 14, 21, 42\}$. Then $A \cap B = \{1, 2, 3, 6\}$ is the set of *common divisors* of 24 and 42, that is, the set of numbers which divide both 24 and 42. Now 6 is the largest member of this last set; thus 6 is the *greatest common divisor* (or largest common factor) of 24 and 42. Likewise, to find the largest common factor of 70 and 44, we write

$$C = \{\text{factors of } 44\} = \{1, 2, 4, 11, 22, 44\},$$
$$D = \{\text{factors of } 70\} = \{1, 2, 5, 7, 10, 14, 35, 70\},$$
$$C \cap D = \{\text{common factors of 44 and 70}\} = \{1, 2\}.$$

Hence the largest common factor of 44 and 70 is 2.

The above procedure, while straightforward, is cumbersome if the number of divisors is large. Moreover, it is not adaptable to theoretical discussions.

Read

To develop a more general procedure let us look at certain properties of the greatest common divisor. Note that, in the first example above, 6 is divisible by each of the common divisors 1, 2, 3, and 6, and, in the second example, 2 is divisible by each of the common divisors 1 and 2. This property is used below to characterize the greatest common divisor (abbreviated gcd). The gcd of x and y will be denoted by (x, y); thus,

$$(24, 42) = 6, \qquad (30, 75) = 15, \qquad (22, 15) = 1.$$

relatively prime — h gcd common f

Definition. The *greatest common divisor* of x and y is d if and only if

(1) d divides each of x and y;

(2) each common divisor of x and y divides d.

It was a simple matter to find d in the preceding example since the numbers 24 and 42 are small. But suppose that we wish to find $(910, 231)$. To do this, we will develop a general procedure, which, along with resulting properties, will be of greater importance in theoretical discussions than in numerical work.

Divide 910 by 231 and express the result in equation form, that is, $910 = 3 \cdot 231 + 217$; then divide the divisor, 231, by the remainder, 217. This yields $231 = 1 \cdot 217 + 14$. Continue this procedure until a zero remainder is obtained; the complete set of equations is

$$910 = 3 \cdot 231 + 217, \tag{1}$$

$$231 = 1 \cdot 217 + 14, \tag{2}$$

$$217 = 15 \cdot 14 + 7, \tag{3}$$

$$14 = 2 \cdot 7 + 0. \tag{4}$$

Let us prove that $(910, 231) = 7$. First, by using a general procedure rather than actual division, let us prove that 7 is a common divisor of 910 and 231. Equation (4) merely shows that 7 divides 14. In Eq. (3), the number 7 divides each term of the right-hand side and hence must divide 217. Now it is known that 7 divides each term of the right-hand side of Eq. (2), and therefore 7 must divide 231. Again, 7 divides each term of the right-hand side of Eq. (1), and therefore 7 divides 910. Accordingly, 7 is a common divisor of 910 and 231.

To show that every common divisor of 910 and 231 divides 7, let us rewrite the above equations in the following form:

$$910 - 3 \cdot 231 = 217, \tag{5}$$

$$231 - 1 \cdot 217 = 14, \quad \text{sub.} \tag{6}$$

$$217 - 15 \cdot 14 = 7. \quad \text{sub. equation} \tag{7}$$

Let g be a common divisor of 910 and 231. By Eq. (5), then, g must divide 217. Since g divides both 231 and 217, it must divide 14, by Eq. (6). Equation (7) then shows that g must divide 7. Thus, since both properties of a gcd are true for the number 7, that number must be the gcd of 910 and 231. Note the use of the general property: since g divides each term of a difference, then it divides the difference.

The procedure used above can be applied to find the gcd of any two counting numbers a and b. The division theorem states that a can be divided by b to yield a quotient q and a remainder r, where q and r are whole numbers and where $0 \leq r < b$. Then b could be divided by r, if $r \neq 0$, to yield a quotient q_1 and a remainder r_1. This can be continued until a zero remainder is obtained; that a zero remainder must be obtained eventually will be shown shortly. This yields

$$a = q \cdot b + r, \qquad\qquad 0 \leq r < b, \qquad\qquad (8)$$

$$b = q_1 \cdot r + r_1, \qquad\qquad 0 \leq r_1 < r, \qquad\qquad (9)$$

$$r = q_2 \cdot r_1 + r_2, \qquad\qquad 0 \leq r_2 < r_1, \qquad\qquad (10)$$

$$\vdots \qquad\qquad\qquad\qquad \vdots$$

$$r_{k-3} = q_{k-1} \cdot r_{k-2} + r_{k-1}, \qquad 0 \leq r_{k-1} < r_{k-2}, \qquad (11)$$

$$r_{k-2} = q_k \cdot r_{k-1} + r_k, \qquad\qquad 0 \leq r_k < r_{k-1}, \qquad (12)$$

$$r_{k-1} = q_{k+1} \cdot r_k + 0. \qquad\qquad\qquad\qquad\qquad (13)$$

This set of equations, obtained by successive application of the division theorem, is known as "Euclid's algorithm."

Now argue as in the numerical example:

r_k divides r_{k-1} from Eq. (13);
then r_k divides r_{k-2} from Eq. (12);
in turn, r_k divides each other r_j, eventually b and a;
accordingly, r_k is a common divisor of b and a.

Let g be any common divisor of a and b:

then g divides r, from Eq. (8);
then g divides r_1, from Eq. (9);
in turn, g divides each r_j, and eventually r_k.

Accordingly, r_k is divisible by each common divisor of a and b. These two lines of argument establish that $r_k = (a, b)$.

The inequalities associated with the above equations require that $b > r > r_1 > r_2 > \cdots$; that is, the remainders form a decreasing sequence of counting numbers. Since b is a given counting number, such a sequence can continue only a finite number of steps before a zero remainder is obtained.

1, 3, 7, 9 21, 63

ɲ

ρ (1, 2, 7, 14, 28)

PROBLEM SET 6–5

eyed 15
done by
sets

1. Use the set procedure to find the gcd of the following.

    (a) 28 and 63   (b) 65 and 51   (c) 36 and 45   (d) 66 and 90

2. Find the greatest common divisor of the following pairs of counting numbers by using Euclid's algorithm.

    (a) 58 and 179   (b) 110 and 315   (c) 421 and 673
    (d) 182 and 612   (e) 243 and 522   (f) 147 and 385

3. Using Eqs. (5), (6), and (7) of the preceding numerical example, perform the following operations.

    (a) Substitute into Eq. 7 the expression for 14 given in Eq. (6). Then collect terms so that 7 is expressed in terms of 217 and 231.

    (b) Substitute the expression for 217, given in Eq. (5), into the equation obtained in part (a).

    (c) The result should be of the form $7 = x \cdot 910 - y \cdot 231$. What are the values of x and y?

read

6–6 PROPERTIES RELATED TO THE GCD

In Problem 3 above it was shown that there are counting numbers x and y for which $7 = x \cdot 910 - y \cdot 231$, where $7 = (910, 231)$. This example illustrates a theorem which has interesting consequences.

Theorem 6–7. If a and b are any counting numbers and $d = (a, b)$, then whole numbers x and y can be found such that

$$d = xa - yb \quad \text{or} \quad d = yb - xa.$$

The proof of Theorem 6–7 follows directly from Eqs. (8), (9), (10), . . . , (12) of the preceding section by using the argument illustrated in Problem 3 of that section. Equation (12) can be used to find r_k; this yields

$$r_k = r_{k-2} - q_k r_{k-1}. \tag{1}$$

In similar fashion, Eq. (11) yields

$$r_{k-1} = r_{k-3} - q_{k-1} r_{k-2}. \tag{2}$$

Replacing r_{k-1} in Eq. (1) by the right-hand side of Eq. (2), we obtain

$$r_k = r_{k-2} - q_k(r_{k-3} - q_{k-1}r_{k-2})$$
$$= (1 + q_k q_{k-1})r_{k-2} - q_k r_{k-3}. \tag{3}$$

Now write the equation which immediately precedes Eq. (11) of Section 6–5:

$$r_{k-4} = q_{k-2}r_{k-3} + r_{k-2}.$$

Using this equation to find r_{k-2}, we obtain

$$r_{k-2} = r_{k-4} - q_{k-2}r_{k-3}. \tag{4}$$

Now substitute the right-hand side of this equation for r_{k-2} in Eq. (3); this produces

$$r_k = (1 + q_k q_{k-1})(r_{k-4} - q_{k-2}r_{k-3}) - q_k r_{k-3}.$$

Collect the terms involving r_{k-4} and r_{k-3} to obtain

$$r_k = (1 + q_k q_{k-1})r_{k-4} - [(1 + q_k q_{k-1})q_{k-2} + q_k]r_{k-3}.$$

Note that the coefficients of r_{k-4} and r_{k-3} are whole numbers. Why? This procedure can be continued until eventually r_k is expressed in terms a and b:

$$r_k = xa - yb \qquad \text{or} \qquad r_k = yb - xa,$$

where x and y are whole numbers. Since r_k is d, the desired expression has been obtained. Theorem 6–7 will be used to obtain Theorem 6–8; that is its principal importance for us. We will not even be interested in actually finding x and y; the fact that they can be found is sufficient.

If $(r, s) = 1$, then r and s are said to be *relatively prime*. Accordingly, 2 and 3 are relatively prime, and so are 14 and 9.

Suppose you have used divisibility ideas discussed previously to show that both 2 and 3 divide a counting number n. Then $n = 2b$, so that 3 divides $2b$. Does it follow that 3 divides b? Try to reason to a "yes" answer. Then $b = 3k$, and consequently $n = 2(3k) = 6k$. This type of argument permits us to show divisibility by a composite number having different prime factors. The above "yes" answer follows from Theorem 6–8.

Theorem 6–8. If p is a prime and $(p, a) = 1$ and p divides the product $a \cdot b$, where a and b are counting numbers, then p divides b.

Theorem 6–8 states that if a prime divides a product and is relatively prime to one factor, then that prime must divide the other factor.

The proof of this theorem is quite short. Since p is relatively prime to a, that is, since $(p, a) = 1$, then, by the preceding theorem,

$$1 = xp - ya \qquad \text{or} \qquad 1 = ya - xp,$$

for some whole numbers x and y. Now multiply both sides of this equation by b to obtain

$$b = xp \cdot b - y \cdot ab \qquad \text{or} \qquad b = y \cdot ab - xp \cdot b.$$

But $ab = p \cdot c$, for some counting number c. Why? Hence

$$\left.\begin{aligned} b &= xb \cdot p - y \cdot pc \\ &= (xb - yc)p \end{aligned}\right\} \quad \text{or} \quad \left\{\begin{aligned} b &= y \cdot pc - xb \cdot p \\ &= (yc - xb)p. \end{aligned}\right.$$

Since $xb - yc$ and $yc - xb$ are counting numbers (why?), then p divides b. This completes the proof of Theorem 6–8.

ILLUSTRATIVE EXAMPLE. Show, without using actual division, that 12 divides 4164.

Solution. Now $12 = 4 \cdot 3$. Since 3 divides $4 + 1 + 6 + 4 = 15$, then 3 divides 4164. Why? Also 4 divides 64, so that 4 divides 4164. Why? Then $4164 = 4 \cdot k$, and 3 divides $4k$. But 3 is relatively prime to 4, so that 3 must divide k. Hence $k = 3c$, and $4164 = 4(3c) = 12c$. Since c is a counting number, then 12 divides 4164.

PROBLEM SET 6–6

1. In each of the following find the greatest common divisor of a and b, and then find x and y, such that $(a, b) = xa - yb$ or $yb - xa$. Use the Euclidean algorithm and the procedure outlined in the proof of Theorem 6–7.
   (a) $a = 17$ and $b = 47$ (b) $a = 22$ and $b = 130$
   (c) $a = 31$ and $b = 77$ (d) $a = 63$ and $b = 165$

2. Without using actual division, show whether or not the following are true.
   (a) 15 divides 375.   (b) 45 divides 585   (c) 75 divides 1350.
   (d) 44 divides 924   (e) 30 divides 1410   (f) 165 divides 2805

3. Show wherein lies the difference between statement (a) and statement (b):
   (a) Both 4 and 6 divide 12; yet $4 \cdot 6$ does not divide 12.
   (b) In the preceding illustrative example it was shown that both 4 and 3 divide 4164, and then the conclusion was drawn that $4 \cdot 3$ divides 4164.

4. Prove the following generalization of Theorem 6–8: If $(n, a) = 1$ and n divides $a \cdot b$, then n divides b.

5. If it is proved that 15 divides n and that 14 divides n, will it follow that $15 \cdot 14$ divides n? Why?

6–7 FUNDAMENTAL THEOREM OF ARITHMETIC

For many years you have written 6 as $2 \cdot 3$ and 50 as $2 \cdot 5^2$. Have you ever wondered whether or not this sort of factorization exists for every counting number, no matter how large? Do you know any other prime factorization for 6 or for 50? Do you think any other can be found? These are interesting questions, which may seem to have obvious answers. It may be interesting, though not too informative at this stage, to be told that there are certain kinds of numbers which can be factored in more than one way. Therefore let us consider the following theorem.

Theorem 6–9. *Unique factorization theorem.* Each counting number larger than one can be written in one *and only one* way (except for order) as a product of one or more primes.

By definition of prime, 13 has no factors other than 1 and itself, and hence 13 does not have two prime divisors. How, then, can 13 be a product of primes? We will consider that the meaning of "product" is broadened to include the case of just one factor. This may seem curious at first since it is artificial. However, if this were not done, it would be necessary to make two statements, one for primes and one for composite numbers.

The number 330 could be written as $22 \cdot 15$, and then 22 written as $2 \cdot 11$, to yield $330 = 2(11 \cdot 15)$; this shows that 330 has a prime factor. A general counting number, n, is either prime or composite. If n is a prime, then n has itself as a prime divisor. If n is composite, then $n = a \cdot b$, where $1 < a < n$ and $1 < b < n$ (prove that $a < n$). Now work with a, applying the same argument as was used on n. If a is a prime, then n has a prime divisor; if a is composite, then $a = c \cdot d$, where $1 < c < a$ and $1 < d < a$. Since n, a, c, etc. are decreasing, there can only be a finite number of such steps. Hence, after a finite number of such steps one of the divisors of n must be a prime. Denote this divisor by p_1 and write $n = p_1 \cdot u$; now $u < n$. Could the same argument be applied to u as was applied to n? Certainly! Hence u would have a prime divisor; denote it by p_2 so that $u = p_2 \cdot w$, where $w < u$. Thus

$$n = p_1 \cdot p_2 \cdot w \quad \text{and} \quad n > u > w.$$

Since the second factors, such as u and w, are decreasing, eventually that factor must be a prime; otherwise we could carry on another step. This occurs after a finite number of steps, say r steps; let the last "second factor" be the prime p_r. Hence

$$n = p_1 \cdot p_2 \cdot p_3 \cdots p_r,$$

and therefore n has a prime factorization.

Now let us prove that this factorization is unique. Let us assume that n has two factorizations; let these be denoted by

$$p_1 \cdot p_2 \cdot p_3 \cdots p_r \quad \text{and} \quad q_1 \cdot q_2 \cdot q_3 \cdots q_s,$$

where the p's and q's are primes. Note that there are r primes in one case and s primes in the other; at this stage it is not known whether or not the number of primes is the same. Thus

$$p_1 \cdot p_2 \cdot p_3 \cdots p_r = q_1 \cdot q_2 \cdot q_3 \cdots q_s.$$

Since p_1 divides the left member of the equation, it must also divide the right member. The right member is a product, so that p_1 must divide one of the factors (see Theorem 6–8). Suppose that p_1 divides q_1. Since both p_1 and q_1 are primes, $p_1 = q_1$. Hence

$$p_1 \cdot p_2 \cdot p_3 \cdots p_r = p_1 \cdot q_2 \cdot q_3 \cdots q_s.$$

Now divide both sides by p_1 to obtain the equation

$$p_2 \cdot p_3 \cdot p_4 \cdots p_r = q_2 \cdot q_3 \cdot q_4 \cdots q_s,$$

which has the same form as the starting equation. The same argument could be applied again to eliminate another prime from the equation. If $r < s$, after r steps of the previous type, we would get

$$1 = \text{a product of } q\text{'s},$$

which is manifestly impossible. If $r > s$, a similar impossible situation would ensue. Hence $s = r$, that is, the number of primes must be the same on each side. Since at the various steps we obtained

$$p_1 = q_1, \qquad p_2 = q_2, \qquad p_3 = q_3, \quad \ldots, \quad p_r = q_r,$$

then the factorizations are the same. This completes the proof.

Theorem 6–9 is so basic in arithmetic that it is often referred to as "the fundamental theorem of arithmetic."

6–8 LEAST COMMON MULTIPLE

The multiples of 3 are the numbers of form $3k$, where k is a counting number. The set of multiples of 3 might be written as

$$A = \{3, 6, 9, 12, 15, 18, 21, 24, 27, 30, 33, \ldots\}.$$

The set of multiples of 5 is

$$B = \{5, 10, 15, 20, 25, 30, 35, \ldots\}.$$

What would be the set of numbers common to these two sets? It would be

$$A \cap B = \{15, 30, \ldots\};$$

the elements of this set are *common multiples* of 3 and 5, that is, both 3 and 5 divide each member of this last set. Obviously, 15 is the smallest of the

after finding least
you can find as many as you want
m- your

common multiples, i.e., the *least common multiple* of 3 and 5. It could also be said that

15 is the smallest counting number divisible by both 3 and 5.

Use the above procedure to show that 60 is the least common multiple of 12 and 5. Now it becomes evident that this procedure is cumbersome and should be superseded. As a general definition, the *least common multiple* of two counting numbers *a* and *b* is the smallest counting number which is divisible by each of them. How can this least common multiple (abbreviated lcm) be found? We begin by factoring each of the numbers *a* and *b*. For example, when $a = 12$ and $b = 5$,

$$12 = 2 \cdot 2 \cdot 3 \quad \text{and} \quad 5 = 5.$$

Let L be the least common multiple of 12 and 5. Since 12 must divide L, then $L = 12k = 2^2 \cdot 3 \cdot k$. Since 5 must also divide L, then 5 must divide $2^2 \cdot 3 \cdot k$. But $(5, 2) = 1$, and $(5, 3) = 1$, so that 5 must divide k. Why? Accordingly, $k = 5t$, and therefore

$$L = 2^2 \cdot 3 \cdot 5t.$$

Now t is some counting number, and for each such value of t, the number L will be a common multiple of both 12 and 5. For what value of t will L be the least such multiple? For $t = 1$, of course! Hence, $L = 2^2 \cdot 3 \cdot 5$.

ILLUSTRATIVE EXAMPLE. Find the lcm of 150 and 315.

Solution. Since

$$150 = 2 \cdot 3 \cdot 5^2 \quad \text{and} \quad 315 = 3^2 \cdot 5 \cdot 7,$$

then $L = 2 \cdot 3 \cdot 5^2 k$. Now $3^2 \cdot 5 \cdot 7$ must divide L. Hence 3^2 must divide $3(2 \cdot 5^2 k)$, so that 3 must divide $2 \cdot 5^2 k$; hence, 3 must divide k. Thus, $k = 3t$, and

$$L = 2 \cdot 3 \cdot 5^2 \cdot 3t = 2 \cdot 3^2 \cdot 5^2 t.$$

The factor 5 of 315 already divides L. The factor 7 must divide L and therefore must divide t. Why? Thus, $t = 7s$ and

$$L = 2 \cdot 3^2 \cdot 5^2 \cdot 7 \cdot s.$$

Now L is a multiple of both 150 and 315 for each counting number s, and $s = 1$ yields the least of these common multiples; hence

$$L = 2 \cdot 3^2 \cdot 5^2 \cdot 7.$$

PROBLEM SET 6–8

1. Use the first method of this section to find the lcm of (a) 14 and 21, (b) 14 and 10.

2. (a) Does 5^3 divide 5^2?
   (b) Name two values of t for which 5^3 will divide $5^2 \cdot t$.
   (c) For what values of k will 5^3 divide $5^3 \cdot k$?
   (d) What is the least value of k in part (c)?

3. (a) The number n is a multiple of 15. Express this in general form, using k. What is k?
   (b) Write the general form of k so that 21 will divide n.
   (c) What is the lcm of 15 and 21.

4. Find the lcm of m and n in each of the following:
   (a) $m = 3 \cdot 5^4 \cdot 7$, $n = 3^2 \cdot 5 \cdot 7^3$ (b) $m = 7^2 \cdot 11$, $n = 11^3 \cdot 13$
   (c) $m = 455$, $n = 275$ (d) $m = 429$, $n = 7623$
   (e) $m = 840$, $n = 4356$ (f) $m = 1800$, $n = 1980$
   (g) $m = 8125$, $n = 4225$ (h) $m = 1235$, $n = 2527$

5. Devise a procedure for finding the lcm of 12, 15, and 21.

6. Find the lcm of m, n, and q in each of the following:
   (a) $m = 75$, $n = 70$, $q = 180$ (b) $m = 56$, $n = 147$, $q = 126$
   (c) $m = 420$, $n = 200$, $q = 189$ (d) $m = 33$, $n = 225$, $q = 4235$

CHAPTER 7

Fractions

What is football? To answer this question one must talk about what certain players are permitted to do under certain circumstances; one must talk about the object of the game and describe how attempts are made to reach the objective in terms of "plays." Certainly the "plays" are governed by the rules of the game. We could even attempt to give reasons for the adoption of certain rules through a discussion of the effect which they have on the movements of players.

Some aspects of mathematics can be likened to a game. We have developed a system of "plays" with whole numbers, these "plays" being carried out according to a set of rules, which includes the definitions and properties already discussed. An attempt has been made to motivate these definitions by discussing what we are trying to do.

Now Canadian football is different from American football; one difference is the use of twelve men on a team. The originator of Canadian football might have said "let us use a twelfth man in the game so as to permit certain types of plays which are not possible in American football." Then and there he had to say how this man was to be used and how the "plays" could be changed so as to fit him into the overall picture.

In mathematics we have reached the stage where we want to do something which cannot be done with whole numbers. Hence we introduce new "men" and state how they are to operate, being certain that the "new men" and "old men" work together so as to produce a workable scheme, i.e., a consistent structure.

7–1 DEFINITION AND EQUALITY OF FRACTIONS

All of us have an intuitive notion of what it means to take a line segment, say one unit in length, and "break" it into 4 parts of equal length, each of which we call one-fourth of the whole. Likewise, a segment of length 3 units could be broken into 5 parts of equal length. Now suppose that a "new" number is associated with each of these parts; the number associated with the part which is one-fourth of a unit will be symbolized by $\frac{1}{4}$, and the number associated with the part which is one-fifth of 3 units will be symbolized by $\frac{3}{5}$. Moreover, we "feel" that 4 of these quarter parts should be equal to

125

the whole unit and that 5 of the "one-fifth parts of 3 units" should be equal to the 3 units. In terms of the numbers involved this could be written

$$4(\tfrac{1}{4}) = 1 \quad \text{and} \quad 5(\tfrac{3}{5}) = 3.$$

Note that an attempt has been made here to distinguish between a number and a length which is associated with the number. This discussion leads to a definition.

Definition. *Common fraction.* A common fraction is a numeral of the form a/b or, as an alternative notation, $\dfrac{a}{b}$, where a and b represent whole numbers, $b \neq 0$, such that

$$b \left(\frac{a}{b} \right) = a.$$

Cannot have
b = 0

This last equation should be thought of as

$$b \cdot \left(\text{the number represented by } \frac{a}{b} \right) = a;$$

hence this is a relationship involving numbers, not numerals. The upper part, a, is called the *numerator*, while the lower part, b, is called the *denominator*. This definition gives not only the form of a fraction, but also a property. This property states, for example, that for the fractions $\tfrac{5}{7}$ and $\tfrac{4}{13}$ the following equations are true:

$$7(\tfrac{5}{7}) = 5 \quad \text{and} \quad 13(\tfrac{4}{13}) = 4.$$

However, the property gives no information about $7(\tfrac{5}{6})$ or even $6(\tfrac{2}{3})$. If $(2 \cdot 3)(\tfrac{2}{3})$ could be written as $2[3(\tfrac{2}{3})]$, progress could be made since we could then say that $6(\tfrac{2}{3})$ would be $2[3(\tfrac{2}{3})] = 2(2) = 4$. Such an associativity property holds for whole numbers, and it is desirable that properties of one type of number hold for other types, if possible. Let us assume that this property does hold, i.e., that

$$(c \cdot b) \left(\frac{a}{b} \right) = c \left[b \left(\frac{a}{b} \right) \right].$$

This will be one of the rules, the statement of which will formulate our new "game."

Henceforth, when a fraction a/b is written, it will be assumed, without explicit statement, that $b \neq 0$. Now, by the preceding property, $(mb)(a/b) = m[b(a/b)]$, so that $(mb)(a/b) = ma$, by the definition. Since $mb(ma/mb)$ is also ma, it follows that ma/mb and a/b should be fractions representing the same number. Accordingly, we will postulate (i.e., assume to be true) one of the most useful properties of fractions.

equivalent fractions represent same number

Equality property E_1. If m is a counting number, then

$$\frac{ma}{mb} = \frac{a}{b}.$$

This property yields such familiar results as

$$\frac{4}{6} = \frac{2 \cdot 2}{2 \cdot 3} = \frac{2}{3} \quad \text{and} \quad \frac{12}{15} = \frac{3 \cdot 4}{3 \cdot 5} = \frac{4}{5}.$$

Read

Hence, $\frac{4}{6}$ represents the same number as $\frac{2}{3}$, and $\frac{12}{15}$ represents the same number as $\frac{4}{5}$. Fractions which represent the same number may be called _equivalent_ fractions. In the last chapter it was seen that any counting number (whole number $\neq 0$) can be written uniquely as a product of primes; this, coupled with E_1, shows why any fraction can be written in a form where numerator and denominator have a gcd of 1. Therefore, in addition to the above examples, we have

$$\frac{30}{42} = \frac{2 \cdot 3 \cdot 5}{2 \cdot 3 \cdot 7} = \frac{5}{7} \quad \text{and} \quad \frac{28}{44} = \frac{2 \cdot 2 \cdot 7}{2 \cdot 2 \cdot 11} = \frac{7}{11}.$$

Can $\frac{2}{3}$ and $\frac{5}{7}$ be written as fractions with the same denominator (a common denominator, actually)? Certainly, by E_1,

$$\frac{2}{3} = \frac{2 \cdot 7}{3 \cdot 7} = \frac{14}{21} \quad \text{and} \quad \frac{5}{7} = \frac{5 \cdot 3}{7 \cdot 3} = \frac{15}{21}.$$

The numerator and denominator of $\frac{2}{3}$ can each be multiplied by 7, the denominator of $\frac{5}{7}$; the numerator and denominator of $\frac{5}{7}$ can each be multiplied by 3, the denominator of $\frac{2}{3}$. Simple, but wait! If we apply this method to $\frac{7}{330}$ and $\frac{11}{390}$, we obtain

$$\frac{7}{330} = \frac{7 \cdot 390}{330 \cdot 390} = \frac{2730}{128700} \quad \text{and} \quad \frac{11}{390} = \frac{11 \cdot 330}{390 \cdot 330} = \frac{3630}{128700},$$

as desired. But the desired result can be obtained more easily and in a form which is better for applications. Consider the fractions

$$\frac{7}{330} = \frac{7}{2 \cdot 3 \cdot 5 \cdot 11} \quad \text{and} \quad \frac{11}{390} = \frac{11}{2 \cdot 3 \cdot 5 \cdot 13}.$$

If we apply E_1 to these fractions, using $m = 13$ for the first and $m = 11$ for the second, we obtain

$$\frac{7}{330} = \frac{7 \cdot 13}{2 \cdot 3 \cdot 5 \cdot 11 \cdot 13} \quad \text{and} \quad \frac{11}{390} = \frac{11 \cdot 11}{2 \cdot 3 \cdot 5 \cdot 13 \cdot 11}.$$

The resulting fractions have a common denominator of $2 \cdot 3 \cdot 5 \cdot 11 \cdot 13 =$

4290, which is much smaller than the 128700 of the previous result. Of course you have noted the reason for this, that the denominators $2 \cdot 3 \cdot 5 \cdot 11$ and $2 \cdot 3 \cdot 5 \cdot 13$ have a common divisor > 1. You have also noted that $2 \cdot 3 \cdot 5 \cdot 11 \cdot 13$ is the least common multiple of $2 \cdot 3 \cdot 5 \cdot 11$ and $2 \cdot 3 \cdot 5 \cdot 13$. The least common multiple of the denominators is called the *least common denominator* (abbreviated lcd).

ILLUSTRATIVE EXAMPLE.   Write $\frac{5}{484}$ and $\frac{7}{198}$ as fractions with a least common denominator.

Solution. Let $b = 484$ and $d = 198$; both b and d can be factored by the methods of Chapter 6:

$$b = 2 \cdot 242 = 2(2 \cdot 121) = 2^2 \cdot 11^2,$$

$$d = 2 \cdot 99 = 2(3 \cdot 33) = 2 \cdot 3(3 \cdot 11) = 2 \cdot 3^2 \cdot 11.$$

Thus the lcd is the

$$\text{lcm of } b \text{ and } d = (2^2 \cdot 11^2)3^2 = 2^2 \cdot 3^2 \cdot 11^2.$$

By what should b be multiplied to get the lcd? The answer is 3^2. Hence both numerator and denominator of $\frac{5}{484}$ are to be multiplied by 3^2. By what should d be multiplied to get the lcd? The answer is $2 \cdot 11$. Hence both numerator and denominator of $\frac{7}{198}$ should be multiplied by $2 \cdot 11$. Thus,

$$\frac{5}{484} = \frac{5}{2^2 \cdot 11^2} = \frac{5 \cdot 3^2}{2^2 \cdot 11^2 \cdot 3^2},$$

$$\frac{7}{198} = \frac{7}{2 \cdot 3^2 \cdot 11} = \frac{7 \cdot (2 \cdot 11)}{2 \cdot 3^2 \cdot 11(2 \cdot 11)} = \frac{2 \cdot 7 \cdot 11}{2^2 \cdot 3^2 \cdot 11^2}.$$

How can it be determined whether or not a/b and c/d are equal, i.e., whether or not they represent the same number? First change them to fractions with a common denominator:

$$\frac{a}{b} = \frac{ad}{bd} \quad \text{and} \quad \frac{c}{d} = \frac{bc}{bd}.$$

When b and d are known, the lcd should be used. To simplify notation, let $ad/bd = r/s$ and $bc/bd = t/s$. If $r/s = t/s$, it follows that

$$s \cdot \frac{r}{s} = s \cdot \frac{t}{s},$$

so that

$$r = t.$$

Conversely, if $r = t$, then

$$\frac{r}{s} = \frac{t}{s}.$$

The "replacement" principle has been used in two places:

(1) Certainly $s \cdot (r/s) = s \cdot (r/s)$, by the reflexive property of equality; if $r/s = t/s$, then one of the r/s can be replaced by t/s.

(2) Certainly $r/s = r/s$, and if $r = t$, then one of the r's can be replaced by t.

Accordingly, we have proved the following property.

Equality property E$_2$. Two fractions with the same denominator are equal if and only if their numerators are equal.

By this property, the fractions $\frac{5}{484}$ and $\frac{7}{198}$ are not equal since, when they are written with a common denominator, $2^2 \cdot 11^2 \cdot 3^2$, their numerators are unequal (see previous work).

PROBLEM SET 7–1

1. Reduce the following fractions to simplest form, i.e., so that the numerator and denominator have a gcd of 1.

   (a) $\frac{86}{44}$ (b) $\frac{84}{70}$ (c) $\frac{153}{209}$

   (d) $\frac{935}{759}$ (e) $\frac{467}{383}$ (f) $\frac{803}{737}$

2. Reduce the following fractions to simplest form. (You may assume that the letters represent whole numbers, the denominators being $\neq 0$.)

   (a) $\dfrac{x^2 y}{yz^2}$ (b) $\dfrac{r^2 s^3 t^4}{rs^1 t^2}$ (c) $\dfrac{u^2 vw^5}{v^3 wz}$

   (d) $\dfrac{ab - ac}{ar - as}$ (e) $\dfrac{(x + y)(x - y)}{(x + y)^2}$ (f) $\dfrac{(ab + ac)(ru - rv)}{a^2 r^2}$

3. In Problem 2(a) you carried out a simplification; could the problem have been simplified further if it is given that

   (a) $x = 3$ and $z = 7$;   (b) $x = 6$ and $z = 3$.

   If so, simplify further.

4. Write the following pairs of fractions with the smallest common denominator possible.

   (a) $\frac{18}{25}$, $\frac{23}{30}$ (b) $\frac{12}{65}$, $\frac{13}{85}$ (c) $\frac{15}{98}$, $\frac{24}{343}$

   (d) $\frac{19}{220}$, $\frac{15}{286}$ (e) $\frac{14}{261}$, $\frac{21}{435}$ (f) $\frac{5}{1518}$, $\frac{7}{2783}$

5. Write each of the following fractions as an equivalent fraction with denominator or numerator as indicated.

(a) $\dfrac{5 \cdot 7}{3 \cdot 11}$, with denominator $3 \cdot 7^2 \cdot 11^3$

(b) $\dfrac{7 \cdot 3}{2 \cdot 5}$, with denominator $2^2 \cdot 3 \cdot 5^3$

(c) $\dfrac{6 \cdot 7}{4 \cdot 5}$, with numerator $2 \cdot 3^2 \cdot 7^3$

(d) $\dfrac{7 \cdot 3}{2 \cdot 5}$, with numerator $3^2 \cdot 7 \cdot 13$

6. In each part below, is the first fraction equal to the second? Why or why not?

(a) $\frac{10}{21}$, $\frac{16}{33}$ (b) $\frac{23}{63}$, $\frac{35}{96}$ (c) $\frac{15}{11}$, $\frac{10}{7}$ (d) $\frac{18}{20}$, $\frac{45}{50}$

7. (a) If $a = c$, is a/b equal to c/d? Why?
   (b) If $b = d$, is a/b equal to c/d? Why?
   (c) If $a/b = c/d$ and $b = d$, what relationship exists between a and c?

7–2 ADDITION OF FRACTIONS

Intuitive ideas will lead us to a suitable definition of addition of fractions. Again thinking in terms of parts of line segments, we feel that two-fifths of a unit and one-fifth of the unit, when placed together, should yield three-fifths of the unit. Since $3 = 2 + 1$, this would suggest the corresponding equation in fractions, $\frac{2}{5} + \frac{1}{5} = (2 + 1)/5$. At this point a definition of addition could be stated arbitrarily. However, any such definition should be linked to the definition of fraction. For this purpose let us assume that the operation

$$b \left(\frac{a}{b} + \frac{c}{b} \right) = b \cdot \frac{a}{b} + b \cdot \frac{c}{b}$$

is valid; this operation is a type of distributivity. The line-segment illustration may be used to show that intuitively this is valid. Since, from the definition of fraction, the right-hand side of this equation is $a + c$, then

$$b \left(\frac{a}{b} + \frac{c}{b} \right) = (a + c).$$

Now, both $a + c$ and b are whole numbers, $b \neq 0$; hence, if $a/b + c/b$ is to be a fraction, that fraction should be $(a + c)/b$. This discussion motivates a definition of addition of fractions.

Definition. *Addition of fractions.* For any fractions a/b and c/b,

$$\frac{a}{b} + \frac{c}{b} = \frac{a + c}{b}.$$

Again it should be emphasized that we are working with *numbers symbolized by fractions;* accordingly, the last equation means that

$$\left(\text{the number symbolized by } \frac{a}{b}\right) + \left(\text{the number symbolized by } \frac{c}{b}\right)$$

$$= \text{the number symbolized by } \frac{a+c}{b}.$$

Note that the fractions being added have the same denominator. This property yields

$$\frac{8}{15} + \frac{4}{15} = \frac{8+4}{15} = \frac{12}{15},$$

which, by previous properties, represents the same number as $\frac{4}{5}$, that is, $\frac{12}{15} = \frac{4}{5}$.

If two fractions have different denominators, they can first be written as fractions with a common denominator, and then the above definition will apply.

ILLUSTRATIVE EXAMPLE. Find $\frac{3}{8} + \frac{13}{20}$.

Solution. Since $8 = 2^3$ and $20 = 2^2 \cdot 5$, then the lcm of 8 and 20 is $2^3 \cdot 5$, so that

$$\frac{3}{8} + \frac{13}{20} = \frac{3 \cdot 5}{2^3 \cdot 5} + \frac{13 \cdot 2}{2^2 \cdot 5 \cdot 2} = \frac{15 + 26}{2^3 \cdot 5} = \frac{41}{40}.$$

Can the answer be reduced? Why or why not?

The above procedure is advised rather than the widely used $(ad + bc)/(bd)$ for $a/b + c/d$ because:

(1) There is a great tendency to use this formula mechanically, all too often without any understanding of background concepts.

(2) In many instances this formula does not produce the least common denominator, and hence possible reductions are often missed.

Reduce fractions before adding them! For example, in adding $\frac{15}{50}$ and $\frac{11}{45}$, first reduce $\frac{15}{50}$ to $\frac{3}{10}$ and then add:

$$\frac{15}{50} + \frac{11}{45} = \frac{3}{2 \cdot 5} + \frac{11}{3^2 \cdot 5} = \frac{3 \cdot 3^2}{2 \cdot 5 \cdot 3^2} + \frac{11 \cdot 2}{3^2 \cdot 5 \cdot 2} = \frac{27 + 22}{2 \cdot 5 \cdot 3^2}.$$

If the reduction had not been performed first, the result of adding would have been $245/2 \cdot 3^2 \cdot 5^2$. Here there is a reduction which should be performed but which may be overlooked.

In the chapter on operations with whole numbers we saw how advisable it was to consider the commutative and associative properties (C_a and A_a).

Do these properties hold for fractions? Since two fractions with different denominators can always be written as fractions with the same denominator, it will still be a general result if we assume, in the proof, that the fractions under consideration have the same denominator. In view of this, are $a/b + c/b$ and $c/b + a/b$ the same or different? We have

$$\frac{a}{b} + \frac{c}{b} = \frac{a+c}{b} \quad \text{and} \quad \frac{c}{b} + \frac{a}{b} = \frac{c+a}{b}.$$

But $a + c$ and $c + a$ are equal, since c and a are whole numbers and the commutative property of addition holds for them. Hence, the fractions resulting from the above additions have the same denominator and the same numerator; accordingly, the results are equal, by the equality property E_2. Hence, the commutative property of addition holds for fractions.

Commutative property of addition.

$$\frac{a}{b} + \frac{c}{d} = \frac{c}{d} + \frac{a}{b}.$$

It is important to note that the proof of C_a for fractions depends on the fact that C_a is true for whole numbers. In subsequent work, C_a will denote the commutative property of addition either for whole numbers or fractions, depending on the type of numbers being considered.

The proof of the associative property of addition for fractions is deferred to a problem.

Associative property of addition.

$$\frac{a}{b} + \left(\frac{c}{d} + \frac{e}{f}\right) = \left(\frac{a}{b} + \frac{c}{d}\right) + \frac{e}{f}.$$

PROBLEM SET 7–2

1. Describe in detail how you would introduce a person to the idea of $\frac{4}{7} + \frac{2}{7}$.

2. (a) What property is illustrated by

$$7(\tfrac{6}{7} + \tfrac{5}{7}) = 7(\tfrac{6}{7}) + 7(\tfrac{5}{7})?$$

(b) Was this property assumed or proved?

3. (a) If it is shown that

$$15(\tfrac{2}{3} + \tfrac{3}{5}) = 10 + 9,$$

what conclusion can be drawn?

(b) What conclusion can be drawn from

$$12(\tfrac{5}{6} + \tfrac{7}{12}) = 10 + 7?$$

4. Perform the following additions, showing all steps. [In parts (g) through (l) it may be assumed that the letters represent whole numbers and that the denominators are nonzero.]

(a) $\frac{11}{15} + \frac{7}{20}$

(b) $\frac{19}{220} + \frac{15}{286}$

(c) $\frac{14}{261} + \frac{21}{435}$

(d) $\frac{5}{1518} + \frac{7}{2783}$

(e) $\frac{66}{70} + \frac{84}{165}$

(f) $\frac{460}{170} + \frac{26}{550}$

(g) $\frac{r}{xy} + \frac{s}{yz}$

(h) $\frac{z}{x^2y} + \frac{t}{xy^2}$

(i) $\frac{u}{a^3bc^2} + \frac{v}{ab^3c}$

(j) $\frac{a}{x + y} + \frac{b}{x - y}$, $(x > y)$

(k) $\frac{a}{x + y} + \frac{b}{(x + y)^2}$

(l) $\frac{x}{(x + y)(x - y)} + \frac{y}{(x + y)^2}$

5. Prove the associative property of addition for fractions.

6. Show that the following are true without performing the calculations. Justify each step.

(a) $(\frac{2}{3} + \frac{3}{7}) + \frac{1}{4} = \frac{3}{7} + (\frac{1}{4} + \frac{2}{3})$

(b) $(\frac{1}{5} + \frac{3}{4}) + (\frac{2}{3} + \frac{1}{7}) = \frac{2}{3} + [(\frac{3}{4} + \frac{1}{7}) + \frac{1}{5}]$

7. (a) Does $\frac{a}{b} + \frac{c}{b} + \frac{e}{b}$ have meaning as yet?

(b) How could it be given meaning?

7–3 MULTIPLICATION OF FRACTIONS

At the intuitive level the fraction $\frac{1}{3}$ is usually associated with the idea of "breaking" a unit into 3 equal parts and taking one of those parts. Hence, the expression $\frac{1}{3}$ of $\frac{1}{5}$ could be associated with the idea of "breaking" the number $\frac{1}{5}$ into 3 equal parts; this would mean that the number 1 would be "broken" into 15 equal parts, each of which would be $\frac{1}{15}$. What does this have to do with $\frac{1}{3} \cdot \frac{1}{5}$? If $\frac{1}{3} \cdot \frac{1}{5}$ is associated with $\frac{1}{3}$ of $\frac{1}{5}$, there would be a link between the abstract and the intuitive. Maybe it would be possible to do a bit better! If $3 \cdot 5(\frac{1}{3} \cdot \frac{1}{5})$ could be written as $3(\frac{1}{3}) \cdot 5(\frac{1}{5})$, then

$$(3 \cdot 5)(\tfrac{1}{3} \cdot \tfrac{1}{5}) = (3 \cdot \tfrac{1}{3})(5 \cdot \tfrac{1}{5})$$
$$= 1 \cdot 1 \qquad \text{(definition of fraction)}$$
$$= 1.$$

Since $3 \cdot 5(\frac{1}{3} \cdot \frac{1}{5}) = 1$, the definition of fraction states that $\frac{1}{3} \cdot \frac{1}{5}$ should be $1/(3 \cdot 5)$. Therefore, assume that

$$(bd) \left(\frac{a}{b} \cdot \frac{c}{d}\right) = b \left(\frac{a}{b}\right) \cdot d \left(\frac{c}{d}\right),$$

and use this equality as one of our ground rules. (Note that we have here a form of associativity, together with commutativity, involving both fractions and whole numbers.) Then

$$(bd)\left(\frac{a}{b}\cdot\frac{c}{d}\right) = a\cdot c \qquad \text{(definition of fraction),}$$

so that

$$\frac{a}{b}\cdot\frac{c}{d} \qquad \text{must be} \qquad \frac{ac}{bd},$$

if it is to be a fraction. This justifies the following definition.

Definition. *Multiplication of fractions.* If a/b and c/d are fractions, then

$$\frac{a}{b}\cdot\frac{c}{d} = \frac{ac}{bd}.$$

This is the only possible definition of multiplication of fractions so long as the special type of associativity and commutativity noted above holds; it comes directly from the definition of fraction. As in previous similar situations this means that

$$\left(\text{the number symbolized by } \frac{a}{b}\right) \cdot \left(\text{the number symbolized by } \frac{c}{d}\right)$$
$$= \text{ the number symbolized by } \frac{ac}{bd}.$$

The commutative and associative properties of multiplication hold for fractions; proofs of these properties are called for in Problem Set 7–3. Similarly, the distributive property of multiplication with respect to addition holds for fractions. These properties are written as follows.

$$C_m: \quad \frac{a}{b}\cdot\frac{c}{d} = \frac{c}{d}\cdot\frac{a}{b},$$

$$A_m: \quad \left(\frac{a}{b}\cdot\frac{c}{d}\right)\frac{e}{f} = \frac{a}{b}\left(\frac{c}{d}\cdot\frac{e}{f}\right),$$

$$D_+: \quad \frac{a}{b}\left(\frac{c}{d}+\frac{e}{f}\right) = \frac{a}{b}\cdot\frac{c}{d}+\frac{a}{b}\cdot\frac{e}{f}.$$

If b is a whole number, then $b/1$ is a fraction, and hence b and $b/1$ seem to represent different types of numbers. However, if we compare

$$a + b = (a + b) \qquad \text{with} \qquad \frac{a}{1} + \frac{b}{1} = \frac{a+b}{1},$$

$$a \cdot b = (ab) \qquad \text{with} \qquad \frac{a}{1}\cdot\frac{b}{1} = \frac{a\cdot b}{1},$$

$$b\left(\frac{a}{b}\right) = a \qquad \text{with} \qquad \frac{b}{1}\left(\frac{a}{b}\right) = \frac{ba}{b\cdot1} = \frac{a}{1},$$

we see that the whole numbers, such as b, and their corresponding fractions, $b/1$, seem to react, in the operations noted, in a similar fashion. For this reason, b and $b/1$ will be considered as representing the same number; hence, we will write $3 = \frac{3}{1}$, $15 = \frac{15}{1}$, etc., meaning that b and $b/1$ are different symbols for the same number. Under this agreement the whole numbers are included in the set of numbers represented by fractions; both calculations and discussion will be simplified as a result of this agreement. Further results of this agreement are

$$a \cdot \frac{1}{b} = \frac{a}{1} \cdot \frac{1}{b} = \frac{a \cdot 1}{1 \cdot b} = \frac{a}{b} \quad \text{and} \quad \frac{1}{b} \cdot a = \frac{1}{b} \cdot \frac{a}{1} = \frac{1 \cdot a}{b \cdot 1} = \frac{a}{b},$$

that is,

$$a \cdot \frac{1}{b} = \frac{a}{b} \quad \text{and} \quad \frac{1}{b} \cdot a = \frac{a}{b}.$$

These results agree with the intuitive notions of

$$\frac{1}{3} \cdot 4 = \frac{4}{3} \quad \text{and} \quad 4 \cdot \frac{1}{3} = \frac{4}{3}.$$

Since

$$1 \cdot \frac{a}{b} = \frac{1}{1} \cdot \frac{a}{b} = \frac{a}{b},$$

the property of one holds for fractions, and either 1 or $\frac{1}{1}$ plays the role of one; by property E_1, we have $\frac{1}{1} = \frac{2}{2} = \frac{7}{7}$, etc., so that any fraction of the form a/a plays the role of one. The property E_1 may be thought of as

$$\frac{a}{b} = \frac{a}{b} \cdot 1 = \frac{a}{b} \cdot \frac{m}{m} = \frac{am}{bm};$$

this thought sequence is useful in some situations.

Likewise,

$$\frac{a}{b} + \frac{0}{1} = \frac{a}{b} + \frac{0}{b} = \frac{a + 0}{b} = \frac{a}{b} \quad \left(\text{why is } \frac{0}{1} = \frac{0}{b} ? \right),$$

so that $\frac{0}{1}$ plays the role of zero. Also,

$$\frac{a}{b} \cdot \frac{0}{1} = \frac{a \cdot 0}{b \cdot 1} = \frac{0}{b} = \frac{0}{1}.$$

In terms of the agreement, $\frac{0}{1}$ can be written as 0, so that

$$\frac{a}{b} \cdot 0 = 0.$$

PROBLEM SET 7–3

1. Without performing the operations indicated, show that the following are true. Justify each step.

   (a) $\frac{1}{2}(\frac{2}{3} + \frac{4}{5}) + \frac{2}{7} = \frac{2}{7} + (\frac{4}{5} \cdot \frac{1}{2}) + (\frac{1}{2} \cdot \frac{2}{3})$ *identify the*

   (b) $\frac{1}{2}(\frac{2}{3} + \frac{4}{5}) + \frac{1}{2} \cdot \frac{5}{8} = [\frac{2}{3} + (\frac{4}{5} + \frac{5}{8})]\frac{1}{2}$ *law used*

   (c) $\frac{1}{2} + 0(\frac{4}{5} \cdot \frac{7}{8}) = \frac{1}{2} \cdot \frac{14}{14}$

   (d) $(\frac{3}{4} + \frac{2}{3} \cdot \frac{1}{5}) + \frac{1}{5} \cdot \frac{3}{7} = \frac{1}{5}(\frac{3}{7} + \frac{2}{3}) + \frac{3}{4}$

   (e) $1(\frac{6}{7} + 0) = \frac{6}{7} + 0 \cdot \frac{1}{4}$

   (f) $(1 + 1)\frac{1}{3} = \frac{2}{3}$

2. Perform the indicated operations and write the answer as a reduced fraction.

   (a) $\frac{4}{7} \cdot \frac{35}{12}$ (b) $\frac{3}{4}(\frac{1}{5} + \frac{2}{3})$ (c) $\frac{15}{14}(\frac{7}{39} \cdot \frac{8}{33})$

   (d) $\frac{1}{2} + \frac{2}{3}(\frac{4}{5} + \frac{3}{4})$ (e) $(\frac{1}{2} + \frac{2}{3})(\frac{4}{5} + \frac{3}{4})$ (f) $\frac{2}{3} + \frac{1}{4}(\frac{2}{3} + \frac{3}{4})$

   (g) $\frac{4}{7}(\frac{15}{11} \cdot 0)$ (h) $(\frac{2}{3} \cdot \frac{4}{5}) \cdot \frac{11}{11}$ (i) $(\frac{2}{3} + 0)\frac{4}{5}$

   (j) $(\frac{4}{7} + 0)(\frac{21}{8} + \frac{9}{5})$

   (k) $\dfrac{x^2}{y} \cdot \dfrac{y^3}{x^4}$ (l) $\dfrac{r^2 s}{t^3} \cdot \dfrac{t}{rs}$ (m) $\dfrac{x}{y}\left(\dfrac{y}{x} + \dfrac{x}{y}\right)$

   (n) $\dfrac{0}{r}\left(\dfrac{u}{v} + t\right)$ (o) $\frac{6}{7} + 5$ (p) $3 + \frac{2}{5}$

   (q) $4 + \frac{1}{3} \cdot \frac{5}{2}$ (r) $(11 + \frac{6}{7})\frac{2}{3}$ (s) $(4 + \frac{1}{3})\frac{5}{2}$

3. Prove the commutative property of multiplication for fractions.

4. Prove the associative property of multiplication for fractions.

5. (a) Prove that if x, y, z, u, and w are whole numbers, $y \neq 0$ and $w \neq 0$, then

$$\frac{x}{y}\left(\frac{z}{w} + \frac{u}{w}\right) = \frac{x}{y} \cdot \frac{z}{w} + \frac{x}{y} \cdot \frac{u}{w}.$$

   (b) From the result of part (a) show how to obtain the general distributive law for fractions.

   Read

7–4 SUBTRACTION AND INEQUALITY

Intuitively, it is quite natural to think of $\frac{5}{7} - \frac{2}{7}$ as $(5 - 2)/7$. How can subtraction be related to the general sequence of ideas? If the distributive property holds for subtraction, then

$$b\left(\frac{a}{b} - \frac{c}{b}\right) = b \cdot \frac{a}{b} - b \cdot \frac{c}{b} = a - c;$$

this requires that $a \geq c$. Hence, if this distributive property is to hold, subtraction must be defined as follows.

Definition. *Subtraction of fractions.* If a/b and c/b are fractions such that $a \geq c$, then

$$\frac{a}{b} - \frac{c}{b} = \frac{a - c}{b}.$$

Accordingly,

$$\frac{5}{3} - \frac{1}{2} = \frac{10}{6} - \frac{3}{6} = \frac{10 - 3}{6} = \frac{7}{6},$$

and

$$\frac{8}{3} - 2 = \frac{8}{3} - \frac{2 \cdot 3}{1 \cdot 3} = \frac{8 - 6}{3} = \frac{2}{3}.$$

The ideas of "less than" and "greater than" were defined and used for whole numbers. Let us define them for fractions.

Definition. *Inequality.* For the fractions a/b and c/b,

$$\frac{c}{b} < \frac{a}{b}, \qquad \text{if } c < a.$$

If two fractions have different denominators, how could one tell which is larger?

ILLUSTRATIVE EXAMPLE. Are $\frac{5}{13}$ and $\frac{6}{17}$ equal? If not, which is the larger?

Solution. Now,

$$\frac{5}{13} = \frac{85}{13 \cdot 17} \qquad \text{and} \qquad \frac{6}{17} = \frac{78}{17 \cdot 13}.$$

When written as fractions with a common denominator, the numerators are different; hence the fractions are not equal.   Since $78 < 85$, then $78/(13 \cdot 17) < 85/(13 \cdot 17)$, by the definition of inequality.   Therefore, $\frac{6}{17} < \frac{5}{13}$.

The equation $\frac{4}{6} = \frac{2}{3}$ states a relationship between the numbers represented by $\frac{4}{6}$ and $\frac{2}{3}$.   For this reason, the sign, "$=$" is the symbol for a *relation*.   Likewise, $\frac{2}{3} < \frac{7}{8}$ states a relationship between $\frac{2}{3}$ and $\frac{7}{8}$; hence the sign "$<$" also symbolizes a relation.   In Section 4–5 the reflexive, symmetric, and transitive properties were discussed for the "equality" relation. Do these properties hold for the "less than" relation?   Certainly it is not true that $\frac{2}{3} < \frac{2}{3}$; hence the reflexive property does not hold for "$<$."   Also, $\frac{2}{3} < \frac{7}{8}$ is true, but $\frac{7}{8} < \frac{2}{3}$ is not true; hence the symmetric property does not hold for "$<$."   In Problem 11 of Problem Set 7–5 you are asked to show that the transitive property does hold for "$<$."   Whenever a new relation is introduced, the truth or falsity of these properties should be investigated.

7–5 DIVISION

Division of one fraction by another seems to give much trouble. Many teachers have given such a problem as $\frac{6}{11} \div \frac{7}{13}$ to a class and were "rewarded" with as many as four different answers, not counting those in which purely computational errors appeared. This seems to be due to complete lack of understanding and hence rote performance in whatever fashion enters the student's mind. Let us investigate carefully!

First, let us consider a related problem. Now,

$$\frac{6}{7} \cdot \frac{7}{6} = \frac{6 \cdot 7}{7 \cdot 6} = 1 \quad \text{and} \quad \frac{4}{13} \cdot \frac{13}{4} = 1;$$

likewise

$$\frac{a}{b} \cdot \frac{b}{a} = \frac{a \cdot b}{a \cdot b} = 1, \quad \text{if } a \neq 0 \text{ and } b \neq 0.$$

0 has no reciprocal

Thus, for each nonzero fraction there exists another fraction such that their product is 1. The fraction b/a is called the *reciprocal* of a/b, if $a \neq 0$ and $b \neq 0$. Hence, $\frac{4}{3}$ is the reciprocal of $\frac{3}{4}$, and $\frac{7}{11}$ and $\frac{11}{7}$ are reciprocals of each other.

What does $12 \div 4$ mean? It is a number r such that $4 \cdot r = 12$. Suppose that division of fractions is handled in a similar fashion. Can we find a number r such that $\frac{7}{13} \cdot r = \frac{6}{11}$? First, if $\frac{7}{13}$ is multiplied by its reciprocal, the result is 1:

$$\frac{7}{13} \cdot \frac{13}{7} = 1.$$

But $\frac{6}{11}$ is desired as a result of the multiplication, so that each side of the above equation should be multiplied by $\frac{6}{11}$, to give

$$\left(\frac{7}{13} \cdot \frac{13}{7}\right) \cdot \frac{6}{11} = \frac{6}{11} \quad \text{or} \quad \frac{7}{13}\left(\frac{13}{7} \cdot \frac{6}{11}\right) = \frac{6}{11}.$$

Accordingly, $r = \frac{13}{7} \cdot \frac{6}{11}$ will satisfy $\frac{7}{13} \cdot r = \frac{6}{11}$. Likewise, if $c \neq 0$, then

$$\frac{c}{d}\left(\frac{d}{c} \cdot \frac{a}{b}\right) = \frac{a}{b},$$

Multiply the reciprocal of divisor

so that $a/b \div c/d$ should be $(d/c)(a/b)$. This leads to the following definition.

Definition. *Division of fractions.* If a/b and c/d are fractions, such that $c \neq 0$, then

$$\frac{a}{b} \div \frac{c}{d} = \frac{a}{b} \cdot \frac{d}{c}.$$

It is the application of this definition which gives trouble. Most people formulate this definition in words, and many apply that formulation improperly. There is an easier way! First, by the definition of division, $\frac{6}{11} \div \frac{7}{13}$ is a fraction, even though when written as at the left below it has four "tiers" instead of the usual two "tiers"; hence

$$\frac{\frac{6}{11}}{\frac{7}{13}} = \frac{\frac{6}{11}}{\frac{7}{13}} \cdot 1 = \frac{\frac{6}{11}}{\frac{7}{13}} \cdot \frac{11 \cdot 13}{11 \cdot 13}$$

$$= \frac{\frac{6}{11} \cdot \frac{11 \cdot 13}{1}}{\frac{7}{13} \cdot \frac{11 \cdot 13}{1}} = \frac{\frac{6 \cdot 11 \cdot 13}{11}}{\frac{7 \cdot 11 \cdot 13}{13}} = \frac{\frac{6 \cdot 13}{1}}{\frac{7 \cdot 11}{1}}$$

$$= \frac{6 \cdot 13}{7 \cdot 11}.$$

Follow each of the above steps carefully, noting how the property of one was used.

The "four-tiered" expressions above are not fractions in the sense of the original definition, since both the numerator and the denominator of a fraction must be whole numbers. These expressions should be considered as formal symbols, the sequence of steps being a means to an end; the end is justified by the definition of division of fractions.

ILLUSTRATIVE EXAMPLE. Perform $a/b \div c/d$, assuming that $c \neq 0$.

Solution.

$$\frac{a}{b} \div \frac{c}{d} = \frac{\frac{a}{b} \cdot bd}{\frac{c}{d} \cdot bd} = \frac{\frac{a}{b} \cdot bd}{\frac{c}{d} \cdot bd} = \frac{ad}{cb}.$$

Using this mode of procedure, we avoid the usual errors, since the actual form keeps the symbols in proper position. Moreover, if property E_1 is kept in mind, it is seen that both the upper and lower parts must be multiplied by the same number. This multiplier is that whole number which will change both the upper and lower parts to whole numbers.

PROBLEM SET 7–5

1. (a) Why is $a \geq c$ needed in the definition of subtraction of fractions?
   (b) Why is $c \neq 0$ needed in the definition of division of fractions?

2. Perform the operations indicated.

(a) $\frac{23}{7} - \frac{17}{13}$

(b) $(\frac{6}{5} - \frac{1}{3}) - \frac{1}{2}$

(c) $\frac{19}{20} - (\frac{3}{4} - \frac{1}{6})$

(d) $\frac{2}{3}(\frac{14}{15} - \frac{7}{20})$

(e) $(7 - \frac{5}{11}) - \frac{19}{5}$

(f) $7 - (\frac{5}{11} + \frac{19}{5})$

(g) $2 - \frac{2}{3}(3 - \frac{1}{5})$

(h) $(2 - \frac{2}{3})(3 - \frac{1}{5})$

3. (a) Is $(\frac{6}{5} - \frac{1}{2}) - \frac{1}{3}$ equal to $\frac{6}{5} - (\frac{1}{2} - \frac{1}{3})$?

(b) Is subtraction associative?

4. Find the reciprocals of each of the following.

(a) $\frac{17}{14}$

(b) $\frac{5}{43}$

(c) $\frac{42}{29}$

5. Perform the following divisions by the method which preceded the definition of division. Write the answers in reduced form.

(a) $\frac{5}{4} \div \frac{4}{7}$

(b) $\frac{13}{5} \div \frac{2}{3}$

(c) $\frac{5}{11} \div \frac{7}{12}$

(d) $\frac{14}{15} \div \frac{7}{5}$

(e) $\frac{8}{15} \div \frac{25}{6}$

(f) $\frac{14}{11} \div \frac{22}{21}$

6. Perform the following divisions by using the property of one (property E_1, if you wish) and write the answers in reduced form.

(a) $\frac{17}{3} \div \frac{4}{7}$

(b) $\frac{5}{6} \div \frac{7}{12}$

(c) $\frac{5}{22} \div \frac{7}{24}$

(d) $\frac{9}{14} \div \frac{5}{21}$

(e) $\frac{7}{16} \div \frac{11}{20}$

(f) $\frac{5}{18} \div \frac{3}{14}$

(g) $\frac{x^2}{y} \div \frac{x}{y^2}$

(h) $\frac{r^2 s^2}{t^2} \div \frac{s}{rt}$

(i) $\frac{uv^2 w}{x} \div \frac{vw}{x^2}$

(j) $\frac{z^2}{xy} \div \frac{1}{x}$

7. (a) Is $(\frac{4}{7} \div \frac{2}{3}) \div \frac{1}{2}$ equal to $\frac{4}{7} \div (\frac{2}{3} \div \frac{1}{2})$?

(b) Is division of fractions associative?

8. (a) Is $\frac{4}{3} \div \frac{3}{7}$ equal to $\frac{3}{7} \div \frac{4}{3}$?   (b) Is division of fractions commutative?

9. In each of the following pairs determine whether $x < y$ or $x > y$.

(a) $x = \frac{17}{22}$, $y = \frac{35}{43}$

(b) $x = \frac{17}{35}$, $y = \frac{12}{23}$

(c) $x = \frac{3}{7} \cdot \frac{10}{12}$, $y = \frac{4}{11} \div \frac{3}{5}$

(d) $x = \frac{5}{14} + \frac{7}{18}$, $y = \frac{14}{15} - \frac{3}{11}$

10. (a) By using sets, show that for natural numbers r, s, and t,

$$\text{if } r < s \text{ and } s < t, \quad \text{then } r < t.$$

(b) What is the name of the property proved in part (a)?

(c) Where was this property used in Section 6–1?

11. Prove that the transitive property for "$<$" holds if the numbers involved are represented by fractions.

12. (a) Prove that

$$\text{if } \frac{x}{y} \cdot \frac{c}{d} = \frac{x}{y} \cdot \frac{r}{s}, \text{ where } x \neq 0, \quad \text{then } \frac{c}{d} = \frac{r}{s}.$$

(b) Choose $d = s = y = 1$ and state a similar property for counting numbers. (This should not be considered a proof.)

$10 \div 3 =$ have a remainder

7-6 MIXED FRACTIONS

A fraction whose numerator is smaller than its denominator (for example, $\frac{2}{3}$ or $\frac{41}{47}$) is called a *proper fraction*. If a/b is a proper fraction, then $a < b$; hence $a/b < b/b$, that is, $a/b < 1$. Since the converse is also true (show it!), then the proper fractions are the fractions less than 1. Note that $\frac{0}{1}$ is a proper fraction. All other fractions are called *improper fractions;* they are the fractions a/b for which $a \geq b$, such as $\frac{5}{5}$, $\frac{4}{3}$, and $\frac{22}{7}$. Now, if $a \geq b$, the division theorem (Section 5–2) states that a can be divided by b to yield a quotient q and a remainder r, where r and q are whole numbers such that $q \geq 1$ and $0 \leq r < b$; also, $a = qb + r$. Hence,

$$\frac{a}{b} = \frac{qb + r}{b} = \frac{qb}{b} + \frac{r}{b} \quad \text{(addition of fractions)}$$

$$= \frac{q}{1} + \frac{r}{b} \quad \text{(by E}_1\text{)}$$

$$= q + \frac{r}{b}, \quad \text{(since } q = q/1\text{)}.$$

Now r/b is a proper fraction, since $r < b$. Accordingly,

an improper fraction = a whole number + a proper fraction.

For example,

$$\frac{17}{5} = \frac{5\cdot 3 + 2}{5} = 3 + \frac{2}{5} \quad \text{and} \quad \frac{45}{7} = \frac{6\cdot 7 + 3}{7} = 6 + \frac{3}{7}.$$

This is true even for such fractions as $\frac{42}{7} = 6 + \frac{0}{7}$, although there is little use for such a representation. It is customary to proceed one step further and write the above as

$$\tfrac{17}{5} = 3\tfrac{2}{5} \quad \text{and} \quad \tfrac{45}{7} = 6\tfrac{3}{7}.$$

When so written, these fractions are called *mixed fractions*. Two facts must be kept clearly in mind:

(1) The symbol $6\frac{3}{7}$ means $6 + \frac{3}{7}$, a sum, and should be read as "6 and $\frac{3}{7}$."
(2) The symbols $6(\frac{3}{7})$ and $6 \cdot \frac{3}{7}$ denote multiplication.

ILLUSTRATIVE EXAMPLE. Change $5\frac{3}{7}$ to improper form.

Solution. Now,

$$5\frac{3}{7} = 5 + \frac{3}{7} = \frac{5}{1} + \frac{3}{7} = \frac{5\cdot 7}{1\cdot 7} + \frac{3}{7} = \frac{35 + 3}{7} = \frac{38}{7}.$$

The preceding examples show that it is always possible to change a fraction from mixed form to improper form or from improper form to mixed form, as we choose. The only reason for using mixed form is that some people feel that it is simpler to visualize $6\frac{2}{3}$ than $\frac{20}{3}$. Such computations as

$$6\tfrac{2}{3} + 3\tfrac{1}{4}, \qquad 6\tfrac{2}{3} - 3\tfrac{1}{4}, \qquad 6\tfrac{2}{3} \times 3\tfrac{1}{4}, \qquad 6\tfrac{2}{3} \div 3\tfrac{1}{4}$$

can always be performed by changing the fractions to improper form and then proceeding as before.

The following procedure should always be used for division:

$$6\frac{2}{3} \div 3\frac{1}{4} = \frac{20}{3} \div \frac{13}{4} = \frac{\frac{20}{3} \cdot 3 \cdot 4}{\frac{13}{4} \cdot 3 \cdot 4} = \frac{20 \cdot 4}{13 \cdot 3} = \frac{80}{39}.$$

Convert the answer to $2\frac{2}{39}$, if you desire.

For multiplication it is usually best to convert and then multiply. For example,

$$6\frac{2}{3} \times 3\frac{1}{4} = \frac{20}{3} \cdot \frac{13}{4} = \frac{20 \cdot 13}{3 \cdot 4} = \frac{5 \cdot 4 \cdot 13}{3 \cdot 4} = \frac{65}{3}.$$

There are some situations where another procedure may be somewhat shorter; for instance,

$$6 \times 2\tfrac{2}{3} = 6(2 + \tfrac{2}{3}) = 6 \cdot 2 + 6 \cdot \tfrac{2}{3} \qquad \text{(by } D_+)$$
$$= 12 + \frac{2 \cdot 3 \cdot 2}{3}$$
$$= 12 + 4 = 16;$$

also,

$$\tfrac{1}{2}(2\tfrac{2}{3}) = \tfrac{1}{2}(2 + \tfrac{2}{3}) = \tfrac{1}{2} \cdot 2 + \tfrac{1}{2} \cdot \tfrac{2}{3} \qquad \text{(by } D_+)$$
$$= 1 + \tfrac{1}{3} = 1\tfrac{1}{3}.$$

However, $6(2\frac{2}{5})$ would probably not be shortened by using mixed form; certainly $\frac{4}{5}(2\frac{2}{3})$ would not be shortened. Try them and see! Hence, why bother with special methods for multiplication?

So far as addition and subtraction are concerned, there is some advantage to using special methods. Let us consider $6\frac{2}{3} + 3\frac{3}{4}$. We have _means sum of 2 h_

$$6\tfrac{2}{3} + 3\tfrac{3}{4} = (6 + \tfrac{2}{3}) + (3 + \tfrac{3}{4})$$
$$= (6 + 3) + (\tfrac{2}{3} + \tfrac{3}{4}) \qquad \text{(by } C_a \text{ and } A_a)$$
$$= 9 + \left(\frac{2 \cdot 4}{3 \cdot 4} + \frac{3 \cdot 3}{4 \cdot 3}\right) \; E,$$
$$= 9 + (\tfrac{8}{12} + \tfrac{9}{12}) \; M. facts$$
$$Add = 9 + \tfrac{17}{12} = 9 + (1 + \tfrac{5}{12})$$
$$= (9 + 1) + \tfrac{5}{12} \qquad \text{(by } A_a)$$
$$= 10\tfrac{5}{12}. \; Notation$$

This procedure follows immediately from the meaning of a mixed fraction and application of the associative and commutative properties for fractions.

Since for subtraction there is neither commutativity nor associativity, it is necessary to develop subsidiary theorems before proceeding. Recall the properties,

PP_1: $(x + y) - z = x + (y - z)$,   if $y \geq z$,

PP_2: $(x - y) - z = x - (y + z)$,   if $x \geq y + z$,

which were proved in Section 4–5 for whole numbers. Similar properties are needed for fractions. Let us prove the property PP_1 for fractions, i.e., let us prove that

PP_1: $\left(\dfrac{a}{b} + \dfrac{c}{d}\right) - \dfrac{e}{f} = \dfrac{a}{b} + \left(\dfrac{c}{d} - \dfrac{e}{f}\right)$,   if $\dfrac{c}{d} \geq \dfrac{e}{f}$.

First we change the fractions to equivalent forms with a common denominator. If $a/b = r/s$, $c/d = t/s$, and $e/f = u/s$, then

$$\left(\frac{a}{b} + \frac{c}{d}\right) - \frac{e}{f} = \left(\frac{r}{s} + \frac{t}{s}\right) - \frac{u}{s}$$

$$= \frac{r + t}{s} - \frac{u}{s}$$

$$= \frac{(r + t) - u}{s} \qquad \text{(definition of subtraction)}$$

$$= \frac{r + (t - u)}{s} \qquad \text{(PP_1 for whole numbers)}$$

$$= \frac{r}{s} + \frac{t - u}{s}$$

$$= \frac{r}{s} + \left(\frac{t}{s} - \frac{u}{s}\right)$$

$$= \frac{a}{b} + \left(\frac{c}{d} - \frac{e}{f}\right).$$

Since a whole number can be considered as a fraction (for example, c can be thought of as $c/1$) and since the statement of the property has the same form for fractions as for whole numbers, PP_1 will denote a single property which is true for either type of number. Likewise, we can prove the property PP_2 for fractions, i.e., we can prove that

PP_2: $\left(\dfrac{a}{b} - \dfrac{c}{d}\right) - \dfrac{e}{f} = \dfrac{a}{b} - \left(\dfrac{c}{d} + \dfrac{e}{f}\right)$,   if $\dfrac{a}{b} \geq \dfrac{c}{d} + \dfrac{e}{f}$.

Problem 7 of the next problem set calls for the proof of PP_2.

Properties PP_1 and PP_2 can be used in a subtraction involving fractions. Let us consider $6\frac{2}{3} - 3\frac{1}{4}$. We have

$$6\frac{2}{3} - 3\frac{1}{4} = (6 + \tfrac{2}{3}) - (3 + \tfrac{1}{4})$$
$$= [(6 + \tfrac{2}{3}) - 3] - \tfrac{1}{4} \qquad (PP_2 \text{ with } a/b = 6 + \tfrac{2}{3})$$
$$= [(\tfrac{2}{3} + 6) - 3] - \tfrac{1}{4} \qquad (C_a)$$
$$= [\tfrac{2}{3} + (6 - 3)] - \tfrac{1}{4} \qquad (PP_1 \text{ applied to } [\,] \text{ with } a/b = \tfrac{2}{3}, c/d = 6)$$
$$= [(6 - 3) + \tfrac{2}{3}] - \tfrac{1}{4} \qquad (C_a)$$
$$= (6 - 3) + (\tfrac{2}{3} - \tfrac{1}{4}) \qquad (PP_1 \text{ with } a/b = 6 - 3, c/d = \tfrac{2}{3})$$
$$= 3 + \frac{8 - 3}{12}$$
$$= 3\tfrac{5}{12}.$$

Application of properties PP_1 and PP_2, as indicated in the example above, would show that if $p/q \geq a/b$ and $m \geq n$, then

$$\left(m + \frac{p}{q}\right) - \left(n + \frac{a}{b}\right) = (m - n) + \left(\frac{p}{q} - \frac{a}{b}\right).$$

Hence the whole numbers can be subtracted in one step, the proper fractions in a second step. In practice, we go directly from the top line of the above example to the sixth line, giving PP_1 and PP_2 as the reasons.

PROBLEM SET 7–6

1. Convert the following to mixed fractions, showing the steps in detail and reasons for them.

   (a) $\frac{19}{8}$ (b) $\frac{55}{12}$ (c) $\frac{47}{13}$ (d) $\frac{88}{15}$

2. Convert the following to improper fractions. Show all steps.

   (a) $7\frac{4}{11}$ (b) $5\frac{3}{8}$ (c) $12\frac{5}{7}$ (d) $4\frac{5}{9}$

3. Perform the following operations.

   (a) $4\frac{2}{7} \times 3\frac{5}{8}$ (b) $3\frac{5}{6} \div 4\frac{2}{3}$ (c) $5\frac{2}{3} \div 2\frac{6}{7}$ (d) $6\frac{1}{4} \times 5\frac{1}{3}$
   (e) $8\frac{1}{2} \times 4\frac{2}{5}$ (f) $7\frac{4}{5} \div 2\frac{1}{6}$ (g) $2\frac{3}{5} \times 6\frac{4}{7}$ (h) $2\frac{3}{5} \div 6\frac{4}{7}$
   (i) $3\frac{1}{4} \div 4\frac{5}{8}$ (j) $3\frac{1}{4} \times 4\frac{5}{8}$

4. Perform the following operations, using mixed form. Show all details and give reasons.

   (a) $4\frac{2}{3} + 3\frac{1}{2}$ (b) $2\frac{5}{8} + 7\frac{1}{3}$ (c) $5\frac{1}{4} + 6\frac{2}{5}$ (d) $7\frac{3}{8} + 4\frac{1}{6}$
   (e) $7\frac{5}{8} - 2\frac{1}{3}$ (f) $6\frac{2}{5} - 5\frac{1}{4}$ (g) $7\frac{3}{8} - 4\frac{1}{6}$ (h) $4\frac{2}{3} - 2\frac{1}{2}$
   (i) $4\frac{2}{5} + 6\frac{2}{3}$ (j) $6\frac{2}{3} - 4\frac{2}{5}$ (k) $7\frac{3}{5} + 2\frac{5}{7}$ (l) $4\frac{2}{3} - 2\frac{7}{8}$

5. Perform the operations indicated in Problem 4 by first converting each fraction to improper form. *i* and *l*

6. In problems such as parts (i) and (l) of Problems 4 and 5, which method is the shorter?

7. Prove property PP$_2$ for fractions.

8. Prove that

$$\left(m + \frac{p}{q}\right) - \left(n + \frac{a}{b}\right) = (m - n) + \left(\frac{p}{q} - \frac{a}{b}\right),$$

if $m \geq n$ and $p/q \geq a/b$, where m, n, p, q, a, and b are whole numbers.

7–7 THE NUMBER LINE

Heretofore, we have identified only those points on the number line which correspond to whole numbers. If the segment from 0 to 1 were bisected, it would seem natural to represent the midpoint by $\frac{1}{2}$. Similarly, it would seem natural to represent the midpoint of the line segment from 3 to 4 by $\frac{7}{2}$. If the segment from 0 to $\frac{1}{2}$ were bisected, what number would be chosen to represent the midpoint? the segment from $\frac{1}{2}$ to 1? from $\frac{7}{2}$ to 4? Continuation of this procedure yields points corresponding to each fraction whose denominator is a power of 2.

How would we find a point which would correspond to $\frac{1}{5}$? We could divide the segment from 0 to 1 into five parts of equal length. The only question is whether or not we know how to do this. A geometric construction, such as that shown in Fig. 7–1, will aid us here. Let us divide the segment AB into five equal parts; more precisely, let us find five congruent segments whose union is AB. To do this, construct *any* half-line from A not lying on the line through A and B, such as A through H; mark on that half-line five segments of equal length, thus obtaining D, E, F, G, and C. Join B and C. Through G construct a line parallel to BC, cutting AB at U. By the same procedure, construct the segments DR, ES, and FT. Since $AD = DE = EF = FG = GC$, what may be said about AR, RS, ST, TU, and UB? Why are they of equal length? Has AB been divided into five equal parts? Now, if AB had been the segment from 0 to 1, what numbers would represent points R, S, T, and U? Could a point now be obtained corresponding to $\frac{6}{5}$? to $\frac{9}{5}$? Explain.

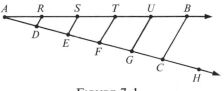

FIGURE 7–1

Since the preceding construction could be used for any counting number just as readily as for 5, we are able to say:

Any fraction can be represented by a point on the number line.

This brief discussion leaves much to be desired. In the main, colloquial language has been used and no reasons have been given as to why certain steps can be taken. Some improvements will be discussed in Chapter 12.

PROBLEM SET 7-7

1. Use a unit segment of sufficient length so that it can be subdivided "comfortably" into six parts of equal length; subdivide it into six equal parts. Mark $\frac{5}{6}$ on the number line. Show, in two ways, how to mark $\frac{11}{6}$ and $\frac{13}{6}$ on the number line.

2. On the number line used in Problem 1, mark $\frac{11}{6} + \frac{1}{12}$ and $\frac{11}{6} - \frac{1}{12}$; also mark $\frac{8}{6} + \frac{1}{12}$ and $\frac{8}{6} - \frac{1}{12}$.

7-8 DECIMALS

A fraction whose denominator is a power of ten, i.e., a *decimal fraction*, can be written in a special form which is particularly advantageous. For instance,

$$\frac{324}{1000} = \frac{3 \cdot 10^2 + 2 \cdot 10 + 4}{10^3} = \frac{3 \cdot 10^2}{10^3} + \frac{2 \cdot 10}{10^3} + \frac{4}{10^3}$$

$$= \frac{3}{10} + \frac{2}{10^2} + \frac{4}{10^3} \qquad \text{(by } E_1\text{)}.$$

Likewise,

$$\frac{567,324}{1000} = 567 + \frac{3}{10} + \frac{2}{10^2} + \frac{4}{10^3}.$$

In this fashion, any decimal fraction can be written as a whole number plus a sum of fractions where each of these last fractions has a numerator b, such that $0 \le b \le 9$. The denominators of these last fractions are 10, 10^2, 10^3, etc. Now, since

$$\frac{1}{10^2} = \frac{1}{10 \cdot 10} = \left(\frac{1}{10}\right)^2, \qquad \frac{1}{10^3} = \frac{1}{10 \cdot 10 \cdot 10} = \left(\frac{1}{10}\right)^3, \quad \text{etc.,}$$

then

$$\frac{567,324}{1000} = 5 \cdot 10^2 + 6 \cdot 10 + 7 + 3 \cdot \frac{1}{10} + 2 \cdot \left(\frac{1}{10}\right)^2 + 4 \cdot \left(\frac{1}{10}\right)^3.$$

$$.309 = \frac{3}{10} + \frac{0}{100} + \frac{9}{1000}$$

The terms to the left of 7 have the form $a \cdot 10^n$, where $0 \leq a \leq 9$, while those to the right of 7 have the form $b \cdot (\frac{1}{10})^n$. Moreover, the powers of 10 increase steadily by 1 as we move to the left from 7, and the powers of $\frac{1}{10}$ increase steadily by 1 as we move to the right from 7. This suggests an extension of the base ten notation.

Definition. *Decimal notation.* The symbol

$$a_k a_{k-1} \ldots a_2 a_1 a_0 . b_1 b_2 b_3 \ldots b_n,$$

where each a_i satisfies $0 \leq a_i \leq 9$ and each b_j satisfies $0 \leq b_j \leq 9$, is an abbreviation for

$$a_k \cdot 10^k + a_{k-1} \cdot 10^{k-1} + \cdots + a_2 \cdot 10^2 + a_1 \cdot 10 + a_0$$
$$+ b_1 (\tfrac{1}{10}) + b_2 (\tfrac{1}{10})^2 + b_3 (\tfrac{1}{10})^3 + \cdots + b_n (\tfrac{1}{10})^n.$$

The above dot between a_0 and b_1 is called the *decimal point;* it is used to separate the *whole part* (i.e., the part involving the a's) from the *fractional part* (i.e., the part involving the b's). This decimal point is written on the line, whereas the dot denoting multiplication is written above the line. The digits in this decimal notation are given names determined by their position. Hence, b_1 denotes tenths; b_2, hundredths; b_3, thousandths; b_4, ten-thousandths; etc. In decimal notation,

$$\frac{324}{1000} \quad \text{is written} \quad 0.324$$

and

$$\frac{567324}{1000} \quad \text{is written} \quad 567.324.$$

When the number is less than one (for example, 0.324), a zero is written to the left of the decimal point to keep the decimal point from being lost. In this case the whole part may be considered as zero.

Can a fraction whose denominator is not a power of ten (for example, $\frac{3}{5}$ or $\frac{4}{7}$) be converted to decimal form? Suppose, first, that the fraction represents a number smaller than one, say $\frac{3}{8}$. Now,

$$\frac{3}{8} = \frac{3 \cdot 10}{8 \cdot 10} = \frac{30}{8} \left(\frac{1}{10}\right) = \left(3 + \frac{6}{8}\right) \frac{1}{10} = \frac{3}{10} + \frac{3}{4} \cdot \frac{1}{10}.$$

Use the same sequence of steps for $\frac{3}{4}$ to obtain

$$\frac{3}{4} = \frac{30}{4} \left(\frac{1}{10}\right) = \left(7 + \frac{2}{4}\right) \frac{1}{10} = \frac{7}{10} + \frac{1}{2} \cdot \frac{1}{10}.$$

Hence, from above,

$$\frac{3}{8} = \frac{3}{10} + \left(\frac{7}{10} + \frac{1}{2} \cdot \frac{1}{10}\right) \frac{1}{10} = \frac{3}{10} + \frac{7}{10^2} + \frac{1}{2} \cdot \frac{1}{10^2}.$$

Use the same procedure on $\frac{1}{2}$ to obtain

$$\frac{1}{2} = \frac{10}{2} \cdot \frac{1}{10} = \left(5 + \frac{0}{2}\right)\frac{1}{10} = \frac{5}{10}.$$

Accordingly,

$$\frac{3}{8} = \frac{3}{10} + \frac{7}{10^2} + \frac{5}{10} \cdot \frac{1}{10^2} = \frac{3}{10} + \frac{7}{10^2} + \frac{5}{10^3} = 0.375.$$

Note that when the procedure was applied to $\frac{1}{2}$, the remainder obtained from the division process was zero; for this reason the procedure terminates.

Applying the same sequence of steps to $\frac{4}{7}$, we have

$$\frac{4}{7} = \frac{40}{7}\left(\frac{1}{10}\right) = \left(5 + \frac{5}{7}\right)\frac{1}{10} = \frac{5}{10} + \frac{5}{7} \cdot \frac{1}{10}$$

$$= \frac{5}{10} + \frac{50}{7} \cdot \frac{1}{10^2} = \frac{5}{10} + \left(7 + \frac{1}{7}\right)\frac{1}{10^2}$$

$$= \frac{5}{10} + \frac{7}{10^2} + \frac{1}{7} \cdot \frac{1}{10^2}$$

$$= \frac{5}{10} + \frac{7}{10^2} + \left(1 + \frac{3}{7}\right)\frac{1}{10^3}$$

$$= \frac{5}{10} + \frac{7}{10^2} + \frac{1}{10^3} + \frac{3}{7} \cdot \frac{1}{10^3}, \quad \text{etc.}$$

No zero remainder has been obtained thus far. No matter how long the procedure is continued, the remainder will never be zero, and hence the decimal expansion will not terminate. This will be proved later. Accordingly,

$$\tfrac{4}{7} = 0.571\ldots,$$

where the dots indicate that further decimal digits (as many as desired) could be obtained.

Consider a general fraction, a/b, where b is not a power of ten. By the division theorem, $a = qb + r$, where q and r are whole numbers, $0 \leq r < b$. Hence

$$\frac{a}{b} = \frac{qb + r}{b} = q + \frac{r}{b}.$$

Now, since $r < b$, then $r/b < 1$, so that r/b is a fraction of the type considered in previous examples. Therefore we can proceed as in those examples, to obtain

$$\frac{r}{b} = \frac{10r}{b}\left(\frac{1}{10}\right).$$

If $r \neq 0$, the division theorem can be applied to $10r$ and b to yield $10r = q_1 \cdot b + r_1$, $0 \le r_1 < b$, so that

$$\frac{a}{b} = q + \frac{q_1 b + r_1}{b} \cdot \frac{1}{10} = q + \left(q_1 + \frac{r_1}{b}\right)\frac{1}{10}$$

$$= q + \frac{q_1}{10} + \frac{r_1}{b} \cdot \frac{1}{10}$$

$$= q + \frac{q_1}{10} + \frac{10 r_1}{b} \cdot \frac{1}{10^2}.$$

Since $r/b < 1$, then $10r/b < 10$; hence

$$\frac{10r}{b} = q_1 + \frac{r_1}{b} < 10 \qquad \text{yields} \qquad q_1 < 10.$$

But q_1 is a whole number and hence must be one of $0, 1, 2, 3, \ldots, 9$; that is, $q_1/10$ is the proper type of term for a decimal expansion. Again, the division theorem can be applied to $10r_1$ and b; this procedure continues as long as the remainder obtained is not zero. Since q is a whole number, it can be written in base ten notation, and therefore it is the whole part of the decimal notation.

Returning to the previous example, would it be correct to write $\frac{4}{7} = 0.571$? Though this use of "=" is incorrect, the number $\frac{4}{7}$ differs from 0.571 by a rather small number, $\frac{3}{7000}$. Hence $\frac{4}{7}$ is "approximately equal to" 0.571. This will be written as

$$\frac{4}{7} \approx 0.571.$$

This concept of approximation is important, especially in applications of mathematics, and hence must be discussed in greater detail. Much of this discussion will be left until later. However, we will proceed a bit further at this stage by considering the equation

$$\frac{4}{7} = 0.571 + \frac{3}{7}\left(\frac{1}{1000}\right).$$

Since $0 < \frac{3}{7} < 1$, then $0 < \frac{3}{7}\left(\frac{1}{1000}\right) < \frac{1}{1000}$; hence

$$0.571 + 0 < 0.571 + \frac{3}{7}\left(\frac{1}{1000}\right) < 0.571 + \frac{1}{1000}.$$

Moreover, since $\frac{3}{7} < \frac{1}{2}$, then $\frac{3}{7}\left(\frac{1}{1000}\right) < \frac{1}{2}(1000)$, so that if we mark these numbers on part of a number line as below, it can be seen that $\frac{3}{7}\left(\frac{1}{1000}\right)$ is nearer to 0 than to $\frac{1}{1000}$.

Hence, $0.571 + \frac{3}{7}(\frac{1}{1000})$ is nearer to $0.571 + 0$ than to $0.571 + \frac{1}{1000}$, so that

$$\frac{4}{7} \text{ is nearer to } 0.571 \text{ than to } 0.572.$$

Accordingly, 0.571 is an approximation to $\frac{4}{7}$, correct to the nearest thousandth. This could be written

$$\frac{4}{7} = 0.571, \qquad \text{correct to the nearest thousandth.}$$

This theory of approximation has nothing to do with representing a fraction in decimal form, but it does give some information as to how "good" the result is when we decide to use only a certain number of decimal places.

PROBLEM SET 7–8

1. Write the following as common fractions. Explain the procedure.
   (a) 7.635   (b) 0.001435   (c) 18.0013
   (d) 0.095   (e) 0.17639   (f) 11.0102

2. Show the detailed steps involved in converting the following to decimal form.
   (a) $\dfrac{1764}{10^4}$ (b) $\dfrac{32,098}{10^6}$ (c) $\dfrac{173,024}{10^5}$

3. Convert the following to decimal form, obtaining three decimal places. Show and justify all steps.
   (a) $\frac{83}{11}$ (b) $\frac{73}{14}$ (c) $\frac{5}{12}$ (d) $\frac{29}{6}$ (e) $\frac{4}{9}$ (f) $\frac{6}{13}$

4. Show that the decimal expansion of $\frac{4}{7}$ will never terminate, by finding at least four more decimal digits than were found in the text.

5. Find the decimal expansion of the following numbers with the accuracy indicated. In each case show why the last digit is chosen.
   (a) $\frac{5}{7}$, correct to the nearest hundredth
   (b) $\frac{8}{11}$, correct to the nearest thousandth
   (c) $\frac{11}{12}$, correct to the nearest thousandth
   (d) $\frac{9}{14}$, correct to the nearest ten-thousandth

6. Show that the decimal expansions of the following numbers terminate.
   (a) $\frac{5}{16}$ (b) $\frac{137}{40}$ (c) $\frac{243}{80}$ (d) $\frac{789}{250}$

7. (a) What would 3.246(seven) mean?
   (b) Write $\frac{1}{7}$, $\frac{4}{7}$, and $\frac{6}{7}$ in base seven notation, using a form similar to decimal notation.
   (c) Write $65/7^2$ and $695/7^3$ as directed in part (b). Apply the same principles as in the decimal system.

8. Write the following numbers in base twelve numerals, having a form similar to decimal form.
   (a) $\frac{1}{2}$ (b) $\frac{2}{3}$ (c) $\frac{7}{3}$

7–9   OPERATIONS WITH DECIMALS

If the meaning of decimal notation is kept in mind, operations with numbers which are symbolized in decimal form are straightforward.

For addition, the commutative and associative properties permit the association of like terms. For example, the addition $1.243 + 7.654$ may be carried out as follows:

$1.243 + 7.654$

$$= [1 + 2(\tfrac{1}{10}) + 4(\tfrac{1}{10})^2 + 3(\tfrac{1}{10})^3] + [7 + 6(\tfrac{1}{10}) + 5(\tfrac{1}{10})^2 + 4(\tfrac{1}{10})^3]$$
$$= (1 + 7) + (2 + 6)\tfrac{1}{10} + (4 + 5)(\tfrac{1}{10})^2 + (3 + 4)(\tfrac{1}{10})^3,$$

or

$$
\begin{array}{r}
1.243 \\
(+)\ 7.654 \\
\hline
8.897
\end{array}
$$

Was any property used other than the associative and the commutative properties? If so, what was the property and where was it used? One other situation must be considered here. This will be exemplified in the following.

$$
\begin{array}{r}
1.28 \\
(+)\ 7.67 \\
\hline
8.95
\end{array}
$$

$$1.28 + 7.67 = (1 + 7) + (2 + 6)\tfrac{1}{10} + (8 + 7)(\tfrac{1}{10})^2,$$
$$(8 + 7)\frac{1}{10^2} = 15(\tfrac{1}{10})^2 = (1 \cdot 10 + 5)(\tfrac{1}{10})^2$$
$$= 1 \cdot 10(\tfrac{1}{100}) + 5 \cdot (\tfrac{1}{10})^2$$
$$= 1 \cdot \tfrac{1}{10} + 5(\tfrac{1}{10})^2 \qquad \text{(by } E_1\text{)}.$$

Hence, the technique of "carrying" must be used, just as it had to be used in adding whole numbers. Since $10 \cdot (\tfrac{1}{10})^2$ equals $1 \cdot \tfrac{1}{10}$, we add 1 to the numbers in the tenths column.

For subtraction the properties PP_1 and PP_2 are needed. By these properties,

$$7.68 - 4.24 = [7 + 6(\tfrac{1}{10}) + 8(\tfrac{1}{10})^2] - [4 + 2(\tfrac{1}{10}) + 4(\tfrac{1}{10})^2]$$
$$= (7 - 4) + (6 - 2)\tfrac{1}{10} + (8 - 4)(\tfrac{1}{10})^2.$$

What should be done with the subtraction

$$7.68 - 4.29 = (7 - 4) + (6 - 2)\tfrac{1}{10} + (8 - 9)(\tfrac{1}{10})^2?$$

Is "borrowing" suggested? Borrow a what? Borrow $1 \cdot \tfrac{1}{10}$ from $6 \cdot \tfrac{1}{10}$; now we can add $\tfrac{1}{10} = 10/10^2 = 10(\tfrac{1}{10})^2$ to $8(\tfrac{1}{10})^2$ to give $18(\tfrac{1}{10})^2$, so that

$$7.68 - 4.29 = (7 - 4) + (5 - 2)\tfrac{1}{10} + (18 - 9)(\tfrac{1}{10})^2.$$

Proceed as before.

To prepare for the multiplication and division of numbers written in decimal form, let us consider the multiplication of a number, c, in decimal form by a power of ten. Write c in decimal form, as in the definition of decimal notation, and apply the distributive law to obtain

$$c \cdot 10^3 = a_k \cdot 10^{k+3} + a_{k-1} \cdot 10^{k+2} + \cdots + a_2 \cdot 10^5 + a_1 \cdot 10^4 + a_0 \cdot 10^3$$
$$+ b_1 \cdot 10^2 + b_2 \cdot 10 + b_3 + b_4 \cdot \tfrac{1}{10} + b_5(\tfrac{1}{10})^2 + \cdots$$
$$+ b_n(\tfrac{1}{10})^{n-3}.$$

In such a representation of c each digit is associated with a unit, and these units together with their names can be arranged as shown in Fig. 7–2. Since

Ten-thousands	Thousands	Hundreds	Tens	Ones	Tenths	Hundredths	Thousandths	Ten-Thousandths
$\cdots \, 10^4$	10^3	10^2	10	1	$\tfrac{1}{10}$	$(\tfrac{1}{10})^2$	$(\tfrac{1}{10})^3$	$(\tfrac{1}{10})^4 \cdots$

FIGURE 7–2

these units increase from right to left, they can be considered as forming a scale of units. It will be said, for example, that

the tens unit   is higher than   the tenths unit,
the tenths unit is higher than   the thousandths unit,
the tenths unit is lower than   the hundreds unit.

This language establishes a sense of direction in the scale. A unit will be "higher" in the scale than a second unit if it is larger than the second.

Now let us multiply 3.2478 by 10^2:

$$\left[3 + 2\left(\frac{1}{10}\right) + 4\left(\frac{1}{10}\right)^2 + 7\left(\frac{1}{10}\right)^3 + 8\left(\frac{1}{10}\right)^4 \right] \cdot 10^2$$

$$= 3 \cdot 10^2 + 2 \cdot \frac{10^2}{10} + 4 \cdot \frac{10^2}{10^2} + 7 \cdot \frac{10^2}{10^3} + 8 \cdot \frac{10^2}{10^4}$$

$$= 3 \cdot 10^2 + 2 \cdot 10 + 4 + 7 \cdot \frac{1}{10} + 8 \cdot \left(\frac{1}{10}\right)^2$$

$$= 324.78.$$

The digits in 324.78 are the same as in 3.2478, but each is associated with a unit which is two places higher in the scale than it was formerly. The net effect is to shift the decimal point two places to the right.

For the general problem of multiplying a number c, in decimal notation, by 10^t,

$$c \cdot 10^t = \left(a_k \cdot 10^k + a_{k-1} \cdot 10^{k-1} + \cdots + a_2 \cdot 10^2 + a_1 \cdot 10 + a_0 \right.$$
$$\left. + b_1 \cdot \frac{1}{10} + b_2 \cdot \frac{1}{10^2} + \cdots + b_n \cdot \frac{1}{10^n} \right) \cdot 10^t ,$$

we will work with individual terms. Since

$(a_k \cdot 10^k)10^t = a_k \cdot 10^{k+t}$, a_k becomes associated with 10^{k+t};

$(a_2 \cdot 10^2)10^t = a_2 \cdot 10^{2+t}$, a_2 becomes associated with 10^{2+t};

$(b_1 \cdot \frac{1}{10})10^t = b_1 \cdot 10^{t-1}$, b_1 becomes associated with 10^{t-1};

$\left(b_2 \cdot \frac{1}{10^2} \right) 10^t = b_2 \cdot 10^{t-2}$, b_2 becomes associated with 10^{t-2};

$\left(b_t \cdot \frac{1}{10^t} \right) 10^t = b_t \cdot 1$, b_t becomes associated with the ones position;

$\left(b_{t+1} \cdot \frac{1}{10^{t+1}} \right) 10^t = b_{t+1}(\frac{1}{10})$, b_{t+1} becomes associated with $\frac{1}{10}$, etc.

Thus, in the result each digit becomes associated with a unit which is t places higher in the scale than it was originally. For example, a_2 becomes associated with 10^{2+t} instead of with 10^2. Accordingly, multiplication by 10^t has the effect of "shifting" the decimal point t places to the right, so that the decimal point will lie between b_t and b_{t+1}. Hence

$c \cdot 10^t$ has the same digits as c;
the decimal point is "shifted" t places to the right.

For example,

$$(6.723516)10^4 = 67235.16 \quad \text{and} \quad (0.139872)10^6 = 139872.$$

Now consider division by a power of ten. For example,

$$678.34 \div 10^2 = \frac{678.34}{10^2}$$
$$= \frac{6 \cdot 10^2}{10^2} + \frac{7 \cdot 10}{10^2} + \frac{8}{10^2} + \frac{\frac{3}{10}}{10^2} + \frac{\frac{4}{10^2}}{10^2}$$
$$= 6 + \frac{7}{10} + \frac{8}{10^2} + \frac{3}{10^3} + \frac{4}{10^4} ,$$

since

$$\frac{\frac{3}{10}}{10^2} = \frac{\frac{3}{10} \cdot 10}{10^2 \cdot 10} = \frac{3}{10^3} \quad \text{and} \quad \frac{\frac{4}{10^2}}{10^2} = \frac{\frac{4}{10^2} \cdot 10^2}{10^2 \cdot 10^2} = \frac{4}{10^4} .$$

Thus,

$$678.34 \div 10^2 = 6.7834;$$

the effect is a shift of the decimal point two places to the *left*. In the resulting number each digit is associated with a unit which is two places *lower* in the scale than it was formerly. That the same is true in general can be seen by noting the effect on individual terms of c; for instance, property E_1 is used to obtain

$$\frac{a_t \cdot 10^t}{10^t} = a_t, \qquad \frac{a_{t-1} \cdot 10^{t-1}}{10^t} = \frac{a_{t-1}}{10}, \qquad \frac{a_{t-2} \cdot 10^{t-2}}{10^t} = \frac{a_{t-2}}{10^2}, \quad \ldots,$$

$$\frac{a_1 \cdot 10}{10^t} = \frac{a_1}{10^{t-1}}, \qquad \frac{a_0}{10^t}, \qquad \frac{b_1(\frac{1}{10})}{10^t} = \frac{b_1}{10^{t+1}}, \qquad \text{etc.}$$

Also,

$$\frac{a_{t+1} \cdot 10^{t+1}}{10^t} = a_{t+1} \cdot 10, \qquad \frac{a_{t+2} \cdot 10^{t+2}}{10^t} = a_{t+2} \cdot 10^2, \quad \text{etc.}$$

Hence, in the result each digit becomes associated with a unit which is t places *lower* in the scale than it was formerly. For example, b_1 becomes associated with $(\frac{1}{10})^{t+1}$ rather than with $\frac{1}{10}$.

Accordingly,

(1) multiplication by 10^t has the effect of shifting the decimal point t places to the right;

(2) division by 10^t has the effect of shifting the decimal point t places to the left.

This discussion can be carried through more readily after negative numbers have been introduced; much apparent confusion can thereby be eliminated.

Use of the previous ideas will enable us to understand multiplication and division operations involving numbers represented in decimal form. For instance,

$$67.32 \times 0.147 = \frac{6732}{10^2} \cdot \frac{147}{10^3}$$

$$= \frac{6732 \times 147}{10^5}.$$

Now, 6732×147 can be performed in the usual manner, obtaining 989604., where the decimal point occurs to the right of the last digit. Division of this product by 10^5 shifts the decimal point five places to the left, yielding the result 9.89604. Since 67.32 has two decimal places and 0.147 has three decimal places, the two numbers have a total of 5 decimal places. Doesn't this explain the usual procedure, which is shown at the left?

$$67.32$$
$$(\times)\ 0.147$$
$$\overline{47124}$$
$$269280$$
$$673200$$
$$\overline{9.89604}$$

Let us divide 67.32 by 0.147, obtaining as a first step

$$\frac{67.32}{0.147} = \frac{(67.32)10^3}{(0.147)10^3} = \frac{67,320}{147}.$$

Using property E_1, we multiplied both numerator and denominator by 10^3. The particular multiplier, 10^3, was chosen so that after the multiplication the denominator would be a whole number. This step reduced the problem to a familiar problem. As a result of dividing 67,320 by 147, we have

$$67.32 \div 0.147 = 457 + \tfrac{141}{147}$$
$$\approx 458, \quad \text{or}$$
$$= 458, \quad \text{correct to the nearest one.}$$

Suppose that an answer had been desired to the nearest hundredth. We could then proceed as follows:

$$\frac{67.32}{0.147} = \frac{67,320\,(10^2)}{147(10^2)} = \frac{6,732,000}{147}\left(\frac{1}{10^2}\right)$$
$$= \left(45795 + \frac{135}{147}\right)\left(\frac{1}{10^2}\right)$$
$$= 457.95 + (\tfrac{135}{147})(\tfrac{1}{100})$$
$$= 457.96, \quad \text{correct to the nearest hundredth.}$$

Why was 6 chosen as the last digit rather than 5? By means such as the above an answer may be obtained correct to any number of decimal places desired.

Now consider $67.32465 \div 0.147$. Since

$$\frac{67.32465}{0.147} = \frac{67,324.65}{147},$$

the problem will assume a familiar form if the numerator and the denominator are each multiplied by 10^2; thus we obtain

$$\frac{6,732,465}{14,700} = \frac{6,732,465}{147} \times \frac{1}{10^2}$$
$$= \left(45,799 + \frac{12}{147}\right)\frac{1}{10^2}$$
$$= 457.99 + (\tfrac{12}{147} \cdot \tfrac{1}{100})$$
$$= 457.99, \quad \text{correct to the nearest hundredth.}$$

When performing divisions such as those above, we should use statements in "horizontal" form in conjunction with the formalized divisions. By so doing, a clear picture can be kept in mind as to what is actually being obtained, and also the size of error committed in stating the answer can be readily seen.

Another difficulty may arise when we divide 6 by 56.7, for example. Since $6/56.7 = \frac{60}{567}$, we obtain a numerator larger than the denominator as follows:

$$\frac{6}{56.7} = \frac{600}{567} \times \frac{1}{10}.$$

Now we can proceed as before. This step may not seem necessary; however, if the step is used, there should be no difficulty in understanding why the decimal point appears where it does.

PROBLEM SET 7–9

1. Perform the following operations, using a horizontal format in each case. Justify each step.

   (a) 16.325 + 1.73   (b) 16.625 − 9.876
   (c) 4.32 − 2.813   (d) 4.01 + 15.895
   (e) 32.901 − 24.69   (f) 0.0327 − 0.0059
   (g) 0.312 + 0.077   (h) 0.312 − 0.077
   (i) 6.735 − 2.699   (j) 6.735 + 2.699

2. Perform the following multiplications. Use horizontal format to explain the procedure.

   (a) 67.13 × 0.154   (b) 0.0135 × 0.0092
   (c) 1.3005 × 0.073   (d) 0.00314 × 16.25
   (e) 91.3 × 4.628   (f) 0.00042 × 0.00000519
   (g) 4.32 × 2.003   (h) 1.678 × 0.0057

3. Perform the following divisions so as to obtain an answer correct to the number of decimal places indicated. Use horizontal format to explain the procedure. In each case use a number line to justify your choice of a last digit.

   (a) 98.476 ÷ 12.23   to the nearest tenth
   (b) 9.73 ÷ 4.28   to the nearest hundredth
   (c) 0.00135 ÷ 0.0892   to the nearest hundredth
   (d) 0.3425 ÷ 897.3   to the nearest hundred-thousandth
   (e) 43.14 ÷ 0.0132   to the nearest one
   (f) 0.000983 ÷ 0.00145   to the nearest hundredth

4. Using inequalities, show how the last digit is chosen in dividing (a) 43.12 by 74.8, to the nearest hundredth; (b) 0.00982 by 0.0345, to the nearest thousandth.

5. (a) Is 98.23 ÷ 7.69 = 12.8? Why?
   (b) Is 0.011 ÷ 0.74 = 0.01? Why?

7-10 SCIENTIFIC NOTATION FOR LARGE AND Sɴ

When numbers are written as

$$6,720,000,000,000 \quad \text{or} \quad 0.000000000235,$$

the notation is cumbersome to say the least. Surely there must be a simₚ
notation! Let's use our knowledge of decimals to write these numbers as

$$6.72 \times 10^{12} \quad \text{and} \quad 2.35 \times \frac{1}{10^{10}} .$$

This form of writing, known as *scientific notation*, is handy for very large
and for very small numbers. In each of the above cases the first factor of the
product is a number ≥ 1 and < 10. A number is written in scientific notation if its symbol has the form

$$b \times \begin{cases} \text{a power of ten} \\ \quad \text{or} \\ 1/(\text{a power of ten}), \end{cases}$$

where b is in decimal form, such that $1 \leq b < 10$.

Scientific notation is used mainly for writing the result of a computation
or a measurement, but it has further application in the theory of logarithms.

PROBLEM SET 7-10

1. (a) Is the number 67.2×10^{8} written in scientific notation? Why or why
not? If not, write it in that form.

   (b) Is the number $0.34 \times \dfrac{1}{10^{6}}$ written in scientific notation? Why or why

   not? If not, write it in that form.

2. Write the following numbers in scientific notation.

   (a) 689,000,000,000   (b) 0.000000014
   (c) 0.0000000005   (d) 8,400,000,000
   (e) 0.000000026   (f) 971,400,000,000

3. (a) Multiply 0.00034 by 0.0000079, and write the answer in scientific notation.

   (b) Divide 67.2 by 0.0000148, and write the answer in scientific notation.

4. (a) Write the numbers 0.00034 and 0.0000079 in scientific form and then
multiply them.

   (b) Which was easier, the procedure of Problem 3(a) or of Problem 4(a)?
Why?

5. Assume that a light wave travels at the rate of 186,000 miles per second. If a light wave takes 6.3 years to travel from a certain star to the earth, find to the nearest million miles the distance from the star to the earth.

Problem 4 above should indicate to you that writing the numbers in scientific form first and then multiplying introduces an extra step. It is easier to multiply by the procedure discussed earlier,

$$0.00034 \times 0.0000079 = \frac{34}{10^5} \times \frac{79}{10^7},$$

and then write the answer in scientific notation.

7–11 WHY IS THE DENOMINATOR CHOSEN $\neq$ 0?

In the definition of fraction it was stated that the denominator should be a whole number different from zero, i.e., a counting number. Let us see why this is done. Suppose, for the moment, that the denominator is zero; then, if the fundamental property of fractions, $b \cdot a/b = a$, is to hold,

$$0 \cdot \frac{a}{0} \qquad \text{should be} \qquad a.$$

But if $a/0$ is to be a fraction, then $0 \cdot$ (this fraction) must be 0. Hence, a must be 0. Accordingly, $\frac{3}{0}$, $\frac{11}{0}$, etc. are meaningless. What about $\frac{0}{0}$? Let us suppose that it does have meaning; let $\frac{0}{0}$ be a number C. Then $0 \cdot C$ would be 0. But this equation holds for any number C, so that $\frac{0}{0}$ could represent any number. Is this a satisfactory situation? Hardly! Hence, to retain some semblance of consistency in having a numeral represent a single specific number, it is advisable to rule out a zero denominator.

CHAPTER 8

Sentences

There is a distinction between a number and a numeral, and on many occasions it is necessary to keep the distinction clearly in mind. The symbols 8, $5 + 3$, eight, acht, huit, $10 - 2$, $16 \div 2$, $\frac{1}{4}[(7 \times 5) - 3]$, VIII are all numerals for the same number. If every time we wanted to talk or think about $4 + 3$ we were forced to say "the number symbolized by 4 plus the number symbolized by 3" or even "the number whose numeral is $4 + 3$," too much time would be consumed and little clarity would result from the mass of words. For the sake of brevity we shall read $4 + 3$ as "the number four plus three" or "the number four plus the number three" or just "four plus three," mentally interpolating the word "number." This seems to indicate that a study of our means of communication would be at least advisable; such a study will now be initiated.

8-1 TRUE AND FALSE SENTENCES

In normal writing we use nouns, verbs, adjectives, adverbs, pronouns, phrases, sentences, etc. to express our thoughts; in general, sentences are "built" of nouns, verbs, etc. Likewise, to express our thoughts in mathematics we need a language which is precise, so that another person will know exactly what is being said or written.

Just as "John is a heavy man" is a sentence, so is "$3 + 4 = 7$" a sentence if the symbol "$=$" is interpreted as "is equal to"; the symbol "$=$" becomes the verb phrase of the sentence. Likewise "$2 < 5$" is a sentence, the verb "is" being part of the verb phrase "is less than," which is symbolized by "$<$." Is "$3 + 4 \neq 9$" a sentence? If so, what is the verb phrase? Is "$4 > 2$" a sentence? Most mathematical sentences that we write in elementary mathematics contain one or more of these verb phrases.

Would "$3 + 4 = 9$" be a sentence? It has the same form as "$3 + 4 = 7$"; it contains a verb, a subject, and a predicate complement. So why should your probable reaction "But, it isn't true!" have anything to do with whether or not it is a sentence! If we agree to call "$3 + 4 = 7$" a *true sentence* and "$3 + 4 = 9$" a *false sentence*, you may feel better about it. If we write, "John is 20 years old" and you know that John is 18 years old, does

159

this knowledge deter you from considering "John is 20 years old" a sentence? Of course not; you say immediately, "That sentence is false." Let us agree that a sentence is either true or false, but not both. With this agreement, all numerical sentences, such as those above, are separated into two categories: those which are true and those which are false.

8–2 VARIABLES AND OPEN PHRASES

Suppose that we have four persons perform the following sequence of operations: choose a number from the set $\{1, 2, 3, \ldots, 20\}$ and add 6; then multiply the result by 3; then subtract the original number and divide the result by 2.

In Table 8–1 we attempt to record the thought sequences of these four

Table 8–1

Person 1	Person 2	Person 3 (Ruth)	Person 4
17	11	R's number	n
23	$11 + 6$	R's number $+ 6$	$n + 6$
69	$3(11 + 6)$	$3(\text{R's number} + 6)$	$3(n + 6)$
52	$3(11 + 6) - 11$	$(3 \cdot \text{R's number} + 18) - \text{R's number}$	$(3n + 18) - n$
26	$\dfrac{3(11 + 6) - 11}{2}$, or 20	$\dfrac{2\,\text{R's number} + 18}{2}$, or R's number $+ 9$	$\dfrac{2n + 18}{2}$, or $n + 9$

persons. The first column indicates results only; the second column indicates, in addition, how the results were obtained. The third person did not want to make a choice initially; consequently her phrases were somewhat more cumbersome, but at the end she could say, "If I now choose any one of the possible numbers, I can give the answer immediately." Hence, the third person gained something over the first two. The fourth person also did not want to make an initial choice, but decided to use a letter instead of the more cumbersome "__'s number." If person 1 wanted to change his original number, he would have to go through the whole sequence of operations again. Person 4 can change from specific number to specific number at will and give the resulting answers immediately.

When a letter is used, as it was by person 4, it will be called a *variable*. Could other letters, such as x, w, a, or p, have been used instead of n? It would not make any difference.

Expressions such as those which appear on each line of column 4 are called *open phrases*, since each expression is open for the substitution of a number for the letter. The permissible numbers or permissible substitutes are called the *values of the variable;* the values of n in the example are 1, 2, 3, ..., 20. The set of permissible numbers is called the *substitution set;* in the example this set is $\{1, 2, 3, ..., 20\}$.

Consider an open phrase in a variable x, say $3(x + 4) - x$. When a value of x is chosen, say 8, then the open phrase becomes a number, $3(8 + 4) - 8$ in this case. Therefore, an open phrase has values which are determined by the specific values chosen for the variable. If the open phrase contains two or more variables, values must be chosen for each of the variables in order that the phrase have a specific value. Let us consider the phrase $2x + y$. If for each of the variables x and y the substitution set is $\{1, \frac{3}{2}, 2\}$, the values of the phrase can be arrayed as in Table 8–2. Since the values of $2x + y$ result from choosing values for x and y, it is advisable to place the values of $2x + y$ in the right-hand column.

Table 8–2

x	y	$2x + y$
1	1	3
1	$\frac{3}{2}$	$\frac{7}{2}$
1	2	4
$\frac{3}{2}$	1	4
$\frac{3}{2}$	$\frac{3}{2}$	$\frac{9}{2}$
$\frac{3}{2}$	2	5
2	1	5
2	$\frac{3}{2}$	$\frac{11}{2}$
2	2	6

In writing the entries in column 4 of Table 8–1, certain operations were performed as we proceeded from step to step; these operations were performed as though n were a number, i.e., one of its permissible substitutes. If this had not been done, the final entry would have been

$$\frac{3(n + 6) - n}{2}.$$

This open phrase is a translation of the original verbal instructions, or worded formulation, into mathematical language. It is also helpful to proceed in the opposite direction. Let us translate the open phrase $7(2n + 5) - 4$ into verbal form. This can be done in many ways, one of which is the following: "A number is doubled, and the result is increased by 5; this sum is multiplied by 7, and the result is decreased by 4."

PROBLEM SET 8–2

1. Translate the following verbal instructions into mathematical language. Use a different letter as variable in each part.
   (a) A number is tripled, and the result decreased by 2; this last number is divided by 3, and that result is increased by 4.
   (b) A number is divided by 2, and the result is increased by 5; the resulting number is multiplied by $\frac{1}{3}$, and this product is increased by 4.
   (c) A number is increased by 7; this result is multiplied by a number which is 3 more than the original number.

2. Translate the following open phrases to verbal form.

(a) $3n - 2$

(b) $2t + 1$

(c) $\frac{1}{2}(x + 4) + 7$

(d) $2(t + 1)$

(e) $6[4 + (3r - 2)]$

(f) $3(2x + y) + 11$

3. For each of the following open phrases and the indicated substitution set for the variable, display the values of the given open phrase.

(a) $3x - 2$, $\{1, 2, 3, 4, 5\}$

(b) $3(x + 4)$, $\{\frac{1}{2}, \frac{3}{2}, \frac{5}{2}, \frac{7}{2}\}$

(c) $\dfrac{x + 2y - 3}{4}$, $\{2, 5\}$ for both x and y

(d) $2x - y + 4$; $\{4, 5\}$ for x, $\{2, 3\}$ for y

4. Each of the following open phrases is coupled with a substitution set. For what members of the set will the phrase have the value indicated?

(a) $2x + 3$, $\{0, 1, 4, 6\}$, value 11

(b) $9 - 2t$, $\{0, \frac{1}{2}, 3, 4\}$, value 1

(c) $2u + v - 1$, $\{1, 2, 3\}$ for both u and v, value 6

(d) $x/2 + \frac{5}{2}$, $\{\frac{1}{3}, \frac{2}{3}, \frac{4}{3}, \frac{7}{3}\}$, value $\frac{19}{6}$

8–3 OPEN SENTENCES

The truth of the sentence "The population of the United States is greater than the population of Canada" can be stated immediately. Is the sentence "The country's population is greater than that of Canada" true or false? You can not answer this question because you do not know what country is referred to. However, let it be stated that the set of countries under consideration is {Holland, Switzerland, United States, China}. Then, if "the country" chosen is

$$
\left.\begin{array}{l}
\text{Holland,} \\
\text{Switzerland,} \\
\text{United States,} \\
\text{China,}
\end{array}\right\}
\quad \text{the sentence is} \quad
\left\{\begin{array}{l}
\text{false;} \\
\text{false;} \\
\text{true;} \\
\text{true.}
\end{array}\right.
$$

Thus, for many English sentences it cannot be stated whether they are true or false until the "objects" referred to are specified precisely.

If "$=$" is given the usual interpretation "is equal to," then "$2x + 1 = x + 5$" has a verb phrase, a subject which is the open phrase "$2x + 1$," and a predicate complement which is the open phrase "$x + 5$." Hence, $2x + 1 = x + 5$ is a mathematical sentence. Is it true or false? Again you cannot tell until a permissible substitute is chosen for x. If the substitution set is specified as $\{1, 2, 3, 4\}$ and a value is chosen for x from this set, it is possible to state that

$$2 \cdot 1 + 1 = 1 + 5 \quad \text{is false,}$$
$$2 \cdot 2 + 1 = 2 + 5 \quad \text{is false,}$$
$$2 \cdot 3 + 1 = 3 + 5 \quad \text{is false,}$$
$$2 \cdot 4 + 1 = 4 + 5 \quad \text{is true.}$$

Hence, the sentence is true for some permissible substitutes, and false for others.

A sentence such as $2x + 1 = x + 5$ is called an *open sentence*. Such a sentence contains one or more variables in the phrases which are used to make up the sentence. Only after a substitution set is specified and values of the variable (or variables) are chosen can it be stated whether the sentence is true or false. In an open sentence the decision as to its truth or falsity is left open until a particular value of the variable is specified.

Is $3x < 2$ an open sentence? Does it have a verb; if so, what is it? Is it true that $3x < 2$ when the value of x is 0? When the value of x is $\frac{1}{2}$? When the value of x is 1?

Is $x + 1 \neq 4$ a sentence? Is it true that $x + 1 \neq 4$ when the value of x is 1? 5? 3?

Sentences of the form $x + 1 = 4$ are called *equations*, while those of one of the forms $x + 1 < 4$, $x + 1 > 4$, or $x + 1 \neq 4$ are called *inequalities*. Values of x for which a sentence is true are called *truth numbers* or *truth values*.

Why are we interested in open sentences? One reason, though not the only reason, is that quite often we wish to use mathematical ideas to find an answer to a question which may have arisen in everyday experience. For example, consider the following problem.

If Mary buys oranges at 3 cents each, how many can she buy for 24 cents?

This problem may appear trivial, but remember that by keeping away from complicated situations we can concentrate on the fundamental ideas involved. Let the number of oranges bought be a value of the variable x. Then

the number of cents in cost of oranges is a value of $3x$.

Also,

the number of cents in cost of oranges is 24,

so that

a value of $3x$ must be 24.

Accordingly, the number (of oranges) must be

a value of x for which $3x = 24$ is true.

Analysis of the problem has led to an open sentence and to the fact that we need to find a value of x for which this sentence is true. When one buys oranges, he usually buys whole oranges, not fractional parts; hence, one might think of buying 3 oranges, but not $3\frac{1}{2}$ oranges. Accordingly, for this problem the substitution set could be chosen as the set of whole numbers. Therefore, when a value of x is sought for which $3x = 24$ is true, the search can be confined to the set of whole numbers. Rather than complete this example, we will proceed to the problem of finding the value (or values) of a variable for which an open sentence is true. Later we will return to this problem of translating a verbal description into mathematical form. At that time the language used in the preceding problem will be simplified considerably.

8–4 TRUTH SETS. EQUATIONS

The *truth set* of an open sentence is the subset of the substitution set for which the sentence is true, i.e., the set of truth numbers. If the substitution set is $\{0, 1, \frac{3}{2}, 2, 3, 4\}$, then

the truth set of $2x + 1 = 3$ is $\{1\}$,
the truth set of $2x + 1 < 3$ is $\{0\}$,
the truth set of $2x + 1 > 3$ is $\{\frac{3}{2}, 2, 3, 4\}$,
the truth set of $2x + 1 \neq 3$ is $\{0, \frac{3}{2}, 2, 3, 4\}$,
the truth set of $2x + 1 > 10$ is Φ.

Note that if the substitution set had been $\{0, 1, \frac{3}{2}, 2, 3, 4, 5, 6\}$, the truth set of $2x + 1 > 10$ would not have been Φ, but $\{5, 6\}$. Thus the truth set depends on both the sentence and the substitution set.

In the above examples the substitution set was finite; each member of that set could be substituted in turn, and the truth or falsity of the resulting sentence could be determined. It could then be stated that the entries in the truth set are truth numbers and that there are no other truth numbers. If the substitution set were infinite, could all members of the set be tried in turn? Obviously not, although trying them one after another may yield a truth number. Accordingly, more general procedures for finding the truth set are needed.

Let us return to the equation $3x = 24$ and determine its truth set. Of course, you can guess one truth number, 8. But are there other truth numbers among the whole numbers? Suppose that the value of x is < 8; then the value of $3x$ is < 24. (What property of whole numbers was used here?) Hence, no number < 8 is a truth number. Similarly, no number > 8 is a truth number. Accordingly, the truth set is $\{8\}$.

Some of the language used up to this point is cumbersome; let us try to simplify it. Each time that the equation $3x = 24$ is considered, numbers

are substituted for x. Hence, the multiplication of a number by 3 is performed in determining the truth set. Instead of saying

$$3 \cdot (\text{a number which is a value of } x) = 24,$$

let us agree to say

$$3 \cdot (\text{a number } x) = 24,$$

or

$$x \text{ is a number such that } 3x = 24.$$

This agreement will simplify the language, but it must be remembered that
the numbers upon which the operations are performed are values of the
variable.

Suppose that we want the truth set of the equation $43x = 2314$. It is
much more difficult to guess a truth number in this instance. Thinking back
to the definition of fraction, we could say that $\frac{2314}{43}$ is a truth number, if
that number is a member of the substitution set. Assuming that such is the
case, there remains the haunting question, "Is it the only truth number?"

Other properties of numbers are needed in order to answer this question
for the above example and for other simple equations. Look again at
property AP of Section 4–5 and note its similarity to one of the properties
below. Let a/b, c/d, and e/f be fractions; then the following properties hold.

Addition property (AP).

$$\text{If } \frac{a}{b} = \frac{c}{d}, \qquad \text{then} \qquad \frac{a}{b} + \frac{e}{f} = \frac{c}{d} + \frac{e}{f}.$$

Subtraction property (SP). Under the restriction that $e/f < a/b$:

$$\text{If } \frac{a}{b} = \frac{c}{d}, \qquad \text{then} \qquad \frac{a}{b} - \frac{e}{f} = \frac{c}{d} - \frac{e}{f}.$$

Multiplication property (MP).

$$\text{If } \frac{a}{b} = \frac{c}{d}, \qquad \text{then} \qquad \frac{e}{f} \cdot \frac{a}{b} = \frac{e}{f} \cdot \frac{c}{d}.$$

You will be asked to prove the above properties in the next problem set.
These properties will be more clearly understood if they are phrased in
words.

AP: if two fractions are equal and the same fraction is added to each of
them, the resulting fractions are equal.

SP: if two fractions are equal and the same fraction is subtracted from
each of them, then the resulting fractions are equal.

MP: if two fractions are equal and each is multiplied by the same fraction,
then the resulting fractions are equal.

By these properties, the following hold:

$$\text{since } \tfrac{1}{2} = \tfrac{3}{6}, \quad \text{then} \quad \tfrac{1}{2} + \tfrac{2}{7} = \tfrac{3}{6} + \tfrac{2}{7},$$
$$\text{and} \quad \tfrac{1}{2} - \tfrac{2}{7} = \tfrac{3}{6} - \tfrac{2}{7},$$
$$\text{and} \quad \tfrac{2}{7} \cdot \tfrac{1}{2} = \tfrac{2}{7} \cdot \tfrac{3}{6}.$$

Now let us return to the equation $43x = 2314$. Since x is to be a number such that

$$43x = 2314,$$

then

$$\tfrac{1}{43} \cdot 43x = \tfrac{1}{43} \cdot 2314 \qquad \text{(by MP)},$$

and therefore

$$x = \tfrac{2314}{43},$$

by the property A_m, the property of reciprocals, and the agreement that a counting number = (the counting number)/1. This thought sequence shows that if x is a number such that $43x = 2314$, then x must be $\tfrac{2314}{43}$; that is, no other truth numbers are possible. Since it was shown earlier that $\tfrac{2314}{43}$ is a truth number, then the truth set of $43x = 2314$ is $\{\tfrac{2314}{43}\}$. There is the additional assumption (at least implied) that this fraction is a member of the substitution set.

ILLUSTRATIVE EXAMPLE. Find the truth set of $11x + 27 = 74$, assuming that the substitution set is the set of all numbers represented by fractions.

Solution.

If

$$11x + 27 = 74,$$

then

$$(11x + 27) - 27 = 74 - 27 \qquad \text{(by SP)},$$

then

$$11x = 47 \qquad \text{(by PP}_1 \text{ and property of zero)},$$

then

$$\tfrac{1}{11} \cdot 11x = \tfrac{1}{11} \cdot 47 \qquad \text{(by MP)},$$

then

$$x = \tfrac{47}{11} \qquad \text{(by } A_m \text{ and reciprocal properties)}.$$

Hence, $\tfrac{47}{11}$ is the only possible truth number. It is not yet known whether or not $\tfrac{47}{11}$ is a truth number, so try it; that is, consider $\tfrac{47}{11}$ as a value of x. Now,

$$11(\tfrac{47}{11}) + 27 = 47 + 27$$
$$= 74.$$

Hence, $\tfrac{47}{11}$ is a truth number, and consequently $\{\tfrac{47}{11}\}$ is the truth set.

The truth set of an equation is often called the *solution set*, and members of the solution set are called *solutions* of the equation. For the above example, $\tfrac{47}{11}$ is *the* solution of $11x + 27 = 74$.

PROBLEM SET 8-4

1. Given the substitution set $S = \{0, 1, 2, 3, 4, 5, 6, 7, 8\}$, find the truth set for each of the following sentences.
(a) $2x + 1 = 7$ (b) $2x + 1 = 4$ (c) $2x < 9$
(d) $4y > 19$ (e) $3z \neq 12$ (f) $3t \neq 14$
(g) $3x < 12$ (h) $3x \leq 12$

2. State, in words, how you found the truth sets in Problem 1.

3. Consider the equation $2x - 1 = x + 4$, along with the following sequence of steps:

$$\text{for } x = 5, \quad \text{left member} = 2 \cdot 5 - 1 = 9;$$
$$\text{right member} = 5 + 4 = 9.$$

(a) What conclusion can be drawn from this work?
(b) Can the truth set be stated at this stage? Why?
(c) If the substitution set is given as $\{10, 11, 12, \ldots, 19\}$, what conclusion can be drawn?

4. Consider the equation $2x - 1 = x + 4$ and the following sequence of steps:

$$2x - 1 = x + 4,$$
$$2x - 1 - x + 1 = x + 4 + 1 - x,$$
$$x = 5.$$

(a) What conclusion can be drawn?
(b) Is 17 in the truth set? Why?
(c) What conclusion can be drawn if the work in both Problems 3 and 4 is taken into consideration?
(d) If the substitution set is the set of whole numbers, how should the answer to part (c) be modified?

5. Find the truth set for each of the following equations (that is, solve each equation) assuming that the substitution set is the set of all fractions. Show all steps, and explain your reasoning.
(a) $3x - 2 = x$ (b) $\frac{3}{4}y + 1 = 4 - \frac{1}{3}y$
(c) $13x = 5 + 11x$ (d) $\frac{4}{5}t - 2 = \frac{2}{3}t + \frac{7}{2}$
(e) $2x - 1 = 5 - 2x$ (f) $\frac{2}{3}x = 7 - \frac{1}{4}x$
(g) $\frac{5}{2}x - 4 = \frac{3}{2}x - \frac{4}{3}$ (h) $\frac{6}{7}x - \frac{2}{3} = \frac{2}{5}x + 4$

6. Prove property AP for fractions along the lines of the proof, given in Section 4-5, of this property for whole numbers.

7. Prove property SP for fractions.

8. Prove property MP for fractions.

9. How is the truth set of $x + 4 \neq 7$ related to the truth set of $x + 4 = 7$.

10. Explain how to find the truth set of $2x - 1 \neq 3 - x$.

11. Find the truth sets of the following inequalities, where the substitution set is the set of all fractions.

(a) $2x - 1 \neq 3 - x$

(b) $5x - 2 \neq 7 - 2x$

(c) $\frac{1}{2}x - 1 \neq 5$

(d) $\frac{2}{3}x - 3 \neq 4 + \frac{1}{2}x$

8–5 INEQUALITY PROPERTIES

In an earlier chapter we proved that if a, b, and c are whole numbers, $c \neq 0$, and $a < b$, then $ca < cb$. Let us show that a similar property holds for fractions a/b, c/d, and e/f.

Inequality property I_2.

$$\text{If} \quad e \neq 0 \quad \text{and} \quad \frac{a}{b} < \frac{c}{d}, \quad \text{then} \quad \frac{e}{f} \cdot \frac{a}{b} < \frac{e}{f} \cdot \frac{c}{d}.$$

The statement $e \neq 0$ ensures that e/f is not the zero fraction. This property yields such results as the following:

$$\text{since} \quad \tfrac{1}{3} < \tfrac{3}{4}, \quad \text{then} \quad \tfrac{2}{5} \cdot \tfrac{1}{3} < \tfrac{2}{5} \cdot \tfrac{3}{4}.$$

To prove this property let $a/b = u/v$ and $c/d = w/v$ (note the common denominator v). Why is this possible? Since $a/b < c/d$, then

$$\frac{u}{v} < \frac{w}{v},$$

and hence $u < w$, from the definition of inequality of fractions. Accordingly,

$$eu < ew \qquad (I_2 \text{ for whole numbers}),$$

$$\frac{eu}{fv} < \frac{ew}{fv} \qquad (\text{definition of inequality for fractions}).$$

Hence

$$\frac{e}{f} \cdot \frac{u}{v} < \frac{e}{f} \cdot \frac{w}{v}.$$

In effect, this property enables us to say:

Given an inequality, each of the numbers appearing therein may be multiplied by the same nonzero number and the resulting inequality holds.

Now suppose that we start with the inequality

$$\frac{e}{f} \cdot \frac{a}{b} < \frac{e}{f} \cdot \frac{c}{d};$$

if $e \neq 0$, then f/e is a fraction, and this fraction may be used as a "multiplier." Hence

$$\frac{f}{e}\cdot\left(\frac{e}{f}\cdot\frac{a}{b}\right) < \frac{f}{e}\cdot\left(\frac{e}{f}\cdot\frac{c}{d}\right) \quad \text{(by I}_2\text{)},$$

so that

$$\left(\frac{f}{e}\cdot\frac{e}{f}\right)\cdot\frac{a}{b} < \left(\frac{f}{e}\cdot\frac{e}{f}\right)\cdot\frac{c}{d} \quad \text{(why?)},$$

$$1\cdot\frac{a}{b} < 1\cdot\frac{c}{d} \quad \text{(property of reciprocals)},$$

$$\frac{a}{b} < \frac{c}{d}.$$

This proves a third inequality property.

Inequality property I₃.

If $e \neq 0$ and $\frac{e}{f}\cdot\frac{a}{b} < \frac{e}{f}\cdot\frac{c}{d}$,   then $\frac{a}{b} < \frac{c}{d}$.

By this property, for example,

if $\frac{2}{3}\cdot\frac{a}{b} < \frac{2}{3}\cdot\frac{c}{d}$,   then $\frac{a}{b} < \frac{c}{d}$.

Now suppose that the inequality $ea < ec$ is given, where a, c, and e are whole numbers, $e \neq 0$. Since this can be written as

$$\frac{e}{1}\cdot\frac{a}{1} < \frac{e}{1}\cdot\frac{c}{1},$$

the property I₃ may be applied to yield

$$\frac{a}{1} < \frac{c}{1}, \quad \text{or} \quad a < c.$$

Hence, it has been shown that

if $e \neq 0$ and $ea < ec$,   then $a < c$.

It is this special case of the property I₃ which was needed earlier (see end of Section 4–8). This case can be proved without using properties of fractions, but such will not be done here. Properties I₂ and I₃ are important for the determination of truth sets of inequalities.

It is true that since $7 < 9$, then $7 + 3 < 9 + 3$ and $7 - 3 < 9 - 3$. Are such results true in general? Let us suppose that $a < b$, where a and b

are whole numbers; then $b - a$ is a whole number, c, such that $b - a = c$. Hence,

$$b = a + c \qquad \text{(why?)},$$

$$b + d = (a + c) + d \qquad \text{(by AP)},$$

$$= (a + d) + c.$$

Therefore,

$$b + d > a + d \qquad \text{(by I}_1\text{)}.$$

This proves the following property.

Inequality property I₄. Let a, b, and d be whole numbers; hence,

$$\text{if} \quad a < b, \quad \text{then} \quad a + d < b + d.$$

Another property can now be stated.

Inequality property I₅. Let a, b, and d be whole numbers such that $d < a$;

$$\text{if} \quad a < b, \quad \text{then} \quad a - d < b - d.$$

Both of the properties I_4 and I_5 hold for fractions; the proof of this is called for in the next problem set. It is desirable to state both properties in words. By the property I_4:

If an inequality is true and a number is added to the numbers appearing on both sides of the inequality, then the resulting inequality is true.

State property I_5 in words.

8–6 TRUTH SETS FOR INEQUALITIES

It is both convenient and helpful to represent the truth sets of inequalities on a number line. If the substitution set is {all whole numbers}, then, for the inequalities $x < \frac{7}{2}$ and $x > \frac{7}{2}$, we obtain the following diagram, where the shaded circles represent truth numbers.

If the substitution set is {all fractions}, then the truth sets must be represented by heavy lines, as below, where an unshaded circle means that the corresponding number is not to be included.

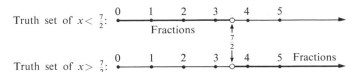

The word "fractions" has been written over or under the shaded part to emphasize the fact that all the fractions corresponding to points on the shaded portion are in the truth set.

Consider the inequality $x - 1 < 3$ for the substitution set {all whole numbers}. If x is a number such that

$$x - 1 < 3,$$

then

$$x < 3 + 1 \qquad \text{(by } I_4\text{)}.$$

Thus, if x is a truth number of $x - 1 < 3$, it must also be a truth number of $x < 4$. Since there are only four possible numbers, 0, 1, 2, and 3, these can be checked in turn and shown to be truth numbers of the original inequality. The truth set is $\{0, 1, 2, 3\}$.

Now consider $x - 1 > 3$ for the same substitution set. Again, if

$$x - 1 > 3,$$

then

$$x > 3 + 1 \qquad \text{(by } I_4\text{)}.$$

In this case the set of *possible* truth numbers is not finite, and hence they cannot all be tried one after the other. What do we do then? Suppose that x is a number in the truth set of $x > 4$; then

$$x - 1 > 4 - 1 \qquad \text{(by } I_5\text{)},$$

that is,

$$x - 1 > 3.$$

Thus x must be a truth number for $x - 1 > 3$. When these two thought sequences are combined, we see that

truth set of $x - 1 > 3$ is the same as   truth set of $x > 4$.

So, the truth set of $x - 1 > 3$ can be represented as follows.

If the substitution set had been {all fractions}, then a thought sequence similar to the above would have been needed for $x - 1 < 3$, as well as for $x - 1 > 3$.

Let us now consider the inequality $2x < 7$ for the substitution set {all fractions}. If x is a truth number for

$$2x < 7,$$

then

$$x < \tfrac{7}{2} \qquad \text{(by } I_3 \text{)}.$$

Hence, the truth set of $2x < 7$ is contained in the truth set of $x < \tfrac{7}{2}$. Conversely, if x is a truth number of

$$x < \tfrac{7}{2},$$

then

$$2x < 7 \qquad \text{(by } I_2 \text{)}.$$

Combining these results, we see that truth set of $2x < 7$ is same as truth set of $x < \tfrac{7}{2}$. Represent this truth set on a number line.

ILLUSTRATIVE EXAMPLE. Find the truth set of $2x - 1 < 7$, and represent it on a number line for the substitution set {all fractions}.

Solution.

If $2x - 1 < 7,$

then $2x < 7 + 1$ (by I_4);

therefore $x < \tfrac{8}{2}$ (by I_3).

Also,

if $x < \tfrac{8}{2},$

then $2x < 8$ (by I_2);

therefore $2x - 1 < 8 - 1$ (by I_5).

Accordingly,

truth set of $2x - 1 < 7$ is same as   truth set of $x < 4$.

This truth set is illustrated below.

Fractions

PROBLEM SET 8–6

1. Find the truth sets for each of the following inequalities, where the substitution set is {all whole numbers}. Give a careful account of your reasoning, using words, such as "if" and "then," which are needed to establish sequential thinking. Represent each truth set on a number line.

   (a) $3x < 11$ (b) $2x - 5 < 8$
   (c) $4x - 17 < 12$ (d) $5x + 4 < 23$

2. Find the truth set for $3x + 2 > 12$, where the substitution set is {all fractions}. Represent this set on a number line. Give a careful account of your reasoning, and draw proper conclusions.

3. Repeat Problem 2 for $4x - 7 < 10$.

4. Find the truth sets of the following sentences for the substitution set indicated.

   (a) $3x - 2 > 11$,   {3, 4, 5, 6, 7, 8}
   (b) $2x - 1 \neq 7$,   {3, 4, 5, 6, 7, 8}
   (c) $4x + 3 = 17 - 2x$,   {all whole numbers}
   (d) $4x + 3 = 17 - 2x$,   {all fractions}
   (e) $3x + 4 < x + 13$,   {all fractions}
   (f) $3x + 4 < x + 13$,   {all fractions larger than 6}
   (g) $4x - 2 > 2x + 15$,   {all whole numbers}
   (h) $3x - 2 \neq x + 7$,   {all fractions}

5. State and prove property I_4 for fractions.

6. Prove property I_5 for whole numbers.

7. State and prove property I_5 for fractions.

CHAPTER 9

Applications

9–1 VERBAL PROBLEMS

So-called verbal problems, or worded problems, prove troublesome to many people. In many cases these people realize that they do not know how to attack such problems, that they do not know where to begin. This psychological situation can be overcome if preconceived notions are thrust aside and a real attempt is made to understand the ideas involved.

Many problems can be solved by using a relatively simple thought sequence, such as that discussed in the following example.

ILLUSTRATIVE EXAMPLE. Mary can buy 5 oranges for 22 cents. Find the cost of 13 oranges.

Solution. A first reading of this problem should indicate that information is given regarding the cost of a certain number of oranges and that we want to find the cost of another number of oranges. The basic idea is that if we know the cost of one orange, we can easily obtain the desired result. We do not know the cost of one orange, but, can we find it readily? Since

$$5 \text{ oranges cost } 22 \text{ cents,}$$

$$1 \text{ orange costs } \tfrac{1}{5} \cdot 22 \text{ cents, or } \tfrac{22}{5} \text{ cents.}$$

Hence,

$$13 \text{ oranges cost } 13 \cdot \tfrac{22}{5} \text{ cents.}$$

Accordingly, the cost of 13 oranges is $\tfrac{286}{5}$ cents, or $57\tfrac{1}{5}$ cents. This cost would probably be stated as 57 cents.

If you are told that a car can travel 15 miles in 13 minutes and you want to find how far it can travel in one minute, which of the two following statements would be more helpful?

(1) A 15-mile distance requires 13 minutes.
(2) In 13 minutes the car can travel 15 miles.

Since time appears first in the second statement, that form is more helpful for finding the answer, i.e., for finding that

$$\text{in 1 minute the car can travel } \tfrac{1}{13} \cdot 15 \text{ miles, or } \tfrac{15}{13} \text{ miles.}$$

In problems such as these there often appear such expressions as "4 feet," "7 hours," and "5 feet per second." Such expressions, in which a number is associated with a unit, are frequently referred to as *denominate numbers*. Denominate numbers will be understood better after the discussion of measurement in Chapter 12. However, it should be realized that while in $\frac{7}{2}$ feet $= 3\frac{1}{2}$ feet two different numerals are used for the same number, in 2 feet $= 24$ inches something else is involved. Two different units are used; 2 and 24 are obviously not different numerals for the same number; we really mean that 2 of the units "foot" are equivalent to 24 of the units "inch." Previously we defined the addition of numbers; now we must define the addition of denominate numbers.

Definition. *Addition of denominate numbers.*

$$b(\text{units}) + c(\text{same unit}) = (b + c)(\text{same unit}).$$

By this definition, 2 inches $+$ 3 inches $= (2 + 3)$ inches. Note that the operation is actually performed on the numbers. What about 2 inches $+$ 3 feet? Is this equal to $2 + 3$ "somethings"? Obviously not! We must convert one of these denominate numbers to the other unit; therefore,

$$2 \text{ inches} + 3 \text{ feet} = 2 \text{ inches} + 36 \text{ inches},$$

or

$$2 \text{ inches} + 3 \text{ feet} = \tfrac{2}{12} \text{ feet} + 3 \text{ feet}.$$

Then we can proceed as before.

PROBLEM SET 9–1

1. Potatoes sell at 10 pounds for 53 cents.
   (a) Find the cost of 1 pound of potatoes.
   (b) Find the cost of 65 pounds of potatoes.
   (c) Find the cost of x pounds of potatoes.

2. A car travels at a steady rate of 12 miles in 13 minutes. Assume that it continues at this rate.
   (a) How far will it travel in 28 minutes?
   (b) How far will it travel in t minutes?
   (c) How long will it take to travel 42 miles?
   (d) How long will it take to travel y miles?

3. Tomato juice is to be served so that a 16-ounce can will yield 5 servings.
   (a) How much tomato juice is needed for 14 servings? for y servings?
   (b) How many servings could be obtained from a 3-pound 4-ounce can?
   (c) Would four 16-ounce cans suffice to serve 19 people? Why?

4. Which is cheaper, a 12-ounce package of soap flakes which costs 34 cents or a 4-pound package which costs $1.76?

5. The speed of a car is 40 miles per hour. Find the equivalent speed in feet per second.

6. A boy runs at the rate of 100 yards in 10 seconds. Find his speed in miles per hour.

7. The scale of a map is to be expressed as 1 inch $\sim$ "so many miles," the symbol "$\sim$" meaning "is equivalent to." Suppose that a distance on the map of $3\frac{1}{2}$ inches $\sim$ 105 miles.
   (a) Find the scale of the map.
   (b) What is the distance represented by w inches on the map?
   (c) What distance on the map would be the equivalent of y miles?

8. Explain carefully the meaning of
   (a) 2.6 seconds $= \frac{13}{5}$ seconds.   (b) 3 hours $= 180$ minutes.
   (c) 2 feet, 3 inches $= 27$ inches.

9–2   VERBAL PROBLEMS, CONTINUED

Many problems are more complicated than those of the previous section and thus require more analysis of the ideas involved. Often it is advantageous to introduce one or more variables, as was done in the "Mary buying oranges" problem of Section 8–3.

We start with a situation described in words, and we wish to describe this situation in mathematical language, so that mathematics can be used as an aid in finding answers to questions. Naturally, this requires that we understand the written words. For some reason many people feel that they should be able to gain this understanding on a single reading. Such is not the case, even for an experienced worker. A first reading can give only a very general idea of what the problem is about. Then it is necessary to break the problem into parts and to describe each of the thoughts expressed in these parts in mathematical language. This will be clearer if we work with an example.

ILLUSTRATIVE EXAMPLE 1.   Mary and Joan go to a store to buy oranges. Mary buys 15 oranges and Joan buys 24 oranges. Joan pays one cent more per orange than Mary does. Together they spend $1.41. How much per orange does Joan pay?

Solution. A first reading should merely indicate that the problem is concerned with "buying oranges" and that certain information is given as to the number of oranges bought, the cost per orange, and the total sum of money spent. We know from experience that in such a situation

(number of oranges bought by Mary) · (price per orange Mary pays)
= Mary's total cost for oranges bought.

This relationship is not specifically stated in the original problem; it is a "fact" which we must bring forth from our experience. It should be expressed in a manner which combines words and mathematical notation, as it is above, and in most cases it should be written down. This combined usage of words and symbols will be called "semi-English."

Now we are ready to break the problem into parts. First, let us consider Mary's purchase. We know the number of oranges she buys, but we don't know how much she pays per orange. In such a case we use a variable:

$$\text{let } x = \text{number of cents Mary pays per orange.}$$

Since we know that

the number of oranges Mary buys is 15,

then

total cost of Mary's oranges $= 15x$ cents.

Now think through Joan's buying situation:

number of oranges Joan buys $= 24$,
number of cents Joan pays per orange $= x + 1$,
total cost of Joan's oranges $= 24(x + 1)$ cents.

Before proceeding, note the following.

(1) A precise description was given for the variable; if this is not done, no one can be sure what the subsequent statements mean.

(2) After the variable is introduced, it can be used to write open phrases, such as $15x$, $x + 1$, and $24(x + 1)$, which in turn are used to state specific information.

There is one bit of information in the original problem which has not been used thus far, the total sum of money spent. Let us again use "semi-English" as follows:

number of cents Mary spends $+$ number of cents Joan spends $= 141$.

In mathematical language this relation becomes an open sentence:

$$15x + 24(x + 1) = 141.$$

We must be careful here! Certainly 40 cents and 60 cents add up to 1 dollar, but is $40 + 60 = 1$? We must watch out for units. Both terms on the left-hand side of the open sentence measure a number of cents; hence the term on the right-hand side must also measure a number of cents. The unit, "cents," should not appear in the equation, although it is used when writing the equation.

Thus, we have concluded the first part of the procedure, which we will call the *analysis and formulation*. Now x is a variable, and the number which is associated with Mary's cost per orange is a value of this variable, a value for which $15x + 24(x + 1) = 141$ is true. Since the cost of an orange is usually expressed as a fraction, the substitution set can be chosen as {all fractions}. Now we need to find the truth set of this open sentence. This part of the procedure will be called the *formal solution*. We have

$$15x + 24(x + 1) = 141,$$

$$15x + (24x + 24) = 141,$$

$$15x + 24x = 141 - 24,$$

$$39x = 117,$$

$$x = 3.$$

Hence no number other than 3 can be in the truth set. For $x = 3$,

$$15x + 24(x + 1) = 15 \cdot 3 + 24 \cdot 4 = 45 + 96 = 141,$$

so that 3 is in the truth set. Accordingly, the truth set is {3}.

The third part of the procedure is called the *recapitulation*. In this part, answers to the questions asked should be given *in words:*

"Joan paid four cents for each orange."

Let us try another example; this time a great portion of the verbal explanation will be omitted.

ILLUSTRATIVE EXAMPLE 2. Jack and Henry drive cars over the same course from location A to location B. Both men drive at constant rates, Jack at 50 miles per hour and Henry at 45 miles per hour. Jack leaves A 30 minutes after Henry leaves; they arrive at B at the same instant. How long did each man take to travel the course?

Solution.

(1) *Analysis and formulation.* This is a rate-time-distance situation; when the rate is constant, as it is here, then

(rate of travel) · (time of travel) = distance traveled,

provided proper units are used. Jack's rate is known to be 50 miles per hour, but his travel time is not known. Hence

let x hours = Jack's travel time.

(Why was the time unit chosen as hours?) Then

$$\text{distance Jack travels} = 50x \text{ miles.}$$

For Henry, we have

$$\text{Henry's rate} = 45 \text{ miles per hour,}$$
$$\text{Henry's travel time} = (x + \tfrac{1}{2}) \text{ hours,}$$
$$\text{distance Henry travels} = 45(x + \tfrac{1}{2}) \text{ miles.}$$

(Why was 30 minutes converted to $\tfrac{1}{2}$ hour?) Remember that Henry's travel time is greater than Jack's; this will aid in obtaining the correct expression for Henry's time.

How do we obtain an equation? They travel the same course, from A to B, so that we have the equation

$$\text{distance Jack travels} = \text{distance Henry travels,}$$

from which we obtain

$$50x = 45(x + \tfrac{1}{2}).$$

The value of x could be a fraction, so that the substitution set is chosen as {all fractions}.

(2) *Formal solution.* Find the truth set of $50x = 45(x + \tfrac{1}{2})$. Now the following statements must hold:

$$50x = 45x + \tfrac{45}{2},$$

$$5x = \tfrac{45}{2},$$

$$x = \tfrac{9}{2}.$$

For $x = \tfrac{9}{2}$,

$$50x = 50(\tfrac{9}{2}) = 225,$$

and

$$45(x + \tfrac{1}{2}) = 45(\tfrac{9}{2} + \tfrac{1}{2}) = 45(\tfrac{10}{2}) = 225.$$

Since, for $x = \tfrac{9}{2}$, the values of the left and right members of the equation are equal, then $\tfrac{9}{2}$ is a truth number. The truth set is $\{\tfrac{9}{2}\}$.

(3) *Recapitulation.* Jack's time is $\tfrac{9}{2}$ hours, or $4\tfrac{1}{2}$ hours, and Henry's time is $(\tfrac{9}{2} + \tfrac{1}{2})$ hours, or 5 hours.

ILLUSTRATIVE EXAMPLE 3. Mary buys oranges at 3 cents each, and Joan buys oranges at 4 cents each. Mary wants to have exactly 6 oranges more than Joan (to make up for the lower quality, supposedly!). Find the largest number they can purchase and still spend less than $1.31.

Solution.

(1) *Analysis and formulation.* Let x = number of oranges Mary buys. Then

> Mary spends $3x$ cents;
> Joan buys $x - 6$ oranges;
> Joan spends $4(x - 6)$ cents.

Since

> cost of Mary's oranges + cost of Joan's oranges < 131,

then

$$3x + 4(x - 6) < 131.$$

The substitution set is {all whole numbers}. (Why?) It is now necessary to find the largest number in the truth set of the above sentence.

(2) *Formal solution.* Since $3x + 4(x - 6) < 131$, then

$$3x + 4x < 131 + 24,$$

$$7x < 155$$

$$x < \tfrac{155}{7}.$$

Conversely, if

$$x < \tfrac{155}{7},$$

then

$$7x < 155,$$

$$3x + 4x < 131 + 24,$$

$$3x + (4x - 24) < 131,$$

$$3x + 4(x - 6) < 131.$$

Hence, formally, the truth set of the sentence consists of all $x < \tfrac{155}{7} = 22\tfrac{1}{7}$. But the substitution set is {all whole numbers}; hence x must be a whole number ≤ 22. The largest such value of x is 22.

(3) *Recapitulation.* Mary can buy 22 oranges, and Joan can buy 16 oranges.

PROBLEM SET 9–2

1. A man wishes to plant tomato plants in rows. If he places 32 plants in each row, how many rows does he need for 992 plants?

2. A man wishes to plant 882 tomato plants in rows. If he has room for 26 rows, find the smallest number of plants he can place in a row so as to use all 882 plants.

3. Harry and Jim plant tomatoes. Harry has 12 rows, and Jim has 9 rows. Jim places 7 more plants per row than Harry. Together they place 714 plants. How many did Jim plant per row?

4. In a certain rectangle the length is related to the width as indicated below. The perimeter is 70 inches. In each case find the dimensions of the rectangle.
   (a) The length is 7 inches more than the width.
   (b) The length is three-halves of the width.
   (c) The width is 7 inches more than one-third of the length.

5. A merchant pays $45 for each suit. His selling price is one-third more than his cost price. How many suits should he sell to have a total profit of $165?

6. A certain college had 3765 students. There were 75 more juniors than seniors. The number of sophomores was twice the number of seniors, and the number of freshmen was twice the number of juniors. How many freshmen attended that college?

7. Find three consecutive whole numbers whose sum is 96.

8. Charles and Stuart form a team for a two-man relay race. Each is to run the same distance. Charles requires 50 seconds for his lap, and Stuart requires 55 seconds. Assume that both run at a constant rate, but that Stuart's rate is two feet per second less than Charles'. How long will it take Stuart to run 100 feet?

9. A rectangular garden is 30 feet wide and 40 feet long. There is a walk of uniform width around the outside of the garden. The outer perimeter of the walk is $\frac{6}{5}$ times the inner perimeter of the walk. Find the width of the walk.

10. A man left an estate of $32,000 to three sons. The eldest son received three times as much as the youngest son; the middle son received $7000 more than the youngest son. How much did each son receive?

11. Jones plants grass seed at the rate of 5 pounds per thousand square feet, and Smith plants grass seed at double that rate. Smith's area to be planted is $1\frac{1}{2}$ times Jones's area. Find the area which Smith plants, if together they use 60 pounds of seed.

12. The number of spectators at a football game was 2710. Students were charged one dollar each, and nonstudents were charged two dollars each. The total proceeds were $3670. How many students attended the game?

13. In a two-digit number the tens digit is twice the ones digit and the sum of the digits is 12. Find the number.

14. In a two-digit number the tens digit is 5 more than its ones digit and the sum of the digits is 13. Find the number.

15. Two cars start at the same instant from points which are 30 miles apart. They travel toward each other until they meet, one at the constant rate of 40 miles per hour and the other at 50 miles per hour. How many minutes do the cars travel?

16. Repeat Problem 15, with the faster car starting 6 minutes after the slower car.

17. How many pounds of chicory worth 24 cents per pound should be mixed with 60 pounds of coffee worth 54 cents per pound, so that the mixture would be worth 42 cents per pound?

18. In a two-digit number in base five, the fives digit is twice the ones digit. The sum of the digits is 11(five). Find the number.

19. In a two digit number in base five, the ones digit is one more than the fives digit. The sum of the digits is 12(five). Find the number.

20. A stream flows at the rate of 5 miles per hour.
    (a) If a boat can travel 15 miles per hour in still water, how far will it travel in one hour, going downstream? Going upstream?
    (b) If a boat can travel x miles per hour in still water, find its rate of travel downstream and also upstream.

21. A stream flows at the rate of 3 miles per hour. A boat can travel 9 miles per hour in still water. It takes 9 hours to travel a distance upstream and back. How far did the boat travel upstream?

22. A wind is blowing from the north at 50 miles per hour. A plane can travel 400 miles per hour in still air. It takes the plane $3\frac{1}{5}$ hours to travel a certain distance north from A to B and back to A. Find the distance from A to B.

9–3 RATIO

Many problems of a mathematical nature can be solved by comparing numbers. The concepts of equality and inequality may be used for this purpose. Thus, $3 = 2 + 1$ and $3 < 4$ state certain comparisons through the use of numbers. Another way to compare numbers is by using the concept of *ratio*. This method is particularly useful in problems of application.

Suppose that there are two sets of marbles, set A containing 6 marbles and set B containing 4 marbles. We often say that "the number of marbles in set A is to the number of marbles in set B as 6 is to 4," thereby describing how these sets compare in "size." The same information is also given by the equation

the number of marbles in $A = \frac{6}{4}$(the number of marbles in B).

Ratios may also be used with pure numbers. Since $6 = \frac{6}{4} \cdot 4$, or $6 = \frac{3}{2} \cdot 4$, the fraction $\frac{3}{2}$ expresses the fractional part of 4 which is 6.

In general we define ratio as follows.

Definition. The ratio of a to b is the fraction a/b; this is sometimes written $a:b$.

If the two ratios a/b and c/d represent the same comparison we write $a/b = c/d$. This equation is frequently called a *proportion* and may be read "*a* is to *b* as *c* is to *d*." (A proportion merely states the equivalence of two different names for the same ratio.)

ILLUSTRATIVE EXAMPLE 1.   The length of the shadow of a flagpole is 34 feet and that of a yardstick is 2.5 feet. Find the ratio of the lengths of the shadows.

Solution. The ratio of shadow lengths is 34/2.5 or 68/5. Note that the unit, feet in this case, does not appear in the ratio.

ILLUSTRATIVE EXAMPLE 2.   A baseball batter went to bat officially 163 times and hit safely 56 times. What is the ratio of the number of hits to the number of times at bat?

Solution. The ratio is $\frac{56}{163}$.

ILLUSTRATIVE EXAMPLE 3.   Find the number which bears the same ratio to 40 as 6 bears to 5.

Solution. Let x be the number. Hence

$$\text{the ratio of } x \text{ to } 40 \qquad \text{equals} \qquad \text{the ratio of 6 to 5,}$$

or

$$\frac{x}{40} = \frac{6}{5}.$$

Accordingly,

$$40 \cdot \frac{x}{40} = 40 \cdot \frac{6}{5}, \qquad \text{so that} \qquad x = 48.$$

Has it been proved that 48 is a truth number? No! Prove it.

ILLUSTRATIVE EXAMPLE 4.   For Illustrative Example 1, find the height of the flagpole.

Solution. Let x feet be the height of the flagpole. The ratio of the height of the flagpole to the length of the yardstick is $x/3$. If the ground is level and both the pole and the yardstick are perpendicular to the ground, then

$$\frac{x}{3} = \frac{68}{5}.$$

(Why is this so?   Where did the "3" come from?)   Accordingly, $x = 3(\frac{68}{5}) = 40\frac{4}{5}$. Does $40\frac{4}{5}$ satisfy the equation? The flagpole is $40\frac{4}{5}$ feet high.

PROBLEM SET 9–3

1. Find a number which bears the same ratio to
     (a) 7, as 11 bears to 14;   (b) 31, as 16 bears to 5;
     (c) 3, as 48 bears to 27;   (d) 14, as 56 bears to 24.

2. In each part below find the ratio of the first number to the second.
     (a) 7, 12   (b) $\frac{2}{3}, \frac{4}{9}$ (c) $\frac{5}{6}, \frac{2}{3}$ (d) $\frac{3}{7}, \frac{2}{5}$

3. In a certain class of 39 persons there are 17 men. Find the ratio of the number of men to the number of women.

4. A certain broker sells $470,000 worth of stocks and $590,000 worth of bonds. What is the ratio of bond sales to stock sales?

5. If the ratio of bond sales to stock sales is the same as in Problem 4 and a broker has a total sale of $5,300,000, find the value of the bond sales.

6. One year the freshman class of a college consisted of 1190 students, of which 600 were men. The next year the freshman class of the same college consisted of 1310 students, of which 650 were women. In which year was the ratio of the number of men to the number of women larger?

7. A baseball player went to bat 163 times and hit safely 56 times. Find the number which bears the same ratio to 100 as this player's number of hits bears to his number of times at bat.

9–4 PERCENTAGE

It is quite easy to compare the ratios $\frac{7}{20}$ and $\frac{9}{20}$. Since the denominators are the same, a glance at the numerators tells us which ratio is the larger. However, the ratios $\frac{7}{20}$ and $\frac{1}{3}$ cannot be compared so quickly. If a speaker states that company A has $\frac{7}{20}$ of its assets in bonds while company B has $\frac{1}{3}$ of its assets in bonds, a listener must convert these fractions to fractions with a common denominator before he can make a comparison. Since our system of numbers is based on "ten-ness," the use of some power of 10 as a common denominator might well be advantageous. It is customary to use 100 as this common denominator.

Therefore, for the moment we will direct our attention to ratios such as $\frac{3}{100}$ and $\frac{247}{100}$, or, in general, to the ratio $b/100$. The fraction notation is clumsy in writing and even more clumsy in printing. Hence, we will use *percent* notation, i.e., we will write $\frac{3}{100}$ as 3% and $\frac{247}{100}$ as 247%, etc.

Definition. *Percent.* The expression "b percent" means $b/100$.

Hence b percent (abbreviated $b\%$) is a numeral which has the form of a fraction with denominator 100. For example, $72\% = \frac{72}{100}$. Since $\frac{72}{100} =$

$72(\frac{1}{100})$, the symbol % can be considered as representing $\frac{1}{100}$. (The choice of the word "percent" is appropriate, since it comes from the Latin "percentum," meaning "out of one hundred.") If decimal notation is kept in mind, the reason for choosing a power of ten as the denominator is obvious. For instance,

$$72\% = \tfrac{72}{100} = 0.72$$

and

$$15\% = \tfrac{15}{100} = 0.15.$$

How can a ratio be converted to percent form? For the ratio $\frac{4}{5}$, we have

$$\tfrac{4}{5} = \tfrac{4}{5} \cdot \tfrac{20}{20} = \tfrac{80}{100} = 80\%.$$

The number 20 is a value of m in property E_1 (see Section 7–1), and in this case it can be determined by "mental arithmetic." For the ratio $\frac{3}{8}$ the value of m would be $12\frac{1}{2}$ or 12.5. For the ratio $\frac{3}{7}$ it is not so easy to determine the value of m; however, the following general procedure can always be used:

$$\frac{3}{7} = \frac{3}{7} \cdot \frac{100}{100} = \left(\frac{3}{7} \cdot 100\right)\frac{1}{100} = \frac{300}{7} \cdot \frac{1}{100} = \frac{42\frac{6}{7}}{100} = 42\tfrac{6}{7}\%.$$

Would it be correct to write $\frac{3}{7} = 42\%$? to write $\frac{3}{7} = 43\%$? to write $\frac{3}{7} = 0.43$? to write $42\frac{6}{7}\% = 0.43$? Would $42\frac{6}{7}\% \approx 0.43$ be correct? Some people write $0.42\frac{6}{7}$ for $42\frac{6}{7}\%$. However, the fraction $\frac{6}{7}$ appearing in decimal notation seems inappropriate, since, according to our discussion, only the digits $0, 1, 2, \ldots, 9$ can appear in that notation. It is suggested that the following forms be used:

$$\tfrac{3}{7} \qquad \text{or} \qquad 42\tfrac{6}{7}\%,$$

or, if approximations are desired,

$$\tfrac{3}{7} \approx 42.9\% \qquad \text{or} \qquad 42.86\%,$$

depending on the accuracy desired.

Applications of percent are usually based on the idea that if a/b is $n\%$, then $a/b = n/100$; this can be thought of as the equality of two ratios, one of which has denominator 100.

ILLUSTRATIVE EXAMPLE 1. What percent of 40 is 16?

Solution. Let the result be $n\%$. Then

$$\frac{16}{40} = \frac{n}{100}.$$

This equation could be solved in any of three ways:

(1) $\dfrac{16}{40} = \dfrac{16(2.5)}{40(2.5)} = \dfrac{40}{100}$; $n = 40$.

(2) $\frac{16}{40} = (\frac{16}{40} \cdot 100)\frac{1}{100} = \frac{1600}{40}(\frac{1}{100}) = 40(\frac{1}{100}) = 40\%$; $n = 40$.

(3) $100(n/100) = 100(\frac{16}{40})$; $n = \frac{1600}{40} = 40$.

It must now be proved that 40 is a truth number, or solution. In general, method 3 above is the most easily applied.

ILLUSTRATIVE EXAMPLE 2. A certain bank pays interest on deposits at the rate of 4% annually. If Mr. Jones has $670 on deposit, find the annual interest he receives.

Solution. Translating this problem to mathematical form, we let the annual interest be $n. Then

$$\frac{n}{670} = 4\%, \qquad \text{so that} \qquad n = \tfrac{4}{100}(670) = 26.80.$$

The annual interest is $26.80.

ILLUSTRATIVE EXAMPLE 3. If Mr. Jones receives $35.60 annual interest from the bank of Illustrative Example 2, how much money does he have on deposit in the bank?

Solution. Suppose that Mr. Jones had $P on deposit. Then, translating the problem to a mathematical sentence, we write

$$\frac{35.60}{P} = \frac{4}{100}.$$

Hence on multiplying each fraction by 100P and using the symmetric property of equality, we obtain

$$4P = 3560, \qquad \text{so that} \qquad P = \tfrac{3560}{4} = 890.$$

Has it been proved that the truth set is {890} ? What should be done to prove that Mr. Jones has $890 on deposit?

ILLUSTRATIVE EXAMPLE 4. Mr. Jones has $450 on deposit in another bank. This bank pays him $15.75 annual interest. Find the rate of interest.

Solution. Let the rate of interest be $i\%$. Then

$$\frac{i}{100} = \frac{15.75}{450}, \qquad \text{so that} \qquad i = \frac{1575}{450} = \frac{7}{2} = 3.5.$$

The interest rate is 3.5%.

The examples above have a common feature which can be used to unify the treatment of percentage problems. In each case an equation of the form

$$\frac{i}{100} = \frac{C}{P} \quad \text{or} \quad \frac{i}{100}P = C$$

was obtained, where

$i\%$ = interest rate,

$\$P$ = number of dollars on deposit,

$\$C$ = number of dollars of interest paid.

In each example two of the numbers i, P, and C were known and the third was to be determined. The solution of a simple equation sufficed to determine the third number. In words, the equation $(i/100)P = C$ becomes

$i\%$ of P is equal to C.

Since most applications of percentage can be phrased in this form, there is no need to treat such problems by subdividing them into three types and treating each separately. This latter procedure wastes time, leads to working by rote, and often results in confusion as to which method to apply.

PROBLEM SET 9–4

1. State the meaning of each of the following.
   (a) 17% (b) 143% (c) 7.4%
   ?—>(d) $\frac{1}{2}$ of 1% (e) $\frac{1}{3}$ of 1% (f) 621%

2. Convert the following fractions to percentage form. Show all steps and give reasons.
   (a) $\frac{5}{8}$ (b) $\frac{17}{4}$ (c) $\frac{4}{3}$
   (d) $\frac{11}{15}$ (e) $\frac{21}{23}$ (f) $\frac{89}{47}$
   (g) $\frac{1}{127}$ (h) $\frac{3}{851}$ (i) $\frac{765}{154}$

3. Write each of the following sentences in mathematical form, and find the truth set.
   (a) 3% of y is 47.   (b) $i\%$ of 625 is 85.
   (c) 5.2% of 160 is w.   (d) $x\%$ of 45 is 220.
   (e) 0.5% of x is 48.   (f) 17.6% of 84 is t.

4. A team played 54 games in a season, winning 37 of them. What percentage of games played were lost?

5. Of a certain class, 45% are men. If the number of men in the class is 81, how many students are in the class?

6. A certain state has a population of 3,425,500, of which 66.8% live in urban areas. How many people in that state live in rural areas?

7. A man has money on deposit in two banks. He has three times as much on deposit in a bank which pays 3.5% per annum as he has in a bank which pays 4% per annum. His total annual interest is $34.80. How much is on deposit at the bank which pays 4%?

8. A person borrows $260 from a loan company which charges 6% per annum. He will pay for this loan in twelve equal monthly payments. What will his monthly payment be? [*Hint:* Interest is added to the principal to obtain the sum due the loan company.]

9. A person borrows $440 from a loan company and agrees to repay the loan in 12 equal monthly installments. The monthly payment is $38.68. Find the interest rate charged.

10. A savings and loan association pays 4% dividends annually. If my annual interest is $50.12, find the sum of money which I have on deposit in the bank.

11. A merchant marks up his prices 30%. Shortly after that, he decides to have a sale, offering a reduction of 20%. Is the sale price more or less than the original price (before the mark-up)?

12. What percent reduction should the merchant of Problem 11 offer in the sale to make the sale price equal to the original price?

13. A salesman receives a commission of 9% of sales. He pays his assistant 40% of his gross receipts. Find the salesman's net receipts as a percent of sales.

14. (a) How many pounds of butterfat are there in 50 pounds of milk containing 3% butterfat?

    (b) If x pounds of milk containing 3% butterfat are mixed with y pounds of milk containing 4% butterfat, how many pounds of butterfat are there in the mixture?

15. A dairyman wishes to produce 100 pounds of milk containing 6% butterfat by mixing a quantity of milk containing 2.5% butterfat with another quantity containing 8% butterfat. How much of each should he use?

CHAPTER 10

Negative Numbers. Rational Numbers

10–1 A BRIEF DISCUSSION OF REAL NUMBERS

When symbols for the counting numbers were being introduced, it was shown how, given any counting number c and a set A, such that $n(A) = c$, another element could be introduced into the set, thus forming a new set B such that $n(B) = c + 1$. That is, from any counting number a new counting number can be formed which is "larger." Since this procedure can be continued indefinitely, the set of counting numbers is an *infinite* set. On the number line this is represented by an arrowhead, indicating that the points which correspond to counting numbers continue beyond the portion shown in the diagram.

Suppose, for the moment, that we confine our attention to numbers between 0 and 1 and the corresponding part of the number line. Some of the numbers between 0 and 1 are displayed in Fig. 10–1. If the implied procedure were continued, what numbers would be placed on the next row? on the row after that? Could the procedure be continued indefinitely? Is the set of such numbers finite or infinite? Has every fractional number between 0 and 1 been considered in developing this display? Has $\frac{1}{3}$ been considered? $\frac{2}{7}$? $\frac{13}{14}$? Now, to each fractional number between 0 and 1 there corresponds a point on the number line, lying on the segment from 0 to 1. Does it seem likely that each point on this segment has a fraction associated

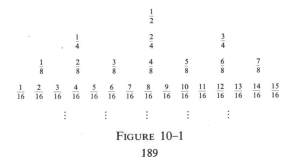

FIGURE 10–1

with it? That is, is the segment "filled up" with points which correspond to fractions? Whatever the answers are to these questions, the same situation holds for the segment from 1 to 2, from 2 to 3, etc.

Recall the Pythagorean theorem from your background in geometry. It can be stated: if a triangle is right-angled, then

$$(\text{length of hypotenuse})^2 = (\text{length of one leg})^2 + (\text{length of other leg})^2.$$

Let us work with a right triangle whose legs are each of length 1 unit and suppose there is a number c which represents the length of the hypotenuse. Then, by the Pythagorean theorem, we have

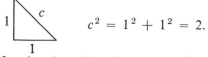

$$c^2 = 1^2 + 1^2 = 2.$$

Is there a fractional number whose square is 2? Let us assume that there is such a number with symbol d/b, where d and b are counting numbers, for which

$$\left(\frac{d}{b}\right)^2 = 2.$$

Since a fraction can always be reduced to simplest form, it can be assumed that d and b have a gcd of 1. Now we write

$$\frac{d^2}{b^2} = 2, \qquad \text{so that} \qquad d^2 = 2 \cdot b^2.$$

The number on each side of the last equation is a counting number, and the right-hand number is even. Hence, d^2 must be even. If d were odd, then d^2 would be odd (prove it!). Thus d must be even, that is, $d = 2 \cdot r$, for some counting number r. Hence, in turn,

$$(2r)^2 = 2b^2, \qquad 4r^2 = 2b^2, \qquad 2r^2 = b^2.$$

By the same reasoning, b must also be even. Now we have both b and d even, in contradiction to the original statement that b and d have a gcd of 1. Since the preceding statements followed from an assumption, that assumption must be false. That is, no fractional number exists whose square is 2. Hence, no fractional number can represent the length of the hypotenuse.

A line segment of length c can be marked on the number line with one end at 0. Since c does not represent a fractional number, the point at the other end of the segment does not have a number associated with it (at least, not of the type we have been considering). Yet it seems reasonable that we would want to have a number which would correspond to such a point. Consequently, we assume that to each point on the number line there is a number which corresponds to it.   Such numbers are called *real numbers* (a more "workable" definition will be given later). Accordingly, both whole numbers and fractional numbers are included in the set of real numbers. Likewise, the number c, such that $c^2 = 2$, is a real number; this number is usually denoted by $\sqrt{2}$.

The word "fraction," as used in mathematics, is somewhat ambiguous, since it usually means any numeral of the form u/v. Now $\sqrt{2}/3$ has this form; yet it is not the quotient of two counting numbers and, from the second last paragraph, cannot be written as such. To overcome this language problem, the term *rational number* is introduced to include those numbers which can be denoted by a/b, where a and b are whole numbers, $b \neq 0$. This new terminology will be used henceforth, even though *we do not have all rational numbers yet*.   Accordingly, symbols of the form a/b, where a and b are whole numbers, $b \neq 0$, represent rational numbers; to simplify the terminology, they will be called "rational numbers." Every real number which is not rational is called an *irrational* number.   Hence $\sqrt{2}$ is an irrational number. You are asked to show that $\sqrt{3}$, $\sqrt{5}$, and $\sqrt{6}$ are irrational in the following problem set. You have used $2\pi r$ as the length of the circumference of a circle. It can be shown that π is a real number; as a matter of fact, that it is an irrational number. Since the proof of this fact is anything but elementary, we are forced to leave it for later discussion.

The relationship between these sets of numbers is shown below.

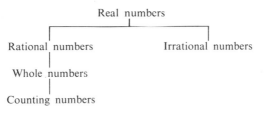

Note that each set is included in the set above it.

The preceding discussion reveals little about real numbers. It does, however, indicate the need for some numbers other than rational numbers. It also indicates that we do "fill in" the number line so that there is a number corresponding to each point.

The type of proof used to show that $\sqrt{2}$ is not rational is another example of an *indirect* proof. Consider the steps of this proof.

(1) The suspected conclusion is assumed not true.
(2) After logical arguments, a contradiction is obtained.
(3) Hence the assumption is false, i.e., the suspected conclusion is true.

Many indirect proofs are more complicated than this example.

PROBLEM SET 10–1

1. Show that the following numbers are irrational.

    (a) $\sqrt{3}$ (b) $\sqrt{5}$ (c) $\sqrt{6}$

2. Assume that $r = \sqrt{2}/3$ is rational.

    (a) What then can be said about $3r$ on the basis of this assumption?
    (b) What is $3r$, and what is known about it?
    (c) Draw a conclusion.

3. (a) Since $(\sqrt{2})^2 = 2$ and $1^2 = 1$, could $\sqrt{2}$ equal 1?

    (b) Could $\sqrt{2}$ equal 2? Why?

    (c) Since $1^2 = 1$, $(\sqrt{2})^2 = 2$, and $2^2 = 4$, what conclusion about $\sqrt{2}$ can be drawn? Use inequalities to express the answer.

    (d) Evaluate $(1.1)^2$, $(1.2)^2$, $(1.3)^2$, and $(1.4)^2$. From these results draw a conclusion about $\sqrt{2}$.

    (e) Evaluate $(1.5)^2$. From this evaluation and part (d) draw a conclusion about $\sqrt{2}$.

    (f) How does the conclusion of part (e) compare with the conclusion of part (c)? Explain why the conclusion of part (e) is better.

    (g) What should be the next step? Perform that step.

    (h) Numbers such as 1.4 and 1.5 are of what type?

    (i) Would the square of any of such numbers ever equal 2? Why?

    (j) Could the "exact value" of $\sqrt{2}$ be found this way?

    (k) Then what does the procedure of this problem accomplish?

4. Use the procedure outlined in Problem 3 to express $\sqrt{3}$ in decimal form, correct to two decimal places.

10–2 CLOSURE

The thought of continuing the discussion of irrational numbers is enticing! However, there are other matters which must be tended to first. Since we know so little about irrational numbers, our attention will be restricted for the present to rational numbers.

If any two counting numbers are added, the result is a counting number; that is, if the operation of addition is performed on any two members of the set C of all counting numbers, the resulting number is in C. This idea is expressed by stating that set C is *closed* with respect to addition. Likewise, the set C is closed with respect to multiplication. Is C closed with respect to division? Obviously not, since $6 \div 4$ is not a counting number. It was for this reason that certain rational numbers were introduced. Our set of rational numbers is closed with respect to division (except by zero) and, also, with respect to both addition and multiplication. Is *this* set of rational numbers closed with respect to subtraction? Certainly $\frac{3}{4} - \frac{1}{3}$ is in the set, but $\frac{1}{3} - \frac{3}{4}$ is *not* in the set. Hence our present goal is to extend our set of numbers so that the new set will be closed with respect to subtraction.

The need for more numbers can be viewed in another light. Every time we have made use of the number line thus far, we have restricted our attention either to that portion of the line extending to the left from the zero point or to that portion extending to the right (usually that to the right). What about the other end? Are there numbers which correspond to points on it? Consider for a moment the scale marked on a thermometer, where the markings extend both above and below the zero point. Below the zero point the markings read -5, -10, -15, etc., where the sign "$-$" denotes temperatures below zero. Similarly, we now introduce numbers which will correspond to points on the "empty" end of the number line and which will also yield closure with respect to subtraction.

10–3 NEGATIVE NUMBERS

The rational numbers, other than zero, which have been discussed thus far are to be called *positive rational numbers* to distinguish them from those numbers to be introduced now. Just as there is a point 3 units to the right of 0 on the number line, there is also a point 3 units to the left of 0. We introduce the numeral $^-3$ to represent the number which corresponds to this point. In a similar fashion, to each counting number n will correspond a new number ^-n (read "negative n"). Let us define a new term.

Definition. *Integers.* The set of integers consists of the counting numbers, the negatives of the counting numbers, and zero.

The counting numbers are then called the *positive integers;* their negatives the *negative integers.* Hence the set of integers contains the subset of positive integers, the subset of negative integers, and the subset $\{0\}$, and could be represented thus:

$$\{\ldots, \, ^-3, \, ^-2, \, ^-1, 0, 1, 2, 3, \ldots\}.$$

Of course, what these negative numbers actually "are" will become evident only as we obtain their properties.

Just as $\frac{5}{2}$ represents a point which is five units of size $\frac{1}{2}$ to the right of 0, the point which is five units of size $\frac{1}{2}$ to the left of 0 could be represented by $^-(\frac{5}{2})$. In other words, to each positive rational number p/q there will correspond a negative rational number $^-(p/q)$. Hence, let us define the complete set of rational numbers.

Definition. *Rational numbers.* The set of rational numbers contains the positive rational numbers, the negative rational numbers, and zero.

Accordingly, the set of rational numbers contains the set of integers, since, for example, 3 and $^-4$ can be written as $\frac{3}{1}$ and $^-(\frac{4}{1})$.

We could denote a number such as 3 by $^+3$ to emphasize its positive nature. These raised prefixes on numerals, such as on $^-4$ and $^+3$, indicate the signs of the numbers. If two numbers have the same sign, they are both positive or both negative; if they have opposite signs, one is positive and the other is negative.

From previous discussion, we know that $\frac{5}{3} < \frac{7}{3}$, since $5 < 7$. Hence the point $\frac{7}{3}$ is to the right of $\frac{5}{3}$ on the number line, since it is a larger number of units (each unit $= \frac{1}{3}$) from 0, and, similarly, $^-(\frac{7}{3})$ will be to the left of $^-(\frac{5}{3})$ on the line since it is a larger number of units from 0. Pay particular attention to the relationships indicated in the following diagram.

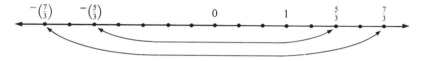

In general, for r_1 and r_2 positive rationals

    if r_1 is to the right of r_2,   then $^-r_1$ is to the left of $^-r_2$.

The numbers r and ^-r, for r positive, are called the *opposites* of each other. Thus $\frac{3}{2}$ and $^-(\frac{3}{2})$ are opposites, and $^-7$ and 7 are opposites. This relationship between numbers will be denoted by a bar set in the middle of the line, rather than raised. For example, the opposite of 3 is denoted by -3 (read: "opposite 3"); the opposite of $^-3$ is denoted by $-(^-3)$; thus $-3 = \ ^-3$, and $-(^-3) = 3$. Further examples are

$$-(^-7) = 7 \quad \text{and} \quad -(7) = \ ^-7,$$
$$-\ ^-(\tfrac{3}{2}) = \tfrac{3}{2} \quad \text{and} \quad -\tfrac{3}{2} = \ ^-(\tfrac{3}{2}).$$

In general, the opposite of a number is defined as follows.

Definition. *Opposite of a Number.* Let r be positive; then

$$-r = \ ^-r \quad \text{and} \quad -(^-r) = r.$$

Also $-0 = 0$.

The definition of -0 is somewhat arbitrary. It is introduced so that every rational will have an opposite, and hence theorems will be easier to state. On the number line, opposites correspond to points at the same distance from 0 but in opposite directions from 0, as in the above figure.

On the number line, we will call the length of the line segment from zero to a specific number the *absolute value* of that number. If r is the number, we will denote its absolute value by $|r|$. For example,

$$|3| = 3 \quad \text{and} \quad |{}^-3| = 3,$$
$$\left|\tfrac{7}{2}\right| = \tfrac{7}{2} \quad \text{and} \quad \left|{}^-(\tfrac{7}{2})\right| = \tfrac{7}{2}.$$

Thus opposites have the same absolute value.

Definition. *Absolute Value.* The absolute value of a number $r \neq 0$ is that member of the pair r and $-r$ which is positive; the absolute value of zero is zero.

The above definition states that

$$|r| = r, \quad \text{if } r \text{ is positive,}$$
$$|r| = -r, \quad \text{if } r \text{ is negative,}$$
$$|r| = 0, \quad \text{if } r \text{ is zero.}$$

Opposites, such as r and $-r$, are at the same distance, $|r|$, from 0.

Does $-r$ represent a positive number or a negative number? As has been noted, $-7 = {}^-7$ is a negative number, but $-({}^-7) = 7$ is a positive number. Accordingly, $-r$ can be either positive or negative, depending on whether r is negative or positive. Do not fall into the trap of thinking that the use of "$-$" as the prefix of a numeral denotes the sign of the number! The definition of absolute value states that $|r| = -r$, if r is negative. Since r is negative, then $-r$ is positive, and hence this statement yields $|r|$ as a positive number, just as it should.

PROBLEM SET 10–3

1. Is the set of whole numbers closed with respect to (a) addition? (b) multiplication? (c) subtraction? (d) division?

2. Write the opposites of the following numbers.

   (a) $^-11$ (b) 4   (c) $\tfrac{5}{3}$ (d) $^-(\tfrac{9}{4})$

3. Find each of the following numbers.

   (a) -5 (b) $-{}^-(\tfrac{6}{5})$ (c) $-\tfrac{5}{4}$ (d) $-{}^-(\tfrac{5}{11})$

4. Find the numbers r for which $|r|$ is given.

   (a) $|r| = 4$ (b) $|r| = \tfrac{2}{3}$ (c) $|r| = 0$ (d) $|r| = \tfrac{4}{9}$

5. For what numbers r is $|r| = {}^-2$?

6. Find the signs of the following numbers.

    (a) $-(^-7)$ (b) $-{}^-(\frac{1}{2})$ (c) $-(^+4)$ (d) ${}^-(\frac{3}{4})$

7. (a) Is zero positive or negative? Explain.
    (b) Write a complete statement as to the sign of r.
    (c) Write a complete statement as to the sign of $-r$.

8. Find r in each of the following cases:
    (a) $|r| = 3$, r positive.
    (b) $|r| = 5$, r negative.

10–4 ADDITION OF RATIONAL NUMBERS

In Section 5–2 addition was illustrated by using the number line. Arrows will now be used in illustrating certain operations. To represent the sum $3 + 4$, draw an arrow from 0 to 3; then draw a second arrow of length 4, starting at the tip of the first arrow and directed to the right. The result, which is represented by an arrow from 0 to 7, is shown below. (Two arrows have been drawn above the line for clarity.)

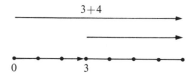

As a practical example, suppose that you want to find your net worth, which can be done by balancing your debts against your assets. We shall represent assets by positive numbers and debts by negative numbers. If your net worth is $3 and you acquire a new asset worth $4, your new net worth will be $(3 + 4)$. This could be represented as shown in the above diagram. However, if you start with a net worth represented by $^-5$ (i.e., debts over-balance assets by $5) when the new asset of $4 is acquired, the number representing your new net worth should be 4 units to the right of $^-5$, as shown below.

Therefore, whether your original worth is represented by a positive or by a negative number, the addition of an asset (which corresponds to a positive number) is represented by moving a certain number of units to the right.

Now suppose that your new acquisition is a debt of $4, rather than an asset. This debt would be represented by a negative number. Two cases are illustrated below.

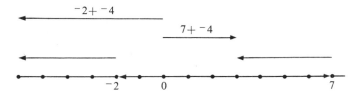

In the first case your original net worth is $7; in the second case you start off with an indebtedness of $2 (represented by $^-2$). The acquired debt of $4 is represented by an arrow 4 units long directed to the left. In each case your new net worth is represented by a number 4 units to the left of that representing the original net worth. Hence the addition of a negative number is represented on the number line by using an arrow directed to the left.

The above ideas pertaining to the addition of rational numbers seem to be natural when assets and debts are interpreted in terms of positive and negative numbers. Now note the following from the examples.

(a) $|3 + 4| = |3| + |4|$
$|^-2 + {}^-4| = |^-2| + |^-4|$ When numbers are of the same sign, $|\text{sum}| = $ sum of absolute values.

(b) $|^-5 + 4| = |^-5| - |4|$
$|7 + {}^-4| = |7| - |^-4|$ When numbers are of different signs, $|\text{sum}| = $ difference of absolute values.

(c) $3 + 4$ is positive
$^-2 + {}^-4$ is negative   When numbers have the same sign, the sign of the sum is the same as that of the numbers being added.

(d) $^-5 + 4$ is negative
$7 + {}^-4$ is positive   When numbers have different signs, the sign of the sum is the same as that of the number having the larger absolute value.

Problem 8 of Problem Set 10–3 indicated that when both the sign and the absolute value of a number are known, the number itself is thereby determined. This discussion motivates the following definition.

Definition. *Addition of Rational Numbers.* The sum of two rational numbers is another rational number, $a + b$, such that

(1) $|a + b| = $ sum of $|a|$ and $|b|$, if a and b have the same sign or at least one of them is zero;

$|a + b| = $ difference of $|a|$ and $|b|$, if a and b have different signs;

(2) if $|a + b| \neq 0$, then $a + b$ has the same sign as that member of the pair, a and b, which has the larger absolute value, if neither a nor b is 0; if either a or b is zero, the sign of $a + b$ is the same as that of the nonzero member.

It should be noted that when this definition is applied to two non-negative numbers, the result is the same as in earlier chapters. Let us apply the definition to $^-7 + 4$. By part (1),

$$|^-7 + 4| = 7 - 4,$$

since the numbers have different signs. By part (2), $^-7 + 4$ is a negative number, since $|^-7|$ is larger than $|4|$. Hence,

$$^-7 + 4 = {}^-(7 - 4) = {}^-3.$$

Remember that when the word "difference" is used, the smaller number is subtracted from the larger. In the preceding example, part (1) of the definition was used to obtain the absolute value of the sum, and part (2) was used to obtain the sign of the sum.

We should now realize that the "arrow" form of addition is an intuitive visualization of the definition of addition. "Arrow" addition can be used as an aid in checking results; in numerical problems it can be used in place of the formal definition. The formal definition will be used in the next section to prove properties of addition.

In the preceding discussion of this section the symbol "$-$" has been used in two different ways. When used to connect two numbers, as in $7 - 4$, it is a symbol for the operation of subtraction. When used with a single number, as in $^-4$, it is a symbol for a negative number. Hence, in the expression $|7| - |^-4|$ the first bar denotes subtraction, and the second bar denotes "negativeness." The earlier use of the bar to denote "opposite," as in -3, should be retained. This somewhat complicated symbolism will be modified later in this chapter.

ILLUSTRATIVE EXAMPLE. Find the sum $^-(\frac{7}{4}) + \frac{2}{3}$.

Solution. Using the number line, we obtain the diagram below.

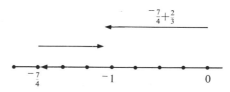

Hence the sum is negative, and its absolute value is $\frac{7}{4} - \frac{2}{3} = \frac{13}{12}$. Therefore, the sum is $^-(\frac{13}{12})$.

Using the formal definition, we have

$$^-(\tfrac{7}{4}) + \tfrac{2}{3} = \,^-(|^-(\tfrac{7}{4})| - \tfrac{2}{3}) = \,^-(\tfrac{7}{4} - \tfrac{2}{3}) = \,^-(\tfrac{13}{12}).$$

PROBLEM SET 10–4

1. Consider the notation $-(-^-3)$.

   (a) Does the middle bar mean "opposite" or "negative"?

   (b) What does the left-hand bar mean?

2. Explain the meaning of the bars in $-(-3)$.

3. In each of the following find the absolute value of the sum.

   (a) $^-8 + (^-3)$ (b) $^-4 + 7$ (c) $3 + (^-5)$

   (d) $^-(\tfrac{4}{3}) + \tfrac{9}{4}$ (e) $^-(\tfrac{5}{2}) + \tfrac{1}{3}$ (f) $^-(\tfrac{5}{7}) + \tfrac{9}{8}$

   (g) $^-2 + \tfrac{3}{4}$ (h) $4\tfrac{1}{3} + (^-6\tfrac{1}{2})$ (i) $3.14 + (^-0.12)$

4. In each part of Problem 3 find the sign of the sum.

5. Perform the following operations, both by using the number line and by using the definition.

   (a) $6 + (^-8)$ (b) $^-3 + (^-7)$ (c) $^-(\tfrac{4}{5}) + \,^-(\tfrac{6}{7})$ (d) $^-(\tfrac{13}{4}) + \tfrac{5}{4}$

   (e) $\tfrac{12}{7} + \,^-(\tfrac{2}{3})$ (f) $^-(\tfrac{6}{7}) + \,^-(\tfrac{5}{4})$ (g) $\tfrac{2}{3} + \,^-(\tfrac{2}{3})$ (h) $^-(\tfrac{5}{4}) + \tfrac{5}{4}$

   (i) $^-(\tfrac{3}{4}) + \tfrac{7}{8}$ (j) $^-(\tfrac{9}{5}) + \tfrac{2}{3}$

6. For each of the following conditions, use the definition of addition to express $r + s$ in a form which will indicate the sign of the sum and its absolute value:

   (a) r and s are negative rational numbers

   (b) r is positive, s is negative, and $|r| > |s|$

   (c) r is positive, s is negative, and $|r| = |s|$

   (d) r is positive, s is negative, and $|r| < |s|$

   (e) r is positive and $s = 0$

   (f) r is negative and $s = 0$

10–5 PROPERTIES RELATED TO ADDITION

The definition of addition can be used to prove several properties of rational numbers. For example:

Theorem 10–1. The commutative property of addition holds for rational numbers.

The proof of this theorem is almost trivial. Both $|a + b|$ and the sign of $a + b$ depend only on the nature of a and b, and not on the order in which they are added. Hence the sum of a and b is not dependent on the order of writing.

The following property of rational numbers can also be proved by applying the definition of addition.

Theorem 10–2.   The associative property of addition holds for rational numbers.

The proof of this property has many different cases. It was proved in Chapter 7 for the case where a, b, and c are all positive or zero. Consider the case where a and b are positive or zero, and c is negative, such that $a + b < |c|$. The results of Problem 6 of the previous problem set will be of assistance here. Since $a + b < |c|$, then $b < |c|$. Hence, applying the definition of addition to $b + c$, we obtain

$$a + (b + c) = a + {}^-(|c| - b).$$

Since ${}^-(|c| - b)$ and a have different signs and since $a + b < |c|$ implies that $a < |c| - b$, then

$$a + {}^-(|c| - b) = {}^-[(|c| - b) - a].$$

Accordingly,

$$a + (b + c) = {}^-[(|c| - b) - a] \qquad \text{(by transitivity of equality)}$$
$$= {}^-[|c| - (b + a)] \qquad \text{(by PP}_2 \text{ of Chapter 7)}$$
$$= {}^-[|c| - (a + b)].$$

Applying the definition of addition to $(a + b) + c$, we obtain

$$(a + b) + c = {}^-[|c| - (a + b)].$$

Hence, in this case, $a + (b + c) = (a + b) + c$. For other cases the proof would follow similar lines, but we will not take the time to complete this lengthy proof here.

From time to time we will be forced to use properties of non-negative rationals which have not been proved previously, or even stated. Such was done above in using the property that $a + b < |c|$ implies $a < |c| - b$; however, you can prove this on the basis of previous work.

What would $-(-a)$ be? Recall that for a positive, $-a = {}^-a$, and for a negative, $|a| = -a$; in the last case, $|a|$ and a are opposites, so that $-|a| = a$. Then

$$-(-a) = -({}^-a) = a, \qquad \text{for } a \text{ positive,}$$
$$-(-a) = -(|a|) = a, \qquad \text{for } a \text{ negative,}$$
$$-(-a) = -(-0) = -0 = 0, \qquad \text{for } a = 0.$$

Accordingly, we can state the following theorem.

Theorem 10–3. For all rational numbers a,

$$-(-a) = a.$$

By this theorem, $-[-(^-3)] = {}^-3$.

Now suppose that in the definition of addition $b = 0$ and a is negative; then

$$a + b = a + 0 = {}^-(|a| + |0|) \qquad \text{(negative since } a \text{ is negative)}$$
$$= {}^-|a|$$
$$= -|a| = -(-a) \qquad \text{(by definition of absolute value)}$$
$$= a \qquad \text{(by Theorem 10-3).}$$

Similarly it can be shown that $0 + a = a$, for a negative. Thus the property of zero holds for a negative so that, in general, the following theorem holds:

Theorem 10–4. The property of zero holds for the set of rational numbers; that is,

$$c + 0 = c = 0 + c, \qquad \text{for all rational numbers } c.$$

Moreover, if a is positive, then

$$|a + {}^-a| = \big||a| - |{}^-a|\big| \qquad \text{(by definition of addition)}$$
$$= |0| \qquad \text{(why?),}$$

so that $a + {}^-a = 0$. (How is the last equation obtained from the previous work?) Also, by the property C_a, we have ${}^-a + a = 0$. Now, if c is positive, let $c = a$; then $-c = {}^-a$, so that $c + (-c) = 0$. If c is negative, let $c = {}^-a$, so that $-c = a$, and hence $c + (-c) = 0$. Does this hold for $c = 0$? Why? The theorem of opposites has now been proved.

Theorem 10–5. *Theorem of opposites.* For each rational number c there is another rational number, $-c$, such that

$$c + (-c) = 0 = (-c) + c.$$

The concepts of "negative" and "opposite" are not the same, since $-(^-3) = 3$ but ${}^-(^-3)$ is meaningless. However, since ${}^-a = -a$ whenever a is positive, each negative number could be denoted by using the sign for "opposite." This we will now do to simplify notation; on occasion, the old notation will be used to emphasize the distinction. However, it must be remembered that we do not know anything about the sign of $-a$ until we know the sign of a; that is,

$-a$ is negative,   if a is positive;

$-a$ is positive,   if a is negative.

We are now ready to make precise statements about the use of the symbol "$-$." In the expression $a - (-b)$ the left-hand bar denotes the operation of subtraction, and the right-hand bar denotes "opposite." In some instances, such as $7 - (-3)$, the symbol for opposite does denote negativity.

PROBLEM SET 10–5

1. Find a simple method of evaluating the following. Explain your procedure.

   (a) $-\frac{2}{3} + (\frac{2}{3} + \frac{7}{5})$ (b) $(\frac{11}{4} + \frac{3}{5}) + (-\frac{11}{4})$

   (c) $-\frac{3}{4} + (\frac{4}{3} + \frac{3}{4})$ (d) $(-\frac{5}{2} + 7) + \frac{5}{2}$

2. Show that the following are true, or evaluate, as the notation requires, first by performing the operations indicated and then by using properties.

   (a) $11 + (-5 + 6) = -5 + (6 + 11)$

   (b) $(-4 + 8) + (-12 + 2) = [-12 + (-4)] + (2 + 8)$

   (c) $-[-(-a)] + [-(-a)]$

3. Perform the following additions, both by using the number line and by using the definition.

   (a) $-\frac{4}{5} + (-\frac{6}{7})$ (b) $\frac{8}{3} + (-3 + \frac{4}{3})$

   (c) $11 + (-7) + (-6)$ (d) $-\frac{3}{8} + \frac{5}{6} + (-\frac{1}{4})$

   (e) $-4\frac{1}{2} + (-5\frac{2}{3})$ (f) $-\frac{5}{2} + \frac{7}{3} - \frac{3}{4}$

4. In Section 4–5 it was proved that for all whole numbers, if $a = b$ then $a + c = b + c$. Refer to the proof of this statement, and show that it holds for all rational numbers.

5. Use the result of Problem 4 to solve the following equations.

   (a) $x + 2 = -7$ (b) $y + (-\frac{2}{3}) = \frac{5}{3}$

   (c) $w + (-4) = -11$ (d) $r + 5 = 3$

   (e) $w + (-5) = -\frac{4}{3}$ (f) $t + \frac{3}{4} = -\frac{7}{2}$

10–6   SUBTRACTION OF RATIONAL NUMBERS

We return for a moment to our "net worth" problem. Whatever your net worth is at the moment, losing $4 would have the same effect on net worth as acquiring a debt of $4. Likewise, for numbers it should be true that

$$3 - 4 = 3 + {}^-4 \quad \text{and} \quad {}^-3 - 4 = {}^-3 + {}^-4.$$

(Illustrate these examples on a number line.) Remember that net worth is made up of assets and debts. Suppose that you were to "lose" a debt of $4; that is, a debt of $4 is taken away from you. Wouldn't the loss of this debt have the same effect on net worth as the acquisition of an asset of $4? For example,

$$7 - {}^-4 = 7 + 4 = 7 + [-({}^-4)],$$
$$^-2 - {}^-4 = {}^-2 + 4 = {}^-2 + [-({}^-4)].$$

(Illustrate these examples on a number line.) Note that, in each of the four illustrations, the same result is obtained by subtracting a number as by adding its opposite.

This discussion should motivate the following definition.

Definition. *Subtraction of rational numbers.* For any rational numbers a and b,

$$a - b = a + (-b).$$

This definition states that

$$a \text{ minus } b \qquad \text{equals} \qquad a \text{ plus the opposite of } b.$$

The new operation, subtraction, has been expressed in terms of something we know how to handle. For example,

$$
\begin{aligned}
-\tfrac{3}{4} - (-\tfrac{5}{3}) &= -\tfrac{3}{4} + [-(-\tfrac{5}{3})] && \text{(by definition)} \\
&= -\tfrac{3}{4} + \tfrac{5}{3} && \text{(by Theorem 10–3)} \\
&= -\tfrac{9}{12} + \tfrac{20}{12} && \text{(why?)} \\
&= {}^+(\tfrac{20}{12} - \tfrac{9}{12}) = \tfrac{11}{12}.
\end{aligned}
$$

Perform the above subtraction, using a number line.

Now, it is also true that

$$
\begin{aligned}
(a - b) + b &= [a + (-b)] + b \\
&= a + [(-b) + b] && \text{(by } A_a) \\
&= a + 0 && \text{(by Theorem 10–5)} \\
&= a && \text{(by Theorem 10–4).}
\end{aligned}
$$

Thus the subtraction property used in earlier chapters holds for rational numbers. This property can be phrased in another form:

$$\text{if} \quad a - b = c, \quad \text{then} \quad a = c + b.$$

Show that the converse of this last statement is also true.

10–7 INEQUALITY. ORDER ON THE NUMBER LINE

Suppose that a and b are two numbers and that on the number line a is to the left of b. Then the following statements hold, at least intuitively.

If a and b are positive or zero, then $a < b$, and therefore $b - a$ is positive.

If a is negative and b is positive or zero, then $b - a = b + (-a)$ is positive, since $-a$ is positive and b is positive or zero.

If a and b are both negative, then $|a| > |b|$, and therefore $b - a = b + (-a) = (|a| - |b|)$ is positive.

We have an intuitive feeling that if a is to the left of b, then a should be less than b, and $b - a$ should be positive. Accordingly, let us define the concept of "less than."

Definition. *Inequality.* If a and b are rational numbers such that $b - a$ is positive, then a is *less than* b. This is denoted by the symbol $a < b$. Also, $b > a$ has the same meaning as $a < b$. Hence,

$$a < b, \quad \text{if} \quad b - a \text{ is positive.}$$

In this discussion, it has been assumed that you are familiar with the notation $a < b$ for numbers a and b which are positive or zero.

Several results follow from the above definition.

(1) If b is positive, then $b - 0 = b + (-0) = b + 0 = b$ is positive, hence $b > 0$. Thus any positive number is > 0.

(2) If a is negative, then $0 - a = 0 + (-a) = -a$ is positive; hence $0 > a$, or $a < 0$. Accordingly every negative number is < 0.

(3) If a is negative and b is positive, then $b - a = b + (-a)$ is positive. Why? Hence $b > a$, or $a < b$. Thus each negative number is less than any positive number.

(4) If a and b are both negative and if $|a| > |b|$, then $b - a = b + (-a) = |a| - |b|$ is positive. On the number line, a would be to the left of b.

Accordingly, this definition agrees with our intuitive ideas, so that the integers could be arranged as follows:

$$\cdots < -3 < -2 < -1 < 0 < 1 < 2 < 3 < \cdots$$

The rational numbers other than integers would fall into their proper places. For example,

$$-\tfrac{3}{2} < -1, \quad \text{since} \quad -1 - (-\tfrac{3}{2}) = -1 + \tfrac{3}{2} = \tfrac{3}{2} - 1 > 0,$$

and

$$\tfrac{5}{4} < 2, \quad \text{since} \quad 2 - \tfrac{5}{4} = \tfrac{8}{4} - \tfrac{5}{4} > 0.$$

Moreover, by using results which follow from this definition, we can write statements in a simpler form, i.e., we can write "$a > 0$," instead of "a is positive," and "$a < 0$," instead of "a is negative."

PROBLEM SET 10–7

1. Perform the following operations, first by using definitions and then by using the number line.
   (a) $-8 - (-4)$ (b) $-8 + 4$ (c) $\frac{5}{3} - (-\frac{4}{3})$
   (d) $-\frac{7}{9} - \frac{5}{9}$ (e) $-\frac{7}{9} - (-\frac{5}{9})$ (f) $\frac{7}{3} - \frac{11}{3}$

2. Answer the following, given that r is positive and s is negative:
   (a) What kind of number is $r - s$?
   (b) Can you tell what kind of number $r + s$ is? If not, what other information do you need?
   (c) Which inequality is true, $s > 0$ or $s < 0$?

3. In each of the following pairs find which member is the larger. Show your work.
   (a) $-\frac{3}{2}, -\frac{5}{2}$ (b) $-\frac{4}{3}, \frac{3}{5}$ (c) $-\frac{7}{9}, -\frac{7}{2}$ (d) $\frac{13}{4}, \frac{25}{8}$

4. (a) Find a number between $\frac{4}{7}$ and $\frac{5}{7}$.
   (b) Find a second number between $\frac{4}{7}$ and $\frac{5}{7}$.
   (c) How many numbers could you find between $\frac{4}{7}$ and $\frac{5}{7}$?

5. Find two numbers between $-\frac{8}{11}$ and $-\frac{7}{11}$.

6. Perform the indicated operations in two ways, by using the number line and by using definitions.
   (a) $\frac{8}{3} - \frac{21}{5}$ (b) $\frac{3}{2} - \frac{9}{4}$ (c) $-\frac{3}{5} - \frac{5}{2}$
   (d) $-\frac{7}{3} - \frac{9}{8}$ (e) $-\frac{3}{5} - (-\frac{5}{2})$ (f) $-\frac{7}{3} - (-\frac{9}{8})$
   (g) $-3\frac{1}{4} - (-5\frac{1}{2})$ (h) $+3\frac{1}{4} - 4\frac{1}{3}$ (i) $2\frac{3}{7} - (3\frac{1}{4})$
   (j) $4\frac{2}{7} - (-5\frac{1}{2})$ (k) $-\frac{17}{5} - \frac{11}{2}$ (l) $+\frac{2}{3} - \frac{13}{4}$

10–8 FURTHER PROPERTIES

The definitions introduced and the properties proved thus far are sufficient for the proof of many other properties; only a few of these will be considered.

It has been shown that for each number a, its opposite satisfies the equation $a + (-a) = 0$. Is there some other number b such that $a + b = 0$? Suppose that $a + b = 0$; then

$$-a + (a + b) = -a + 0,$$

$$(-a + a) + b = -a + 0 \qquad \text{(by } A_a),$$

$$0 + b = -a + 0 \qquad \text{(by property of opposites),}$$

$$b = -a \qquad \text{(by property of zero).}$$

The preceding work proves the following property.

Theorem 10–6. The opposite of a rational number a is the only number which, when added to a, yields zero.

This theorem could also be phrased as follows: "the opposite of a rational number is *unique*."

Application of this theorem yields further results. For instance,

$$[-a + (-b)] + (a + b) = (-a + a) + (-b + b) \qquad \text{(by } C_a \text{ and } A_a\text{)}$$
$$= 0 + 0$$
$$= 0.$$

Hence, by Theorem 10–6, the number $-a + (-b)$ must be the opposite of $a + b$, that is, $-a + (-b) = -(a + b)$. This proves another property.

Theorem 10–7. For any rational numbers a and b,

$$-(a + b) = -a + (-b).$$

Thus, we have

$$-(-3 + 7) = -(-3) + (-7) = 3 + (-7) = 3 - 7.$$

By this last theorem,

$$-(a - b) = -[a + (-b)]$$
$$= -a + [-(-b)]$$
$$= -a + b \qquad \text{(by Theorem 10–3)}$$
$$= b - a.$$

Hence, we have proved the following property.

Theorem 10–8. For any rational numbers a and b,

$$-(a - b) = b - a.$$

The proof of the next theorem will be left to the reader. Note that special cases of this theorem were proved in Chapter 4 and that these statements are the so-called "laws of parentheses" in algebra.

Theorem 10–9. For any rational numbers a, b, and c,

$$a + (b - c) = (a + b) - c,$$
$$a - (b + c) = (a - b) - c,$$
$$a - (b - c) = (a - b) + c.$$

These statements should be much easier to prove at this stage than they were in earlier chapters.

PROBLEM SET 10–8

1. Prove Theorem 10–9.
2. Find the truth set of $x + \frac{3}{4} = -\frac{2}{3}$ in the two ways indicated below. Justify each step and be certain that your logic is complete.

   (a) Subtract an appropriate number from each member of the sentence.
   (b) Add an appropriate number to each member of the sentence.

3. Find the truth sets of the following:

   (a) $y - 5 = -7$ (b) $z + \frac{4}{3} = \frac{2}{5}$
   (c) $u - 3 = \frac{2}{3}$ (d) $w + \frac{5}{7} = -\frac{3}{5}$

4. Without performing the indicated operations, show that the following equations are true. Give reasons for each step.

   (a) $-\frac{2}{3} - (\frac{3}{4} - \frac{7}{8}) = \frac{7}{8} + (-\frac{2}{3} - \frac{3}{4}) = \frac{7}{8} - (\frac{2}{3} + \frac{3}{4})$
   (b) $\frac{3}{4} + (-\frac{7}{2} - \frac{1}{5}) = (\frac{3}{4} - \frac{7}{2}) - \frac{1}{5}$
   (c) $\frac{5}{3} - (-\frac{5}{2} + \frac{2}{3}) = (\frac{5}{3} + \frac{5}{2}) - \frac{2}{3} = (-\frac{2}{3} + \frac{5}{3}) + \frac{5}{2}$
   (d) $-(-\frac{5}{3} - \frac{3}{4}) = \frac{3}{4} + \frac{5}{3}$

10–9 MULTIPLICATION OF RATIONAL NUMBERS

The "rules" for multiplication, when negative numbers are involved, seem mysterious to many people. In this section, we shall try to motivate an understanding of these. In previous work, properties such as

   (1) the associative, commutative, and distributive properties,
   (2) $a \cdot 0 = 0 = 0 \cdot a$

proved to be quite useful. We would hope that, however multiplication is defined for the larger set now under consideration, these same properties would hold. Let us suppose that there is a multiplication for which they do hold. Then, for example,

$$
\begin{aligned}
(-2)5 &= (-2)5 + 0 & &\text{(by } P_{0,a}) \\
&= (-2)5 + (2 \cdot 5 + [-(2 \cdot 5)]) & &\text{(by property of opposites)} \\
&= [(-2)5 + 2 \cdot 5] + [-(2 \cdot 5)] & &\text{(by } A_a) \\
&= (-2 + 2)5 + [-(2 \cdot 5)] & &\text{(by } D_+) \\
&= 0 \cdot 5 + [-(2 \cdot 5)] & &\text{(by property of opposites)} \\
&= 0 + [-(2 \cdot 5)] & &\text{(by property (2) above)} \\
&= -(2 \cdot 5) & &\text{(by } P_{0,a}).
\end{aligned}
$$

That is, $(-2)5$ must be equal to $-(2 \cdot 5)$. Also,

$$
\begin{aligned}
(-2)(-5) &= (-2)(-5) + 0 \\
&= (-2)(-5) + [-(2 \cdot 5) + 2 \cdot 5] \\
&= (-2)(-5) + [(-2)5 + 2 \cdot 5] \qquad \text{(by preceding result)}, \\
&= [(-2)(-5) + (-2)5] + 2 \cdot 5 \\
&= (-2)[-5 + 5] + 2 \cdot 5 \\
&= (-2)0 + 2 \cdot 5 \\
&= 0 + 2 \cdot 5 \\
&= 2 \cdot 5.
\end{aligned}
$$

Hence $(-2)(-5)$ must be equal to $2 \cdot 5$. From this discussion, if a and b are positive numbers, then it is desirable that

$$
\begin{aligned}
(-a)b & \qquad \text{should be} \qquad -(ab), \\
(-a)(-b) & \qquad \text{should be} \qquad ab.
\end{aligned}
$$

Accordingly, let us define multiplication for rational numbers.

Definition. *Multiplication of rational numbers.* Let a and b be rational numbers. Then

$$
\begin{aligned}
a \cdot b &= |a| \cdot |b|, & \text{if } a \text{ and } b \text{ have the same sign}; \\
a \cdot b &= -(|a| \cdot |b|), & \text{if } a \text{ and } b \text{ have different signs}; \\
a \cdot b &= 0, & \text{if either of } a \text{ and } b \text{ is zero}.
\end{aligned}
$$

If you feel that we have deliberately defined multiplication in such a way as to "get what we want," e.g., $(-2)(-3) = 6$, you are correct. However, it has been shown that this particular definition is necessary if the desired properties are to hold, and this is deemed advisable. The important idea now is to see what properties do hold as a result of this definition. To this end, let us state and prove, in part, a theorem.

Theorem 10–10. For all rational numbers a, b, and c, each of the following equations is true:

(1) $a \cdot 0 = 0 = 0 \cdot a$ $(P_{0,m})$,
(2) $ab = ba$ (C_m),
(3) $a(bc) = (ab)c$ (A_m),
(4) $a(b + c) = ab + ac$ (D_+).

That (1) is true follows directly from the definition of multiplication.

The proof of (2) also follows from the definition of multiplication, which shows that the result of multiplying depends only on the nature of the numbers, and not on their order. For example, if $a < 0$ and $b > 0$, then $ab = -(|a| \cdot |b|)$ and $ba = -(|b| \cdot |a|) = -(|a| \cdot |b|)$, since the product inside the parentheses involves positive numbers only.

Several cases must be considered in the proof of (3). For example, if $a > 0$, $b > 0$, and $c < 0$, then applying the middle part of the definition to bc, we have

$$a(bc) = a[-(|b| \cdot |c|)].$$

From this equation, we obtain

$$a(bc) = -[|a|(|b| \cdot |c|)],$$

again by applying the middle part of the definition, since we are dealing with the product of a positive number by a negative number. Finally,

$$a(bc) = -[a(b \cdot |c|)],$$

since a and b are positive. Also, it is true that

$$(ab)c = -[|ab| \cdot |c|] \qquad \text{(product of a positive by a negative)}$$
$$= -[(ab) \cdot |c|].$$

Now, $a(b \cdot |c|) = (ab)|c|$, since the associative property of multiplication holds for positive numbers. Hence, in this case, $a(bc) = (ab)c$. Proofs of other cases are called for in the next problem set.

In the proof of (4) several cases must again be considered. If any one of a, b, or c is zero, we can obtain the desired result immediately by using (1). If $a > 0$, $b > 0$, and $c < 0$, where $|c| > |b|$, then

$$a(b + c) = a[-(|c| - |b|] \qquad \text{(by definition of addition)}$$
$$= -[a(|c| - |b|)],$$

by the middle part of the definition of multiplication. This yields

$$a(b + c) = -[a|c| - a|b|],$$

since $r(s - t) = rs - rt$ for positive numbers, where $s > t$. Applying Theorem 10–8 to this last equation, we have

$$a(b + c) = a|b| - a|c| = ab - a|c|.$$

Also,

$$ab + ac = ab + [-|a| \cdot |c|] = ab + [(-a) \cdot |c|]$$
$$= ab - a|c| \qquad \text{(by definition of subtraction)}.$$

Hence in this case $a(b + c) = ab + ac$. Proofs of other cases are similar to this proof; some of them are called for in the next problem set.

The definition of multiplication yields the following specific statements:

The product of two positive numbers is positive.
The product of two negative numbers is positive.
The product of a positive number by a negative number is negative.

Does it follow from the above statements that $(-a)b = -ab$? It does if $a > 0$ and $b > 0$, but it does not in other cases. However, it may be readily proved that in all cases $(-a)b = -ab$.

Theorem 10–11. For any rational numbers a and b,

(1) $(-a)b = -ab$,   (2) $(-a)(-b) = ab$.

This theorem states directly, for example, that

$$[-(-3)](-7) = -[(-3)(-7)],$$

by using $a = -3$ and $b = -7$. This equality can be proved by using the definition of multiplication as follows:

$$[-(-3)](-7) = 3(-7) = -(3 \cdot 7),$$

and

$$-[(-3)(-7)] = -(3 \cdot 7).$$

Theorem 10–11 states how opposites interact in a multiplication, while the definition states how positive and negative numbers interact in a multiplication.

Consider the following proof of the first part of Theorem 10–11:

$$\begin{aligned}
(-a)b &= (-a)b + 0 = (-a)b + [ab + (-ab)] \\
&= [(-a)b + ab] + (-ab) \\
&= (-a + a)b + (-ab) \\
&= 0 \cdot b + (-ab) \\
&= 0 + (-ab) \\
&= -ab.
\end{aligned}$$

Justify each step of the above. Then prove the second part of the theorem.

The following theorem is an extension of properties proved earlier for positive numbers.

Theorem 10–12. For any rational numbers a, b, and c,

(1) $a(b - c) = ab - ac$,   (2) $1 \cdot a = a$ (property of one).

The proof of part (1) is called for in Problem 5 below.

In the proof of (2), if $a \geq 0$, the result follows from a previous chapter. If $a < 0$, then

$$1 \cdot a = -(1 \cdot |a|) = -(|a|) = a.$$

Justify each step.

PROBLEM SET 10–9

1. Perform the following operations.

   (a) $(-3)(-9)$ (b) $(-\frac{2}{3})\frac{7}{9}$ (c) $\frac{3}{4}(-\frac{8}{3})$ (d) $(-\frac{4}{5})(-\frac{15}{2})$

   (e) $\frac{2}{3}(-\frac{2}{3})$ (f) $(-\frac{3}{4})\frac{4}{3}$ (g) $(-\frac{7}{6})(-\frac{6}{7})$ (h) $(-\frac{5}{4})(-\frac{7}{15})$

   (i) $(-4\frac{1}{2})(-7\frac{2}{3})$ (j) $(1\frac{2}{3})(-3\frac{1}{7})$

2. Perform the indicated operations, assuming that the letters represent integers.

   (a) $\left(-\dfrac{x}{2y}\right)\left(\dfrac{y}{2x}\right)$ (b) $\left(\dfrac{3x}{y}\right)\left(-\dfrac{y}{2}\right)$

   (c) $\left(-\dfrac{x^2}{y^2}\right)\left(-\dfrac{y}{2x}\right)$ (d) $\dfrac{x^3}{y^2}\left(-\dfrac{3xy}{4}\right)$

3. If w, x, y, and z represent rational numbers, show that

   (a) $(-x)(-y - z) = xy + xz;$

   (b) $-x(y + z) + xw = x(w - y) - xz.$

4. Show in two ways that $(-1)a = -a.$

5. Prove part (1) of Theorem 10–12.

6. Show that each of the following holds. Justify each step.

   (a) $(-2)3 + (-3)(-4) = 3(-2 + 4)$

   (b) $2 \cdot 5 - (-5)7 = 5(2 + 7)$

   (c) $-[(-2) \cdot 4] = 4 \cdot 2$

   (d) $-[b(-a)] = ab$

7. List all the cases which should be considered in a proof of the associative property of multiplication.

8. Prove the associative property of multiplication for the following cases.

   (1) $a > 0, \quad b < 0, \quad c < 0$

   (2) $a < 0, \quad b < 0, \quad c < 0$

9. Prove the distributive property for the following cases.

   (1) $a > 0, \quad b > 0, \quad c < 0,$ where $|c| < |b|$

   (2) $a < 0, \quad b < 0, \quad c < 0,$ where $|b| < |c|$

10. Without using Theorem 10–11 or the definition of multiplication, show that the equality $(-4)(-5) = 4 \cdot 5$ should be true.

11. Prove part (2) of Theorem 10–11, if you have not done so heretofore.

12. Prove that if a, b, and m are rational numbers, then $a = b$ implies $ma = mb$.

10–10 RECIPROCAL AND DIVISION

Such a result as $(-\frac{2}{3})(-\frac{3}{2}) = \frac{2}{3} \cdot \frac{3}{2} = 1$ is a consequence of the definition of multiplication and previous results for positive rationals. Just as in the case of positive rationals, $-\frac{3}{2}$ is called the reciprocal of $-\frac{2}{3}$.

Definition. *Reciprocal.* If $a \neq 0$ is a rational number, then the reciprocal of a is a number b such that

$$a \cdot b = 1.$$

We denote the reciprocal of a by $1/a$. (Note that, conversely, a would be the reciprocal of $1/a$.)

If c has a reciprocal, then $-c$ also has a reciprocal, since

$$(-c)\left(-\frac{1}{c}\right) = c \cdot \frac{1}{c} = 1.$$

Thus each negative rational number has a reciprocal, since we have already learned that each positive rational has a reciprocal. Is there any number b such that $0 \cdot b = 1$? Suppose that there is such a number; then since $0 \cdot b = 0$, it follows that $0 = 1$. You probably feel that this is a contradiction, but do you really know that it is? If you think of 0 and 1 as whole numbers, then a consequence of $0 = 1$ would be that the empty set, Φ, would have to match the set $\{\Box\}$. Since this is a contradiction, then $0 \neq 1$; hence 0 does not have a reciprocal.

You probably cannot name any reciprocal of $-\frac{1}{2}$ other than -2. But can we prove that -2 is the only reciprocal of $-\frac{1}{2}$?

Theorem 10–13. The reciprocal of a rational number is unique.

Let b and c both be reciprocals of a. Then

$$ab = 1 \qquad \text{and} \qquad ac = 1,$$

so that

$$ab = ac.$$

Hence

$$b \cdot ab = b \cdot ac,$$

$$(ba)b = (ba)c,$$

$$1 \cdot b = 1 \cdot c,$$

$$b = c.$$

Accordingly, a number has only one reciprocal. Since a is the reciprocal of $1/a$, then we could say that a and $1/a$ are the reciprocals of each other. Previous examples indicate the truth of the following theorem.

Theorem 10–14. The reciprocal of a positive rational number is positive; the reciprocal of a negative rational number is negative.

Suppose that b is a negative number; if $1/b$ were positive, then $b(1/b)$ would be negative, i.e., the number 1 would be negative. Another contradiction! Hence $1/b$ must be negative (why not zero?).

We now know that each nonzero rational number has a unique reciprocal. Moreover, reciprocals are related to each other as shown by the arrows in the following diagram (see Problem 12 of the next problem set for the general result).

Construct once again a diagram indicating how a number is related to its opposite, and note the difference between this diagram and that above.

Remembering that subtraction is defined as $a - b = a + (-b)$, let us now define division.

Definition. *Division for Rational Numbers.* If a and b are rational numbers, $b \neq 0$, then a divided by b is $a(1/b)$, or, using the usual symbol for division, we write

$$a \div b = a \cdot \frac{1}{b}.$$

For example,

$$-2 \div 3 = -2 \cdot \tfrac{1}{3} = -(2 \cdot \tfrac{1}{3}),$$
$$-\tfrac{3}{4} \div (-\tfrac{4}{7}) = (-\tfrac{3}{4})(-\tfrac{7}{4}) = \tfrac{3}{4} \cdot \tfrac{7}{4}.$$

By this definition, division is related to multiplication in much the same way that subtraction is related to addition:

$a - b$	equals	a plus the opposite of b;
$a \div b$	equals	a times the reciprocal of b.

When we considered positive rationals, we related the idea of the division $a \div b$ to a number which satisfies $bx = a$. Does a similar result hold for all rationals?

Theorem 10–15. If $b \neq 0$, then $a(1/b)$ is the unique truth number of the equation $bx = a$, for a and b rational numbers.

As the first step in the proof of this theorem,

$$b\left(a \cdot \frac{1}{b}\right) = a\left(b \cdot \frac{1}{b}\right) = a \cdot 1 = a.$$

Thus $a(1/b)$ is a truth number. Moreover, if x is a truth number of $bx = a$, then

$$\frac{1}{b}(bx) = \frac{1}{b} \cdot a,$$

$$\left(\frac{1}{b} \cdot b\right)x = a \cdot \frac{1}{b},$$

$$1 \cdot x = a \cdot \frac{1}{b},$$

$$x = a \cdot \frac{1}{b}.$$

Hence the truth number must be $a(1/b)$; it is unique.

As previously, another notation can be used for the result of division:

$$a \div b = a \cdot \frac{1}{b} \quad \text{or} \quad a \div b = \frac{a}{b}.$$

Accordingly, $\frac{-2}{3}$ is the unique truth value of $3x = -2$. Also $-\frac{2}{3}$ is the unique truth value of $3x = -2$, since

$$3(-\tfrac{2}{3}) = -(3 \cdot \tfrac{2}{3}) = -2.$$

Hence, $\frac{-2}{3}$ must be the same number as $-\frac{2}{3}$. In general, $\frac{-a}{b}$ is the unique truth number of $bx = -a$; however,

$$b\left(-\frac{a}{b}\right) = -\left[b \cdot \frac{a}{b}\right] \quad \text{(by Theorem 10–11)}$$

$$= -a,$$

so that $-\frac{a}{b}$ is a truth number of $bx = -a$. Hence

$$\frac{-a}{b} = -\frac{a}{b}.$$

Now consider $\frac{a}{-b}$. Certainly this is the same as $a \cdot \frac{1}{-b}$. Now $\frac{1}{-b}$ is the reciprocal of $-b$. But since

$$-b\left(-\frac{1}{b}\right) = b \cdot \frac{1}{b} = 1,$$

then $-\frac{1}{b}$ is also the reciprocal of $-b$. Accordingly, $\frac{1}{-b} = -\frac{1}{b}$, so that

$$\frac{a}{-b} = a \cdot \frac{1}{-b} = a\left(-\frac{1}{b}\right) = -\left(a \cdot \frac{1}{b}\right) = -\frac{a}{b}.$$

These results are summarized in the following theorem.

Theorem 10–16. For any rational numbers a and b, $b \neq 0$,

$$\frac{-a}{b} = \frac{a}{-b} = -\frac{a}{b} .$$

Probably the simplest way to use the above results in practice is illustrated below; this involves the property $(-1)c = -c$, which is true, since

$$(-1)c = -(1 \cdot c) \qquad \text{(by Theorem 10–11)}$$
$$= -c.$$

The following examples illustrate the preceding statement:

$$-\frac{2}{3} = (-1)\frac{2}{3} = \frac{-1}{1} \cdot \frac{2}{3} = \frac{(-1)2}{1 \cdot 3} = \frac{-2}{3} ,$$

and

$$\frac{-2}{3} = 1 \cdot \frac{-2}{3} = \frac{-1}{-1} \cdot \frac{-2}{3} = \frac{(-1)(-2)}{(-1)3} = \frac{2}{-3} .$$

10–11 SUMMARY

In this chapter negative numbers have been introduced so as to complete the set of rational numbers. With the introduction of these numbers subtraction of any two rational numbers is possible. The many properties obtained serve to give these rational numbers meaning. These properties were seen to be a natural outgrowth of the various definitions. In turn, reasons for making the specific definitions were given.

PROBLEM SET 10–11

1. Find the reciprocals of the following numbers. In each case show why it is the reciprocal.

   (a) -4 (b) $-\frac{7}{2}$ (c) $\frac{2}{3}$ (d) -5

2. (a) The number -3 is the reciprocal of what number?

   (b) Write an equation whose truth number is the reciprocal of -3. Be certain that your equation indicates this reciprocal relationship.

3. Repeat Problem 2 for the number $-\frac{1}{4}$.

4. Use the definition to find the following. Write your answers in simplified form.

   (a) $-4 \div 3$ (b) $-4 \div (-6)$ (c) $-\frac{2}{3} \div \frac{1}{4}$ (d) $-\frac{2}{7} \div (-\frac{6}{5})$

5. (a) Given that $m \neq 0$ is a rational number, prove that the equations

$$bx = a \qquad \text{and} \qquad mbx = ma$$

have the same truth set.

(b) Use part (a) to prove that $ma/mb = a/b$.

6. Give formal reasons for each step in the following procedure:

$$-\tfrac{3}{4} \div (-\tfrac{9}{8}) = \frac{-\tfrac{3}{4}}{-\tfrac{9}{8}} = \frac{\tfrac{3}{4}}{\tfrac{9}{8}}$$

$$= \frac{\tfrac{3}{4} \cdot \tfrac{8}{9}}{\tfrac{9}{8} \cdot \tfrac{8}{9}} \qquad (\text{why use } \tfrac{8}{9}?)$$

$$= \tfrac{3}{4} \cdot \tfrac{8}{9}$$

$$= \tfrac{2}{3}.$$

7. Using a procedure similar to that of Problem 6, find the following.

(a) $-\tfrac{12}{7} \div \tfrac{5}{8}$

(b) $-\tfrac{11}{3} \div (-\tfrac{8}{9})$

(c) $\tfrac{3}{8} \div (-\tfrac{5}{4})$

(d) $\tfrac{7}{12} \div (-\tfrac{14}{3})$

(e) $-\tfrac{17}{11} \div \tfrac{4}{11}$

(f) $-\tfrac{5}{7} \div (-\tfrac{5}{14})$

(g) $\left(-\dfrac{r}{s}\right) \div \dfrac{2s}{r}$

(h) $-\dfrac{r^2}{s^2} \div \left(-\dfrac{2r}{s}\right)$

(i) $\left(-\dfrac{x^2}{y}\right) \div \dfrac{2xy}{3}$

(j) $\dfrac{x}{2y^2} \div \left(-\dfrac{x^2}{2y}\right)$

(k) $-\dfrac{uv^2}{w} \div \dfrac{u}{w}$

(l) $-\dfrac{u}{v} \div \left(-\dfrac{u^2}{2v^2}\right)$

8. Show that $-r/-s = r/s$, where r and s are integers, $s \neq 0$.

9. Prove that $-\dfrac{4}{5}$ and $\dfrac{-4}{5}$ are the same number, without using Theorem 10–16.

10. Prove that $\dfrac{7}{-8}$ and $-\dfrac{7}{8}$ are the same number, without using Theorem 10–16.

11. Show that the following equations are true.

(a) $-\dfrac{1}{x - y} = \dfrac{1}{y - x}$

(b) $\dfrac{-1}{2x - y} = \dfrac{1}{y - 2x}$

(c) $1 - \dfrac{1}{r - 2s} = \dfrac{1}{2s - r} + 1$

(d) $\dfrac{r - 2s}{r - s} = \dfrac{2s - r}{s - r}$

12. Prove the following statements.

(a)   If $c > 0$ and $c > 1$, then $(1/c) < 1$.

(b)   If $c > 0$ and $c < 1$, then $(1/c) > 1$.

(c)   If $c < 0$ and $c < -1$, then $(1/c) > -1$.

(d)   If $c < 0$ and $c > -1$, then $(1/c) < -1$.

CHAPTER 11

Real Numbers

11–1 MEANING OF REAL NUMBERS

In Section 10–1 it was indicated how we might think about a number symbolized by $\sqrt{2}$. It was shown that there is no rational number whose square is 2; thus $\sqrt{2}$ is a number of a "new" type. To merely consider $\sqrt{2}$ as a number whose square is 2 is not very productive of further results. Let us try to improve the situation somewhat, though we will be forced by the difficulties involved to leave things far short of completion.

Let us consider that $\sqrt{2}$ is a number and that our task is to find approximations to it; that is, we will find numbers whose squares are "close" to 2. Since

$$1^2 = 1, \quad (\sqrt{2})^2 = 2, \quad 2^2 = 4,$$

and since $1 < 2 < 4$, it should follow that $\sqrt{2}$ lies between 1 and 2, that is, $1 < \sqrt{2} < 2$. This limits $\sqrt{2}$ to an interval of length 1. Also, the equalities

$$1.4^2 = 1.96, \quad (\sqrt{2})^2 = 2, \quad 1.5^2 = 2.25$$

should show that $\sqrt{2}$ lies between 1.4 and 1.5. The numbers 1.4 and 1.5 are picked from the set $\{1.0, 1.1, 1.2, \ldots, 1.8, 1.9, 2.0\}$ by squaring each member of the set and choosing the consecutive pair between whose squares the number 2 lies. After some experience such numbers can be selected without squaring each number. The result $1.4 < \sqrt{2} < 1.5$ is better than the inequality $1 < \sqrt{2} < 2$ since the interval within which $\sqrt{2}$ should lie is smaller, being of length 0.1. Continuation of this procedure yields, for example,

$$1.41^2 = 1.9881, \quad (\sqrt{2})^2 = 2, \quad 1.42^2 = 2.0164;$$

$$1.414^2 = 1.999396, \quad (\sqrt{2})^2 = 2, \quad 1.415^2 = 2.002225.$$

Consequently, $\sqrt{2}$ should lie between 1.41 and 1.42, or, more precisely, between 1.414 and 1.415. The pairs of numbers obtained by this procedure, along with their differences, are shown below.

Differences

1	< 2	1 = 2 − 1
1.4	< 1.5	0.1 = 1.5 − 1.4
1.41	< 1.42	0.01
1.414	< 1.415	0.001
⋮	⋮	⋮

Since these numbers are rational, none of them when squared would yield 2. Accordingly, the procedure can be continued indefinitely. No matter how many times the procedure is applied, it can be applied again; there is no last step. The differences shown above are decreasing steadily toward zero. Moreover, the numbers on the left side of the inequalities are increasing steadily from step to step, while those on the right are decreasing steadily. We probably feel intuitively that there is a number determined by this set of inequalities. Whenever we have such a set of inequalities involving rational numbers whose differences decrease steadily toward zero, and where the left members of the inequalities increase while the right members decrease, we shall say that a *real number* is thereby determined and that this real number has a decimal expansion.

In the example above, the decimal expansion, which is determined by the left members of the inequalities, is infinite, i.e., it does not terminate. Our intuitive feeling is that there is a number which lies between the pair of rational numbers in each and every inequality. Let us denote this number by α. Since these rational numbers are getting closer together (why?), we have a feeling that as we proceed from one inequality to the next we are obtaining a closer approximation to α. Moreover, if the fifth line of the set of inequalities were found, the numbers on that line would be between 1.414 and 1.415. Hence numbers in the left-hand column following 1.414 must have 1.414 as the first four digits. Each number on the left is a decimal and each step produces another digit in the decimal; it is nonterminating because the set of inequalities itself is nonterminating. It will be said that this infinite set of inequalities determines a number whose decimal expansion is 1.414 . . . , where the dots denote that the expansion continues indefinitely. It is in this sense that $\sqrt{2}$ is a number with the decimal expansion 1.414 . . . .

Let us assume that each infinite set of inequalities of the following type determines a number:

$$r_1 < t_1,$$
$$r_2 < t_2,$$
$$r_3 < t_3,$$
$$\vdots$$

where

(a) all r's and t's are finite decimals (and hence rational numbers),
(b) the differences $t_1 - r_1$, $t_2 - r_2$, $t_3 - r_3$, etc. decrease steadily toward zero,
(c) $r_1 \leq r_2 \leq r_3 \leq \cdots$ and $t_1 \geq t_2 \geq t_3 \geq \cdots$

Then a real number can be defined as follows:

Definition. *Real Number.* A number which is determined by a set of inequalities such as that described above is called a *real number.*

If the r's and t's are positive rationals, the number determined will be called a *positive real number.* In this case, the r's will determine a decimal, such as in the preceding example; this decimal expansion and the real number can be considered as one and the same.

Consider the number $\frac{1}{3}$. Applying to this number the procedure of decimal expansion discussed in Chapter 7, we obtain 0.333 .... Now let us use this decimal expansion to set up an infinite set of inequalities:

		Differences
0.3	< 0.4	0.1
0.33	< 0.34	0.01
0.333	< 0.334	0.001
⋮	⋮	⋮

By the above assumption and definition, this set determines a real number whose decimal expansion is 0.333 .... Show that $\frac{1}{3}$ lies between 0.3 and 0.4, between 0.33 and 0.34, between 0.333333 and 0.333334. It can be shown that $\frac{1}{3}$ lies between the numbers which appear in each inequality. This gives some meaning to the idea that the infinite decimal 0.333 ... is $\frac{1}{3}$.

The rational numbers in these inequalities can be thought of as approximations of the real number. For example, both 0.3 and 0.4 are approximations of 0.333 .... Similarly, 0.33 and 0.34 are approximations of 0.333 .... The latter are better approximations than 0.3 and 0.4; note also that $0.3 < 0.33 < 0.333 < \cdots < 0.34 < 0.4$. The numbers on each line of the set of inequalities are better approximations than those on the preceding line.

Consider $\frac{1}{4} = 0.25$ in a similar fashion. We could write the following set of inequalities:

		Differences
0.2	< 0.3	0.1
0.25	< 0.26	0.01
0.250	< 0.251	0.001
0.2500	< 0.2501	0.0001
⋮	⋮	⋮

The real number determined by this set of inequalities would be 0.250000 . . . . Also,

$$0.2 < \tfrac{1}{4} < 0.3,$$
$$0.25 \leq \tfrac{1}{4} < 0.26,$$
$$0.250 \leq \tfrac{1}{4} < 0.251, \quad \text{etc.}$$

(Note the necessity of using $\leq$ in some of these inequalities). Hence the number determined here should be $\tfrac{1}{4}$ and its decimal expansion can be written either 0.25 or 0.25000 . . . , as desired. Consequently the decimal expansion of $\tfrac{1}{4}$ can be considered as either terminating or nonterminating. In the manner of this and the preceding paragraph it can be shown that each rational number is also a real number.

Start with any infinite decimal, say 0.121121112 . . . , where each 2 is preceded by a group of 1's, the number of 1's in each group being one more than in the preceding group. Wouldn't this decimal expansion be the number determined by the following set of inequalities?

$$0.1 \quad < 0.2$$
$$0.12 \quad < 0.13$$
$$0.121 \; < 0.122$$
$$0.1211 < 0.1212$$
$$\vdots \qquad \vdots$$

In this manner, it can be shown that each decimal expansion is a real number. Since each real number is also a decimal expansion, the real numbers are the decimal expansions.

To each positive real number there corresponds another real number, called a *negative real number*. For example, if $\alpha = $ 0.121121112 . . . , then, from the set of inequalities for α we could write the following set of inequalities (see Problem 3 of the next problem set):

$$-0.2 \quad < -0.1$$
$$-0.13 \quad < -0.12$$
$$-0.122 \quad < -0.121$$
$$-0.1212 < -0.1211$$
$$\vdots \qquad \vdots$$

This set is of the prescribed type for a real number. The real number determined will be denoted by $-\alpha$. The decimal expansion for $-\alpha$ will be determined by the right-hand numbers of the above inequalities.

PROBLEM SET 11–1

1. Use the method of the text to set up inequalities which will determine each of the following numbers and then write the decimal expansion.

   (a) $\sqrt{5}$, to three decimal places   (b) $\sqrt{23}$, to two decimal places
   (c) $\sqrt{71}$, to two decimal places   (d) $\sqrt[3]{12}$, to two decimal places

2. Write a set of inequalities containing the indicated number of lines which would determine each of the following numbers.

   (a) 3.43 (five lines)   (b) 0.674 (five lines)
   (c) $\frac{4}{3}$ (four lines)   (d) $\frac{5}{6}$ (three lines)
   (e) $-\sqrt{5}$ (four lines)   (f) $-\sqrt{23}$ (three lines)
   (g) $-\sqrt{71}$ (three lines)   (h) $-\sqrt[3]{12}$ (three lines)

3. Let x and y be positive rational numbers such that $x < y$. Prove that $-y < -x$.

11–2 ADDITION OF REAL NUMBERS. ZERO

Let us write, side by side, the sets of inequalities for $\frac{1}{3}$ and $\frac{1}{4}$:

$$\frac{1}{3} \qquad\qquad\qquad \frac{1}{4}$$

$$0.3 \quad < 0.4 \qquad\qquad 0.2 \quad < 0.3$$
$$0.33 \ < 0.34 \qquad\qquad 0.25 \ < 0.26$$
$$0.333 < 0.334 \qquad\qquad 0.250 < 0.251$$
$$\vdots \qquad \vdots \qquad\qquad\quad \vdots \qquad \vdots$$

Now we add corresponding left members of the two sets of inequalities and corresponding right members, to obtain

$$0.3 \ \ + 0.2 \ \ = \ \ 0.5 \ \ < 0.7 \ \ \ = 0.4 \ \ + 0.3$$
$$0.33 \ + 0.25 \ = \ \ 0.58 \ < 0.60 \ \ \ = 0.34 \ + 0.26$$
$$0.333 + 0.250 = \ \ 0.583 < 0.585 \ \ = 0.334 + 0.251$$
$$\vdots \qquad\qquad \vdots \qquad \vdots \qquad\qquad \vdots$$

Do the differences decrease steadily toward zero? Is this set of inequalities of the type that can be used to determine a real number? Now $\frac{1}{3} + \frac{1}{4} = \frac{7}{12}$; show that $\frac{7}{12}$ lies between the numbers in each inequality. This example should indicate how the addition of two real numbers could be defined. Note that the left-hand numbers again produce a decimal expansion; in the above case, 5 and 8 are the first two decimal digits, but we cannot be certain of the third decimal digit until the next inequality is obtained. Why?

Try this procedure for $\frac{1}{3} + (-\frac{1}{3})$. You should obtain

$$-0.1 \quad < 0.1$$
$$-0.01 \quad < 0.01$$
$$-0.001 < 0.001$$
$$\vdots \qquad \vdots$$

What number seems to be determined by this set of inequalities? Wouldn't it be zero? Hence, zero should be a real number whose decimal expansion is 0.000 .... As before, $\frac{1}{3} + (-\frac{1}{3}) = 0$.

Since subtraction can be considered as a special case of addition, i.e., since $a - b = a + (-b)$, nothing more need be said about it.

PROBLEM SET 11–2

1. For each of the following find a set of inequalities which consists of four lines.

   (a) $1.23 + 0.25$ (b) $2 + \sqrt{5}$ (c) $\sqrt{5} + \sqrt{2}$

   (d) $\frac{1}{3} + 1.12$ (e) $-1.23 + \sqrt{5}$ (f) $-1.12 - \sqrt{5}$

   (g) $0.45 - 0.012$ (h) $\frac{3}{7} + \frac{2}{3}$

2. Write the first part of a decimal expansion for the number determined by each part of Problem 1, and give information concerning the next digit.

11–3 MULTIPLICATION AND DIVISION OF REAL NUMBERS

The multiplication $10 \times \frac{1}{3}$ could be based on the following inequality sets for 10 and $\frac{1}{3}$:

	10		$\frac{1}{3}$
10	< 11	0.3	< 0.4
10.0	< 10.1	0.33	< 0.34
10.00	< 10.01	0.333	< 0.334
$\vdots$	$\vdots$	$\vdots$	$\vdots$

Now we multiply corresponding left-hand numbers and corresponding right-hand numbers to produce

$$10 \quad \times 0.3 \quad = \quad 3 \qquad < 4.4 \qquad = 11 \quad \times 0.4$$
$$10.0 \quad \times 0.33 \quad = \quad 3.300 \qquad < 3.434 \qquad = 10.1 \quad \times 0.34$$
$$10.00 \times 0.333 = \quad 3.33000 < 3.34334 \qquad = 10.01 \times 0.334$$
$$\vdots \qquad\qquad \vdots \qquad\qquad \vdots \qquad\qquad\qquad \vdots$$

Does this set of inequalities determine a real number? Would its decimal expansion be 3.3 . . . ? The next inequality will show that the third digit is actually a three; show this. This should indicate how multiplication of real numbers can be defined. It should also indicate that, as for finite decimals, the expansion for 10×0.333 . . . can be obtained from 0.333 . . . by shifting the decimal point one place to the right. This can actually be proved.

Using the inequalities definition of $\frac{1}{3}$, how could we find $1/\frac{1}{3}$, the reciprocal of $\frac{1}{3}$? First, for example, since $5 < 6$, then $\frac{1}{5} - \frac{1}{6} = (6 - 5)/30$ is positive, that is, $\frac{1}{5} > \frac{1}{6}$. In general, if x and y are positive rational numbers and $x < y$, then the number

$$\frac{1}{x} - \frac{1}{y} = \frac{y - x}{xy}$$

is positive, that is,

$$0 < x < y \qquad \text{implies} \qquad \frac{1}{x} > \frac{1}{y}.$$

Thus, from the set of inequalities for $\frac{1}{3}$ the following inequalities could be obtained:

$$\left. \begin{array}{c} \dfrac{1}{0.4} < \dfrac{1}{0.3} \\[2mm] \dfrac{1}{0.34} < \dfrac{1}{0.33} \\[2mm] \dfrac{1}{0.334} < \dfrac{1}{0.333} \\[2mm] \vdots \qquad \vdots \end{array} \right\} \quad \text{or} \quad \left\{ \begin{array}{l} 2.5 \quad < 3.34 \\[2mm] 2.94 \;< 3.04 \\[2mm] 2.994 < 3.004 \\[2mm] \vdots \qquad \vdots \end{array} \right.$$

The right-hand numbers in the second set of inequalities were obtained by finding the first few decimal places for the fractions on the right in the left-hand display and then doing a bit of "juggling"; for example,

$$\frac{1}{0.3} = \frac{10}{3} = 3 + \frac{1}{3} = 3.33 + \frac{1}{300}$$

$$= 3.33 + (\text{a number} < 0.01)$$

$$< 3.33 + 0.01 = 3.34.$$

Looking at the inequalities in the right-hand block above we see that the differences are decreasing toward zero. Hence this new set of inequalities is of the proper type to determine a real number. Intuitively, we feel that this set determines the number 3, which is the reciprocal of $\frac{1}{3}$. This procedure could be used to define the reciprocal of a real number, whether it be, for example, $1/\sqrt{2}$ or $1/0.27$.

Once again look at the preceding set of inequalities determining the number 3. The left-hand numbers seem to be generating the decimal 2.999 . . . , while those on the right seem to be generating 3.000 . . . . Both of these are considered as decimal expansions for 3; in this case, the decimal expansion is not unique. This difficulty can be overcome by arbitrarily selecting one of these expansions. In a similar manner, the decimal expansion for 5.17 could be taken as either 5.17000 . . . or 5.16999 . . . . An attempt will be made later to allay any fears you may have because of this lack of uniqueness (see Section 11–9).

Now suppose it is desired to consider $3/\sqrt{2}$. Let us define this to mean $3 \cdot 1/\sqrt{2}$. Since $\sqrt{2}$ now has meaning, $1/\sqrt{2}$ could be found by the above procedure, and then $3 \cdot 1/\sqrt{2}$ would have meaning in terms of the multiplication of real numbers.

PROBLEM SET 11–3

1. Consider the inequalities determining the number 3 which were obtained in this section. The right-hand side of the middle inequality was obtained by replacing $1/0.33$ by 3.04.

   (a) Show that $1/0.33$ is closer to 3.03 than to 3.04.

   (b) Show why 3.04 was used.

   (c) Could 3.03 have been used? Why?

2. For $100(\frac{5}{6})$ find a set of inequalities which contains three lines. Will this set determine the tenths digit? What is determined about this digit?

3. Find a set of inequalities, containing three lines, which would determine each of the following, and indicate which decimal digits are determined.

   (a) $\sqrt{2} \times \sqrt{5}$ (b) $\frac{1}{3} \times \sqrt{2}$

11–4 ABSOLUTE VALUE AND INEQUALITY

The absolute value of a rational number was defined in Section 10–3. Let us now define it for a real number.

Definition. *Absolute value of a real number.* Let α be a real number. Then

$$|\alpha| = \alpha, \qquad \text{if } \alpha \text{ is positive;}$$

$$|\alpha| = -\alpha, \qquad \text{if } \alpha \text{ is negative;}$$

$$|\alpha| = 0, \qquad \text{if } \alpha \text{ is zero.}$$

Hence, both the notation and the definition of absolute value are the same for real numbers as for rational numbers.

For inequality let us work with real numbers in decimal expansion form. The following will be satisfactory so long as neither α nor β comes under the exceptional case discussed in Section 11–9. If $\alpha = n \cdot a_1 a_2 a_3 \ldots$ and $\beta = m \cdot b_1 b_2 b_3 \ldots$, where m and n are whole numbers and the a's and b's are decimal digits (α and β being positive or zero), we shall say that $\alpha < \beta$ either if

$$n < m$$

or if

$$n = m, \quad a_1 = b_1, \quad a_2 = b_2, \quad \ldots, \quad a_k = b_k, \quad a_{k+1} < b_{k+1},$$

for some counting number k.

Thus, by the first case,

$$2.34 \ldots < 7.36 \ldots,$$

and, by the second case,

$$2.345 \ldots < 2.346 \ldots.$$

11–5 PROPERTIES OF REAL NUMBERS

In most of the preceding discussion of real numbers, formal definitions were not stated, but it was indicated, by examples, how they could be stated. Let us suppose that these formal definitions have been stated. Meaning has now been given to real numbers, to the absolute value of a real number, to the addition or multiplication of two positive real numbers, to the difference of two positive real numbers, and to inequalities involving positive real numbers. Refer to the definition of addition in Section 10–4, and wherever "rational number" appears substitute "real number." Wouldn't this then serve to define the addition of any two real numbers? Since Theorem 10–1 followed directly from the definition of addition, wouldn't it hold for real numbers? For the same reason, Theorem 10–2 would hold for real numbers. Continue in this fashion with the theorems of Sections 10–5 through 10–10 using the definitions for real numbers. Would not each theorem be true for real numbers?

The above indicates that the properties of rational numbers stated in Sections 10–5 through 10–10 also hold for real numbers. Hence formal manipulations with real numbers would be carried through just as for rational numbers. For example,

$$\frac{2}{\sqrt{3}} + \frac{3}{5} = \frac{10 + 3\sqrt{3}}{5\sqrt{3}}; \qquad \frac{6}{7} \cdot \frac{1}{2\sqrt{3}} = \frac{6}{14\sqrt{3}}; \qquad -\frac{\sqrt{2}}{\sqrt{3}} = -\frac{5\sqrt{2}}{5\sqrt{3}};$$

$$\frac{\sqrt{2}}{\sqrt{3}} + 5 = \frac{\sqrt{2}}{\sqrt{3}} + \frac{5\sqrt{3}}{\sqrt{3}} = \frac{\sqrt{2} + 5\sqrt{3}}{\sqrt{3}}; \qquad \frac{\sqrt{2}}{\sqrt{3}} \cdot \frac{\sqrt{5}}{\sqrt{7}} = \frac{\sqrt{2} \cdot \sqrt{5}}{\sqrt{3} \cdot \sqrt{7}}.$$

11–6 FURTHER PROPERTIES OF EXPONENTS

Only counting numbers have been used as exponents thus far. In terms of the definition given in Section 4–3 for x^k, where x is positive and k is a counting number, the notation x^0 would be meaningless. After stating the definition of x^k, an example was used to illustrate a proof of the multiplication property for exponential notation. This property states that $x^k \cdot x^t = x^{k+t}$. Suppose we assume that however x^0 is to be defined, the property of exponents stated above should hold for k and t any counting numbers or zero. Then

$$x^k \cdot x^0 = x^{k+0} = x^k,$$

and hence,

$$x^0 = \frac{x^k}{x^k} = 1,$$

since $x \neq 0$. Accordingly, x^0 should be, and will be, defined as 1. It can now be shown that the above multiplication property holds for k and t whole numbers (see Problem Set 11–6).

With the preceding in mind, 5^3 could be written as $5^3 \cdot 7^0$ or $5^3 \cdot 13^0$, if it seems to be desirable. Moreover, an operation such as

$$x^k \cdot x^{t-k} = x^{k+(t-k)} = x^t$$

has meaning even if $t = k$.

Certainly,

$$(xy)^3 = xy \cdot xy \cdot xy = (x \cdot x \cdot x)(y \cdot y \cdot y),$$

by the properties A_m and C_m. Similarly,

$$
\begin{aligned}
(xy)^s &= xy \cdot xy \cdot xy \cdots \text{to } s \text{ factors} \\
&= (x \cdot x \cdot x \cdots \text{to } s \text{ factors})(y \cdot y \cdot y \cdots \text{to } s \text{ factors}) \\
&= x^s \cdot y^s.
\end{aligned}
$$

Since this result holds also for $s = 0$, then

$$(xy)^s = x^s \cdot y^s, \qquad \text{for } s \text{ any whole number.}$$

This power property for exponential notation will be used in two types of applications. It can be used in a straightforward manner, such as $10^4 = (2 \cdot 5)^4 = 2^4 \cdot 5^4$, to simplify, or reduce, fractions. For example,

$$\frac{28}{10^4} = \frac{2^2 \cdot 7}{2^4 \cdot 5^4} = \frac{7}{2^2 \cdot 5^4} \qquad (\text{by } E_1).$$

It can also be used in a reversal of the above procedure in which we change $7/(2^2 \cdot 5^4)$ to an equivalent fraction whose denominator is a power of 10. In this instance, we multiply numerator and denominator by 2^2, obtaining

$$\frac{7}{2^2 \cdot 5^4} = \frac{7 \cdot 2^2}{2^2 \cdot 5^4 \cdot 2^2} = \frac{7 \cdot 4}{2^4 \cdot 5^4} = \frac{28}{(2 \cdot 5)^4} = \frac{28}{10^4}.$$

How was the multiplier 2^2 determined? We need the same powers of 2 and 5 in the denominator, and in this case it must be the 4th power, the larger of the two exponents. Since $2^2 \cdot 2^{4-2} = 2^{2+(4-2)} = 2^4$, then 2^{4-2} should be used as the multiplier. Show why 5^{6-3} should be used to change $3/(2^6 \cdot 5^3)$ to $375/10^6$. In general, to change $a/(2^r \cdot 5^s)$ to a fraction with a power of 10 in the denominator, use property E_1 as follows:

If $r > s$, multiply numerator and denominator by 5^{r-s}.

If $r < s$, multiply numerator and denominator by 2^{s-r}.

Do not memorize the above; determine what is needed in a specific problem. Perform the operations indicated to see why the desired effect is obtained.

In an earlier chapter we learned why $10^5 \div 10^2 = 10^3$; now, since $10^3 = 10^{5-2}$, then $10^5 \div 10^2 = 10^{5-2}$. In similar fashion, $10^2 \div 10^5 = 1/10^3 = 1/10^{5-2}$. In general, if $x \neq 0$, then

$$x^k \div x^t = \frac{x \cdot x \cdot x \cdots \text{ to } k \text{ factors}}{x \cdot x \cdot x \cdots \text{ to } t \text{ factors}}.$$

Hence,

if $k > t$, $\quad x^k \div x^t = x \cdot x \cdot x \cdots \text{ to } k - t \text{ factors} = x^{k-t}$;

if $k < t$, $\quad x^k \div x^t = \dfrac{1}{x \cdot x \cdot x \cdots \text{ to } t - k \text{ factors}} = \dfrac{1}{x^{t-k}}$;

if $k = t$, $\quad x^k \div x^t = 1.$

The preceding statement will be referred to as the "division property for exponential notation." This property is not applicable to the problem $5^7 \div 3^4$. Why?

PROBLEM SET 11-6

1. What, if anything, can be done to simplify $2^3 \cdot 5^7$? Show why no property of exponents used above is applicable.

2. Write the following in an equivalent form, using properties of exponents.
   (a) $(3 \cdot 4)^7$
   (b) $(u \cdot v)^4$
   (c) $(uv^2)^4$
   (d) $(x^2 y^3)^3$
   (e) $(x^3 y)^0$
   (f) $(3 \cdot 4^5)^0$
   (g) $4^3 \cdot (3 \cdot 4)^2$
   (h) $(3 \cdot 4)^5 \cdot (3 \cdot 4)^6$
   (i) $(x \cdot y)^4 \cdot (x \cdot y)^5$

3. Write each of the following as an equivalent fraction whose denominator is a power of 10.

(a) $\dfrac{7}{2^3 \cdot 5}$ (b) $\dfrac{11}{2^3}$ (c) $\dfrac{13}{2 \cdot 5^2}$ (d) $\dfrac{7}{2^2 \cdot 5^6}$ (e) $\dfrac{17}{2^4 \cdot 5^7}$ (f) $\dfrac{11}{2^7 \cdot 5^3}$

4. Can $7/(2^4 \cdot 3)$ be written as an equivalent rational number whose denominator is a power of 10? Why, or why not?

5. Simplify each of the following.

(a) $7^4 \cdot 7^8$ (b) $11^{13} \div 11^5$ (c) $11^4 \div 11^6$

(d) $5^6 \div 5^4$ (e) $5^r \div 5^s$, if $r < s$ (f) $7^r \div 7^s$, if $r > s$

(g) $x^4 y^2 \div x^2 y$ (h) $a b^4 c \div b^2 c^5$ (i) $(x^2 y)^3 \div x^0 \cdot y^2$

(j) $(uv)^5 \div u^2 (uv)^3$ (k) $(x + y - z)^0$ (l) $u^3 v^5 \div u^2 vw^4$

6. Show that $x^k \cdot x^t = x^{k+t}$, where k and t are counting numbers.

7. Using x^0 as defined, show that $x^k \cdot x^t = x^{k+t}$, for k and t whole numbers.

11–7 RATIONAL NUMBERS WITH DENOMINATOR OF FORM $2^r \cdot 5^s$

Whenever a real number has been mentioned there was always a decimal expansion closely associated with it. At one time it was stated that a real number is a number which has a decimal expansion. Later a real number was defined as being determined by a set of inequalities which satisfy certain properties, but here again the inequalities determined a decimal expansion. Sometimes the decimal expansion determined by the set of inequalities terminated after a finite number of steps, i.e., had all zeros after a certain position, and sometimes the expansion was unending or non-terminating. The question to be considered now is whether or not there is some way of knowing what type of expansion should be obtained.

Before you proceed in this section, it is advisable to review Section 7–8, since several ideas to be used here were introduced at that time. For instance, it was shown in that section that the rational number, $324/10^3$, whose denominator is a power of ten, has a finite decimal expansion. A general result of this nature will now be obtained. Consider the positive rational number $b/10^k$. Since b is a counting number, it can be written as

$$a_r \cdot 10^r + a_{r-1} \cdot 10^{r-1} + \cdots + a_2 \cdot 10^2 + a_1 \cdot 10 + a_0,$$

where r and the a's are whole numbers. If $r < k$, then

$$\frac{b}{10^k} = \frac{a_r \cdot 10^r}{10^k} + \frac{a_{r-1} \cdot 10^{r-1}}{10^k} + \cdots + \frac{a_1 \cdot 10}{10^k} + \frac{a_0}{10^k}$$

$$= \frac{a_r}{10^{k-r}} + \frac{a_{r-1}}{10^{k-r+1}} + \cdots + \frac{a_1}{10^{k-1}} + \frac{a_0}{10^k}.$$

This is certainly a terminating decimal expansion, where the whole number portion of the decimal form is zero. If $r \geq k$, then

$$\frac{b}{10^k} = a_r \cdot 10^{r-k} + a_{r-1} \cdot 10^{r-k-1} + \cdots + a_s + \cdots + \frac{a_1}{10^{k-1}} + \frac{a_0}{10^k},$$

where a_s is that term in the sum which has, before simplification, the same power of 10 in both numerator and denominator. In decimal notation this terminating decimal expansion would be written $a_r a_{r-1} \ldots a_s \cdot a_{s-1} \ldots a_1 a_0$. This sequence of operations will be more clearly understood if it is applied to a specific number, such as $237{,}458/10^3$. (In so doing, do not simply "shift" the decimal point mechanically.)

Now, by the preceding section, any rational number of the form $a/(2^r \cdot 5^s)$ can be written in an equivalent form, $b/10^k$. This statement, coupled with the results of the preceding paragraph, yields the following.

If a rational number has the form $b/(2^r \cdot 5^s)$, where b is a positive integer and where r and s are whole numbers, then it has a terminating decimal expansion.

For example, since $7/(2^3 \cdot 5^6) = (7 \cdot 2^3)/10^6$, then $7/(2^3 \cdot 5^6)$ must have a terminating decimal expansion. When b is negative, the situation can be handled as follows:

$$\frac{-3}{2 \cdot 5^2} = -\frac{3 \cdot 2}{2^2 \cdot 5^2} = -\frac{6}{10^2} = -0.06.$$

Since this procedure is applicable whenever a numerator is negative, henceforth results will be proved only for fractions with positive numerators.

The converse of the result proved above would be stated as follows.

If a decimal expansion terminates, then it represents a rational number of the form $b/(2^r \cdot 5^s)$.

The proof of this statement is straightforward. If the decimal notation is

$$a_r a_{r-1} \ldots a_1 a_0 \cdot c_1 c_2 \ldots c_k,$$

then

$$a_r a_{r-1} \ldots a_1 a_0 \cdot c_1 c_2 \ldots c_k$$
$$= a_r \cdot 10^r + a_{r-1} \cdot 10^{r-1} + \cdots + a_1 \cdot 10 + a_0 + \frac{c_1}{10} + \frac{c_2}{10^2} + \cdots + \frac{c_k}{10^k}$$
$$= \frac{a_r \cdot 10^{r+k} + a_{r-1} \cdot 10^{r-1+k} + \cdots + a_0 \cdot 10^k + c_1 \cdot 10^{k-1} + \cdots + c_k}{10^k}.$$

The numerator of this last fraction is an integer, which may have 2 or 5 (or both) as a factor; in that case the situation would be similar to

$$1 \cdot 10 + 2 + \frac{0}{10} + \frac{7}{10^2} + \frac{5}{10^3} = \frac{1 \cdot 10^4 + 2 \cdot 10^3 + 0 \cdot 10^2 + 7 \cdot 10 + 5}{10^3}$$

$$= \frac{12075}{10^3} = \frac{5^2(483)}{2^3 \cdot 5^3} = \frac{483}{2^3 \cdot 5},$$

where the denominator of the resulting rational number is the product of a power of 2 by a power of 5.

The two major statements proved above are combined in the following:

Theorem 11-1. A decimal expansion is terminating if and only if it represents a rational number of the form $b/(2^r \cdot 5^s)$, where r and s are whole numbers.

To be precise, a rational number does not have a denominator, but its fractional numeral does have a denominator. However, in accordance with the agreement made in Section 10-1, we shall continue to speak of the rational number a/b; in that context we may speak of the denominator of a rational number.

PROBLEM SET 11-7

1. Find the decimal expansion for each of the following.

   (a) $\dfrac{34161}{2^4 \cdot 5^2}$ (b) $\dfrac{164}{5^2}$ (c) $\dfrac{379}{2^4}$ (d) $\dfrac{16283}{2 \cdot 5^4}$ (e) $\dfrac{78432}{2^2 \cdot 5^5}$ (f) $\dfrac{672}{5^3}$

2. Write each of the following in the simplest possible rational form.

   (a) 6.704   (b) 0.9352   (c) 17.675
   (d) 0.0034   (e) 4.0512   (f) 3.1415

3. Would $\frac{2}{11}$ have a finite decimal expansion? Why? What about $5/(2^3 \cdot 7)$? Why?

4. Let the rational number represented by 3.457 be a/b, in reduced form. Without actually finding b, can you tell whether or not it is divisible by 3? by 11? Explain your answer.

5. Write two rational numbers whose decimal expansions would not terminate.

11-8 RATIONAL NUMBERS WITH DENOMINATOR DIVISIBLE BY A PRIME OTHER THAN 2 OR 5

Now consider a rational number b/c, in reduced form, where c is divisible by at least one prime other than 2 or 5 and where b and c are positive. Could b/c have a terminating decimal expansion? According to Theorem 11-1 it could not; hence its decimal expansion must be nonterminating.

However, more than this can be stated! To obtain this "more" let us think through the procedure developed in Section 7–8.

Since $c \neq 0$, there exist integers q and r such that $b = q_1 c + r_1$, $0 < r_1 < c$. (What theorem justifies this conclusion? Why cannot r_1 be zero?) Hence,

$$\frac{b}{c} = q_1 + \frac{r_1}{c}, \qquad \text{where} \quad \frac{r_1}{c} < 1 \qquad (\text{why?}).$$

As shown previously, r_1/c can be written as $(10 r_1/c)\frac{1}{10}$. The division theorem can then be applied to $10 r_1$ and c to yield $10 r_1 = q_2 \cdot c + r_2$, $0 < r_2 < c$. Accordingly,

$$\frac{b}{c} = q_1 + \left(q_2 + \frac{r_2}{c}\right) \frac{1}{10} = q_1 + \frac{q_2}{10} + \frac{r_2}{c} \cdot \frac{1}{10}.$$

It was shown in Section 7–8 that q_2 had to be one of the digits from 0 to 9, inclusive. Moreover, $r_2 \neq 0$, since the decimal expansion cannot terminate. As before, the fraction $(r_2/c)\frac{1}{10}$ can be written as $(10 r_2/c)(1/10^2)$, and the division theorem can be applied to $10 r_2$ and c to yield $10 r_2 = q_3 \cdot c + r_3$, $0 < r_3 < c$. Thus,

$$\frac{b}{c} = q_1 + \frac{q_2}{10} + \left(q_3 + \frac{r_3}{c}\right) \frac{1}{10^2}$$

$$= q_1 + \frac{q_2}{10} + \frac{q_3}{10^2} + \frac{r_3}{c} \cdot \frac{1}{10^2}.$$

We can continue this procedure indefinitely, obtaining more and more terms of the nonterminating decimal.

When the division theorem was applied in each step above, the remainder r_i was always smaller than c, that is, $r_i < c$ for $i = 1, 2, 3$, etc. Since $r_i > 0$ and since only a finite number of integers exist between 0 and c, there is only a finite number of possibilities for the r_i's. Hence, after a finite number of steps, we must obtain a remainder equal to a remainder obtained previously. For $\frac{4}{7}$ the only possible remainders are 1, 2, 3, 4, 5, and 6. Suppose that $r_k = r_j$, where $k > j$. In the next step, $10 r_k$ would be divided by c to obtain $10 r_k = q_{k+1} c + r_{k+1}$, where $0 < r_{k+1} < c$. Now, in an earlier step we obtained $10 r_j = q_{j+1} c + r_{j+1}$, and since $10 r_k = 10 r_j$, then $q_{k+1} = q_{j+1}$ and $r_{k+1} = r_{j+1}$. The last two equations result from the fact that in a division process both quotient and remainder are unique, by the division theorem. Again, $10 r_{k+1}$ would be divided by c to obtain a quotient and a remainder, but these must be the same as those obtained on dividing $10 r_{j+1}$ by c. Apparently we are obtaining the same set of q's following q_k as had previously been obtained following q_j. That is, the q's are beginning to repeat. After a certain number of steps, the same as the number of steps between r_j and r_k, we would obtain $r_t = r_k$, so that repetition of the q's begins again. Since these q's are the digits in the decimal expansion, this expansion is a *repeating* decimal expansion.

Some of the preceding steps which are not shown in notational detail will be clearer if we work through a numerical example. Let us obtain the decimal expansion for $\frac{2}{7}$ (the early steps are left for the reader). This expansion is

$$\frac{2}{7} = 0 + \frac{2}{10} + \frac{8}{10^2} + \frac{5}{10^3} + \frac{7}{10^4} + \frac{1}{10^5} + \frac{4}{10^6} + \frac{2}{7} \cdot \frac{1}{10^6}$$

$$= 0.285714 + \frac{20}{7} \cdot \frac{1}{10^7}.$$

The first term, $\frac{2}{10}$, was obtained from $\frac{20}{7} \cdot \frac{1}{10} = (2 + \frac{6}{7})\frac{1}{10}$; the next term of the above expansion will be obtained from $(2 + \frac{6}{7})(1/10^7)$. Hence the digits in the expansion will repeat from this point on, and there are six terms in the repeating part. Accordingly,

$$\frac{2}{7} = 0.285714\ 285714\ 285714\ldots.$$

There are several notations which can be used to abbreviate such an expansion; two of these are

$$0.\dot{2}8571\dot{4} \quad \text{or} \quad 0.\overline{285714},$$

where the repeating part is indicated by dots or a bar.

The following statement was proved above.

For a rational number, in reduced form, whose denominator is divisible by a prime other than 2 or 5, the decimal expansion is repeating.

Definite means are available for determining the number of digits in the repeating part; however, the mathematics involved in the discussion of that problem is beyond us at present.

Now let us consider the converse of the above statement, i.e., let us try to determine what type of real number is represented by a repeating decimal expansion. Consider the example $x = 0.\dot{3}2\dot{7}$:

$$x = 0.327327327\ldots,$$

so that

$$10^3 x = 327.327327\ldots$$

$$= 327 + 0.327327\ldots$$

$$= 327 + 0.\dot{3}2\dot{7}$$

$$= 327 + x.$$

The multiplication of a real number by a power of 10, such as that performed above, was considered in Section 11–3, in connection with multiplication of real numbers. It was shown, by example, that the decimal expansion of the product was obtained by the usual "shift" of the decimal point. Now, from the preceding equation,

$$(10^3 - 1)x = 327, \qquad \text{so that} \qquad x = \tfrac{327}{999}.$$

Accordingly, x is a rational number.

To prove a general statement, let $x = 0.\dot{a}_1 a_2 a_3 \ldots \dot{a}_k$. Hence

$$x = 0.a_1 a_2 a_3 \ldots a_k a_1 a_2 a_3 \ldots a_k \ldots,$$
$$10^k x = a_1 a_2 a_3 \ldots a_k.a_1 a_2 a_3 \ldots a_k \ldots$$
$$= a_1 \cdot 10^{k-1} + a_2 \cdot 10^{k-2} + \cdots + a_{k-1} \cdot 10 + a_k + 0.\dot{a}_1 a_2 a_3 \ldots \dot{a}_k$$
$$= N + x,$$

where N is the integer $a_1 \cdot 10^{k-1} + a_2 \cdot 10^{k-2} + \cdots + a_{k-1} \cdot 10 + a_k$. Hence

$$(10^k - 1)x = N,$$

so that

$$x = \frac{N}{10^k - 1}.$$

Since both N and $10^k - 1$ are integers, then x is a rational number.

Now consider a somewhat more general type of expansion, in which the repeating part does not start in the tenths place. For example, let $y = 0.46\dot{3}2\dot{7}$. Now $10^2 y = 46.\dot{3}2\dot{7} = 46 + x$, where $x = 0.\dot{3}2\dot{7}$ was determined previously. Hence

$$100y = 46 + \frac{327}{999} = \frac{46{,}281}{999}.$$

Accordingly, $y = 46{,}281/99{,}900$, a rational number. For the general problem, let $y = 0.b_1 b_2 \ldots b_t \dot{a}_1 a_2 \ldots \dot{a}_k$. As before,

$$10^t y = b_1 b_2 \ldots b_t.\dot{a}_1 a_2 \ldots \dot{a}_k$$
$$= b_1 \cdot 10^{t-1} + \cdots + b_{t-1} \cdot 10 + b_t + 0.\dot{a}_1 a_2 \ldots \dot{a}_k$$
$$= M + x,$$

where M is the integer $b_1 \cdot 10^{t-1} + \cdots + b_{t-1} \cdot 10 + b_t$ and x is of the form considered previously. Since x has been proved rational, then $M + x$ is rational. Thus, $y = (M + x) \div 10^t$ is also rational, since a rational number divided by a nonzero rational number is again rational.

In all expansions considered thus far the integral portion was zero. The following numerical example will suffice to indicate what happens when the integral part is nonzero. If $z = 62.\dot{3}2\dot{7}$, then $z = 62 + 0.\dot{3}2\dot{7} = 62 + x$. Since x is rational, then $62 + x$ is rational, so that z is rational. The denominator of the rational number z must be divisible by a prime other than 2 or 5. (Why?)

The results of the last four paragraphs can be summarized as follows.

If a decimal expansion is repeating, then the number it represents is a rational number.

This statement and the previous main statement can be combined in a theorem (for an exceptional case see Section 11–9).

Theorem 11–2. A real number has a repeating decimal expansion *if and only if* it is a rational number, b/c, where c is divisible by a prime other than 2 or 5 and where b and c are relatively prime.

Theorems 11–1 and 11–2 can be combined into a single theorem.

Theorem 11–3. A real number is rational if and only if its decimal expansion is either terminating or repeating.

These theorems enable us to classify real numbers according to the type of decimal expansion which the real number has. Information is thereby obtained about a number by considering one of its numerals, in particular its decimal expansion. See the problems below for further details.

PROBLEM SET 11–8

1. Find the decimal expansion for each of the following.

   (a) $\frac{5}{7}$ (b) $\frac{7}{11}$ (c) $\frac{5}{6}$ (d) $\frac{4}{9}$ (e) $\frac{5}{12}$ (f) $\frac{9}{14}$

2. Find the rational number represented by each of the following.

   (a) $6.7\dot{3}$ (b) $2.34\dot{2}\dot{5}$ (c) $0.4783\dot{5}\dot{2}$

   (d) $0.67\dot{1}\dot{8}$ (e) $1.32\dot{5}\dot{6}$ (f) $6.72\dot{8}$

3. Describe the decimal expansions for each of the following numbers. Give a reason for your answer.

   (a) $\sqrt{2}$ (b) $\sqrt{5}$ (c) $\sqrt{7}$

4. Define $x = 0.121121112\ldots$, where the number of 1's increases by one from block to block.

   (a) Is x a real number? Why?
   (b) Is x a rational number? Why?
   (c) What word is often used to describe x?

5. Assume that π is a real number and that it is not rational.

   (a) What can be said about the decimal expansion for π?
   (b) Is $\pi = \frac{22}{7}$? Why? How is $\frac{22}{7}$ related to π?
   (c) Is $\pi = 3.14159$? Why?
   (That π is irrational is anything but easy to prove. This fact was first proved about the middle of the nineteenth century.)

6. (a) Prove that $\sqrt[3]{2}$ is irrational.

   (b) What form of decimal expansion does $\sqrt[3]{2}$ have?

7. Are Theorems 11–1 through 11–3 properties of numbers or numerals? Why?

11–9 DECIMAL EXPANSIONS ENDING IN NINES

Let $x = 0.2\dot{9}$. Then

$$10x = 2.\dot{9},$$

$$10x - 2 = 0.\dot{9},$$

$$10(10x - 2) = 9.\dot{9},$$

$$100x - 20 = 9 + (10x - 2),$$

$$90x = 27,$$

$$x = \tfrac{27}{90} = \tfrac{3}{10} = 0.3.$$

In this example a repeating decimal ending in nines turned out to be the same as the terminating decimal 0.3. This is the exceptional case which we referred to just before Theorem 11–2. By the type of proof used in the last section, it can be shown that any decimal expansion ending in nines actually represents a rational number whose denominator is a power of 10; hence it also has a terminating decimal expansion representation.

The procedure used in the last section for finding the decimal expansion of a rational number would never produce a repeating nine. Prove this by an indirect type of proof. However, other procedures would produce such an expansion. For instance, consider the following set of inequalities in terms of the ideas of Section 11–1:

$$0.3 \quad < 0.4$$
$$0.37 \quad < 0.38$$
$$0.379 \quad < 0.380$$
$$0.3799 < 0.3800$$
$$\vdots \qquad \vdots$$

This example actually gives the decimal form ending in repeated zeros as well as the form ending in repeated nines.

The decimal expansion of a real number is unique unless the expansion ends in repeated nines. A proof of this statement will not be attempted here. Something should be left for the future!

CHAPTER 12

Measurement: A Mathematical Approach

Measurement is common both in everyday experience and in scientific work. We measure lengths or distances in inches, feet, miles, centimeters, etc. Areas enclosed by rectangles and circles may be measured in square feet or square centimeters; time may be measured in hours or days; a volume of liquid may be measured in quarts or gallons. Our purpose in this chapter is to gain real understanding of the basic concepts of measurement rather than to discuss special "units." To do this it is necessary to spend some time on the relationship of real numbers to points on a line. In turn, this calls for a discussion of certain geometric concepts.

12–1 GEOMETRY

In elementary geometry we study interrelationships between points, straight lines, planes, triangles, rectangles, circles, etc. All of us have intuitive notions of what we mean by points and straight lines; we feel we know what is meant when a point on the floor is designated in some fashion or when the edge of a table is referred to as a straight line. When we refer to points and straight lines (henceforth called "lines") in geometry, we are thinking of "idealizations" of physical reality. We study these idealizations carefully, logically, in the hope that the body of ideas to be developed will have some application to the real world. The most carefully drawn "line" contains many irregularities and hence is not a line in the mathematical sense, although it may approximate such a line quite closely. A line in geometry is a *mathematical model* of what is termed a line in the real world. The structure of elementary geometry, as developed in high school, is a mathematical model of the space in which we exist, or at least a portion of that space.

Points, lines, and planes are treated as undefined, and certain assumptions are made about them. These assumptions, or postulates, form the basis of the mathematical model, and they are actually properties of the "things" being discussed. The following are examples of such assumptions.

(1) Through each two points there will pass one and only one line (or, on each two points there will be one and only one line).

(2) If three points do not lie on the same line, there is one and only one plane on (or through) these points.

No attempt will be made in this chapter to discuss fully the basis of geometry. However, we shall discuss rather carefully certain concepts which are basic for a study of measurement.

12–2 LINES, SEGMENTS, RAYS

A line is a set of points. Since a line "extends indefinitely in both directions," only a portion of the line can be shown in any sketch. This "indefinite extension" is often indicated by placing arrow heads at the ends of the portion drawn, as shown below.

If two points, say A and B, are designated on a line then the set of all points on the line which lie between A and B, as well as A and B themselves, is called a *line segment*. (Note that we do not distinguish between the point and the name of the point; to always speak of "the point whose name is A" would be awkward.) This line segment is denoted by AB. The points A and B are called the *endpoints* of the segment.

The set of points consisting of A and all those points on the line to the right of A is called a *ray;* with reference to the above illustration, this ray could be denoted by $\overrightarrow{AB}$. The set consisting of A and those points (on the line) to the left of A is also a ray. This ray is denoted by $\overrightarrow{AC}$. Is $\overrightarrow{BA}$ a ray? Is $\overrightarrow{BA}$ the same ray as $\overrightarrow{BC}$? For the ray $\overrightarrow{AB}$, the point A is called the *endpoint*.

Suppose that two line segments, such as AB and CD below, are given, and the question is asked, "Are they the same size; if not, which is larger?" To answer this question we may talk about moving AB until it lies on the ray $\overrightarrow{CD}$, so that A coincides with C. Then if B coincides with D, we would say that AB and CD are *congruent* segments. If B lies between C and D, we would say that AB is "smaller" than CD. If B lies "beyond" D, then

AB is said to be "larger" than *CD*. This procedure gives some information as to the relative "sizes" of *AB* and *CD*, but not enough to suffice for many purposes. Draw diagrams illustrating the three possible cases.

The language of the last paragraph was largely intuitive, even physical in its implication. Do we know that a line segment can be moved? If so, how do we know and how is it done? Actually, we are not really interested in the answers to these questions. Our only interest is whether or not there *is* a line segment on ray $\overrightarrow{CD}$ which has one endpoint at *C* and which is congruent to *AB*. This will be a basic assumption of the geometry.

Property 1. Given a segment *AB* and a ray $\overrightarrow{CD}$, there is (or there exists) one and only one segment on $\overrightarrow{CD}$ which has one endpoint at *C* and which is congruent to *AB*.

Do not be misled by your knowledge of constructions; with geometric instruments only reasonable facsimiles can be drawn.

PROBLEM SET 12-2

1. Assume that a number scale has been established on a line and that points *A*, *B*, and *C* correspond to −3, 2, and 7, respectively.
   (a) Find the intersection of $\overrightarrow{BC}$ and $\overrightarrow{CB}$.
   (b) Find the intersection of $\overrightarrow{BC}$ and $\overrightarrow{BA}$.
   (c) Find the intersection of $\overrightarrow{AC}$ and $\overrightarrow{BC}$.
   (d) Find the union of $\overrightarrow{AC}$ and $\overrightarrow{BC}$.

2. Define the concept of line segment in terms of two rays, using the concept of set intersection.

12–3 LENGTH

In previous chapters when number lines were constructed we were somewhat casual in our approach. Now we can do a better job! Let us start with a line, a point *O* on the line, and any convenient line segment *MN*. Choose one of the rays with endpoint *O*. On this ray there is a segment *OA* congruent to *MN*, by Property 1. Similarly, there are segments *AB*, *BC*, and *CD*, each congruent to *MN*. These segments are to be nonoverlapping, in the sense that adjacent segments have only an endpoint in common. Moreover, the union of *OA* and *AB* is *OB*, and the union of *OA*, *AB*, *BC*, and *CD* is *OD*. Now we will compare *OB* with *OA* by saying that *OB* is twice as long as *OA*, since OB is the union of two segments each congruent to OA. Similarly, OD is four times as long as OA. To simplify the language, let us refer to MN as "the *unit*" and then state that

the *length* of $OB = 2$ units;   the length of $OD = 4$ units.

Basically, this is the concept of *measurement of length* of a line segment; however, it is only an introduction to that concept. As before, we will associate the number 1 with A, 2 with B, 3 with C, etc. to obtain the beginnings of a number scale. Note that when 4 is the number associated with D in the number scale with zero at O, then

the length of $OD = 4$ units.

If *any* counting number is named specifically, whether it be 11, 87, or 1563, for example, the preceding discussion enables us to state that there is a point on the ray $\overrightarrow{OA}$ corresponding to the number named. Does this mean that corresponding to every counting number there is a point on the line? Since it is impossible to name specifically each and every counting number, mathematicians do not like to give a "yes" answer to that question, based on such "evidence." However, if we assume that there is a point P corresponding to the counting number n, then by Property 1 there is a point Q to the right of P, such that PQ is congruent to MN and hence Q corresponds to $n + 1$.

This states, in effect, that if there is a point corresponding to a certain counting number, then there is a point corresponding to the "next" counting number. There is a property of counting numbers which would say that since the preceding sentence is true and since there is a point corresponding to 1, then there is a point corresponding to each counting number. This property is called the "principle of mathematical induction." (Actually the principle of mathematical induction was used twice in previous work, although it was not formally stated.)

In essence, the preceding discussion gives a set of points, $O, A, B, C, D, \ldots$, which determine nonoverlapping congruent segments on ray $\overrightarrow{OA}$. Intuitively, we feel that this set of segments would be the "same" as ray $\overrightarrow{OA}$, in the sense that every point P on $\overrightarrow{OA}$ would lie on one of these segments (two segments, if P is an endpoint). Actually this must be assumed, as it is in the following property.

Property 2.   The ray $\overrightarrow{OA}$ is the union of the segments OA, AB, BC, $CD, \ldots$ (notation indicated above).

Now each point on the ray will belong to at least one of the segments constituting the ray.

In Section 7–7 we used a familiar construction to divide a line segment into five equal parts. We can now rephrase the ideas presented in that section so as to eliminate the "construction" terminology. Given a line segment RS, there are points P_1, P_2, P_3, and P_4 such that RS is the union of five non-overlapping, congruent segments RP_1, P_1P_2, P_2P_3, P_3P_4, and P_4S. More-

over, the fact that these points exist is based on primary assumptions and theorems of the geometry studied in high school, such as the following:

(1) Given a line and a point not on the line, there is one and only one line through the given point and parallel to the given line.

(2) A transversal makes congruent angles with parallel lines.

(3) If two angles and a side of one triangle are congruent, respectively, to two angles and a side (corresponding) of a second triangle, then the triangles are congruent.

Perform the construction and note where such properties are used in the determination of P_1, P_2, P_3, and P_4.

In similar fashion, CD (see Fig. 12–1) is the union of ten nonoverlapping, congruent segments. Since C and D correspond to the numbers 3 and 4, then the points determining these subsegments would, as usual, be assigned the numbers 3.1, 3.2, . . . , 3.9. Let us introduce the notation $P_{3.1}$ for the

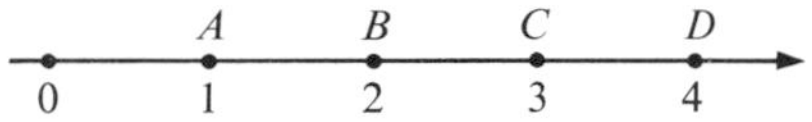

FIGURE 12–1

point corresponding to 3.1; then $P_{3.2}, \ldots, P_{3.9}$ would denote the other points which determine the subsegments (see Fig. 12–2). Thus, for example,

$$\text{the length of } OP_{3.2} = 3.2 \text{ units.}$$

Here again the length of a line segment is expressed in terms of the number on the number line which is associated with that endpoint of the segment which is not at O.

The ideas of the preceding paragraph will suffice for line segments which have one endpoint at O and the other endpoint associated with a rational number. For instance, CD might have been separated into seven nonoverlapping, congruent segments to obtain points corresponding to numbers such as $3\frac{2}{7}$ or $3\frac{6}{7}$.

Are there points on the ray $\overrightarrow{OA}$ (Fig. 12–1) which are not associated with any rational number, but which can be associated with a real number? In

Section 10–1 it was shown that $\sqrt{2}$ is not a rational number; however, according to the discussion of Section 11–1, $\sqrt{2}$ is a real number. Intuitively we feel that there should be a point on the ray corresponding to the real, but nonrational, number $\sqrt{2}$. To cover the general situation it is necessary to assume the following property.

Property 3. To each positive real number there will correspond a point on a ray.

What can we say about the converse of this assumption? We choose a point, P, on the ray $\overrightarrow{OA}$. By Property 2, the point P is on one of the segments whose union is the ray. Either P is the endpoint of such a segment, or it lies between two consecutive endpoints. Thus, either P is associated with a counting number, or it is not associated with a counting number. In the first case, there is a number which corresponds to P, the counting number. In the second case, P must lie between two points associated with consecutive counting numbers, say between C and D. Now suppose we sketch the segment CD in a magnified form, and mark on this segment the points $P_{3.0} = C$, $P_{3.1}, P_{3.2}, \ldots, P_{3.9}, P_{4.0} = D$. Certainly P must coincide with one of the

FIGURE 12–2

points $P_{3.1}, P_{3.2}, \ldots, P_{3.9}$, or it must lie between two consecutive points designated by C, the P's, and D. If P coincides with $P_{3.5}$, for example, then 3.5 corresponds to P. If P lies between $P_{3.5}$ and $P_{3.6}$, for example, then we proceed as before. The segment $P_{3.5} P_{3.6}$ is separated into 10 congruent, nonoverlapping subsegments with endpoints $P_{3.50}, P_{3.51}, P_{3.52}, \ldots, P_{3.60}$. If P coincides with one of these points, then P has a number associated with it; if not, P must lie between two of these points which are consecutive, and we proceed as before. If at some stage of this procedure P coincides with an endpoint of a subsegment, then P has a rational number associated with it. If this does not happen at any stage of the procedure, then P is contained within each subsegment of an "infinite" set of subsegments, where each subsegment is contained in the preceding. Moreover, this procedure develops a set of rational numbers which satisfy the set of inequalities

$$3 \quad < 4,$$
$$3.5 \quad < 3.6,$$
$$3.57 \quad < 3.58, \text{ say},$$
$$3.576 < 3.577, \text{ say},$$
$$\vdots \qquad \vdots$$

Now, this set of inequalities is of the type which determines a real number, that real number whose decimal expansion is 3.576 .... This number, 3.576 ... , is assigned to the point P. In this manner, to each point P on the ray there is assigned a real number. This statement, coupled with Property 3, yields the following property.

Property 4. To each point on a ray there corresponds a positive real number, or zero, and conversely.

Proceeding from the above discussion, we can state the following definition.

Definition. *Length of a line segment.* For the segment OP,

$$\text{length of } OP = \alpha \text{ units},$$

if α is the number associated with P in a number scale which has been set up on $\overrightarrow{OP}$ so that zero is associated with the point O.

For the preceding example, the length of $OP = (3.576 \ldots)$ units.

In the case where P never coincides with an endpoint of one of the sub-segments, the following property was used, but not stated.

Property 5. For each counting number n, a line segment may be separated into n nonoverlapping, congruent segments.

In the above, P was chosen on a line on which there was an existing number scale, and the length of OP was determined. Now, if AB is any given segment whose length is desired, a number scale can be set up on the ray $\overrightarrow{AB}$, with 0 at A, but in order to do this, a unit must first be chosen. Then the length of AB is determined as before.

Suppose that various units are used to construct number scales. Would not the measurement of the length of AB depend on the unit used? In actual practice, such standard units as the inch (in.), foot (ft), mile (mi), centimeter (cm), or meter (m), are usually used. If the length of AB were 11 ft, then the length of AB could also be stated as 132 in. A ruler is simply a practical number scale based on a standard unit, such as the inch.

A measurement of length involves two things, a number and a unit. If the length of a line segment is given as 2 ft, the number "2" is often called the *measure;* in this case, we say that

"the measurement is 2 ft,"   or   "the measure, in feet, is 2."

Suppose that the unit is changed, say to inches; then we say that "the measurement is 24 in.," or "the measure, in inches, is 24." Would "the measure is 3" have any meaning? To answer this, we ask the question, "What is the corresponding measurement?" This cannot be answered until the unit is stated; hence "the measure is 3" is meaningless, unless the unit is implied by the context.

Remember that thus far we have discussed only the mathematical idea of measurement. In practice, many other concepts, such as precision of measurement, become important. These will be discussed in the next chapter.

PROBLEM SET 12–3

1. Set up the "usual" construction for showing that a line segment can be separated into three congruent, nonoverlapping segments.
   (a) Show where each of the three assumptions or theorems listed on page 240 was used.
   (b) State an assumption not listed on page 240 which was actually used, and show where it was used.

2. (a) If R and S are points on a number line corresponding to 6 and 7, respectively, describe how to find points corresponding to $6\frac{1}{4}$ and $6\frac{3}{4}$.
   (b) What is the length of $OP_{6.75}$?
   (c) If RS is separated into five nonoverlapping congruent segments, what numbers would correspond to the endpoints of these segments?
   (d) Repeat part (c) for separation into 7 segments.

3. Describe how to find points corresponding to the following numbers.
   (a) 3.42   (b) 2.03   (c) $4\frac{1}{6}$

4. On what basis do we *know* that there is a point on a number line corresponding to 673425.68?

5. Change the following "measurement" statements to "measure" statements, or vice versa.
   (a) The measurement is 3.2 mi.
   (b) The measure, in millimeters, is 15.7.
   (c) The measure, in feet, is 6.
   (d) The measurement is 3.7 yd (yards).

12–4 SIMPLE CLOSED CURVES

If A and B are points on a plane, then the *distance* from A to B (or from B to A) is defined as the length of the segment AB. If we represent this distance by $|AB|$ units, then $|AB|$ is the measure of the length of the segment. A circle is often defined as "the set of all points on a plane which lie at a constant distance from a fixed point in the same plane." Let A be a point on a circle with center O. If $|OB| < |OA|$, then B would *not* lie on the circle. The set of all points such as B, for which $|OB| < |OA|$, would constitute the *interior* of the circle. The union of the circle and its interior is called a *closed* circular region.

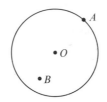

A circle is one example of a class of plane curves called *simple closed curves*. Other examples are shown in Fig. 12–3. Examples of curves which are not simple closed curves are shown in Fig. 12–4. In each diagram of Fig. 12–3 the point B is in the interior of the simple closed curve; in each case, the curve is the *boundary* of the interior; the union of the boundary and the interior is a *closed region*.

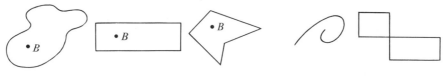

FIGURE 12–3   FIGURE 12–4

We have an intuitive feeling that each closed region has "size"; the term *area of a closed region* is used for this concept of size. Thus we speak of "the area of a closed circular region" or "the area of a closed rectangular region." Strictly speaking, neither a circle nor a rectangle has area, and therefore it is incorrect to speak of "the area of a rectangle." However, this commonly used phraseology is not in serious error *if* we remember that it is only an abbreviation of the correct phraseology.

It is now our purpose to discuss the mathematical background of the determination of the area of a closed rectangular region. Remember that we are dealing with mathematical idealizations of configurations which are found in the real world.

12–5 AREA OF A CLOSED RECTANGULAR REGION

It will be assumed that what is meant by a "rectangle" is well understood; that it is the union of four line segments which are called its "sides," such that opposite sides are of equal length and each pair of adjacent sides determines a right angle. It will also be assumed that a square is a rectangle whose adjacent sides are of equal length. A knowledge of right angle is assumed, for the present; this concept is discussed in more detail in Section 12–7.

To measure a line segment *OP*, a unit line segment, *OA*, was chosen, and *OP* was "compared" with this unit. If *OP* was the union of *m* non-overlapping segments, where each segment was congruent to *OA* and where *m* was a counting number, then the length of *OP* was said to be *m* units. If *OP* was not the union of *m* nonoverlapping segments congruent to the unit, then it was shown how to use the number scale based on this unit to find the length of *OP*.

In many respects our discussion of the area of a closed rectangular region will be similar to our discussion of the length of the line segment *OP*. The question of a unit comes to mind first. Does it seem reasonable that we should choose as a unit of area some "small" closed region? Would either of the regions shown below seem to be reasonable choices? If you think in terms of

cutting facsimiles of the regions shown out of paper and trying to fit them on a rectangular region, would it be likely that their union would "come close" to being the rectangular region? Obviously, it would not. Suppose then that we decide to use a rectangular region as unit, but to leave the de-

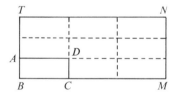

FIGURE 12–5

cision as to exactly which rectangular region unanswered for now. We would certainly want to be able to say that the area of region *BMNT* = 9 · (area of region *ABCD*), since region *BMNT* is the union of nine nonoverlapping regions each of which is congruent to *ABCD*.

The preceding intuitive discussion seems to require that we assume certain properties of regions and areas.

Property 6. If two closed regions are congruent, they have the same area.

Property 7. In any desired position there is a rectangular closed region which is congruent to a given rectangular closed region.

In the preceding example it was desired to have a "copy" of the rectangular region *ABCD* so that one side would coincide with *CD*, and an adjacent side would lie on *CM*. Property 7 guarantees the existence of this copy. Now let us state a property which will relate the areas of certain regions.

Property 8. If a closed region, *A*, is the union of nonoverlapping closed regions, *B*, *C*, *D*, etc., then the area of region *A* is the sum of the areas of the regions *B*, *C*, *D*, etc.

The statement of this property presupposes that we know how to "add" two areas; actually, we do not have this knowledge as yet, but discussion of it will be left until the end of the next section.

FIGURE 12–6

Let us start with any rectangle *ABCD*, such as that shown in Fig. 12–6. Subdivide *AB* into ten congruent subsegments; this determines ten subrectangles, each of which is congruent to *AEFD*. By Property 6, the subrectangles are of equal area and, by Property 8, this area must be $\frac{1}{10}$ · (area of *ABCD*). Actually, *AB* could have been subdivided into any desired number of parts, and a corresponding relationship would have existed between the areas.

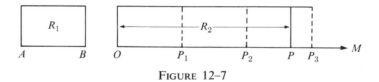

FIGURE 12–7

Suppose that two rectangular regions, say R_1 and R_2 of Fig. 12–7, are given such that a side of one is congruent to a side of the other. It is desired to compare the areas of R_1 and R_2. Mark on $\overrightarrow{OM}$ a number scale using *AB* as the unit. For purposes of illustration suppose that *P* lies between P_2 and P_3 on this scale. By Properties 7 and 8, there exist two rectangular closed regions, determined by P_2 and P_3, whose areas are 2 · (area of R_1) and 3 · (area of R_1), respectively. Intuitively, the area of R_2 should lie between these two areas, i.e., the area of R_2 should lie between

$$2 \cdot (\text{area of } R_1) \quad \text{and} \quad 3 \cdot (\text{area of } R_1).$$

Now if a rectangle is obtained whose area is $\frac{1}{10}$ · (area of R_1), as discussed in the preceding paragraph, there are ten nonoverlapping copies of this rectangle based on the segment P_2P_3. If P coincides with $P_{2.6}$, say, then

$$\text{area of } R_2 = 2 \cdot (\text{area of } R_1) + \tfrac{6}{10} \cdot (\text{area of } R_1)$$
$$= (2.6) \cdot (\text{area of } R_1) \qquad \text{(by Property 8).}$$

If P lies between $P_{2.6}$ and $P_{2.7}$, we subdivide the rectangle whose area is $\tfrac{1}{10} \cdot (\text{area of } R_1)$ into ten congruent nonoverlapping rectangles, each of area $\tfrac{1}{100} \cdot (\text{area of } R_1)$. A somewhat magnified diagram of the portion between $P_{2.6}$ and $P_{2.7}$ is shown below. The area of the rectangle with base $P_{2.6}P_{2.7}$

is $\tfrac{1}{10} \cdot (\text{area of } R_1)$; the area of the rectangle with base $P_{2.6}P_{2.61}$ is $\tfrac{1}{100} \cdot (\text{area of } R_1)$. If P is in the position indicated, then intuitively we feel that the area of R_2 should lie between $(2.64) \cdot (\text{area of } R_1)$ and $(2.65) \cdot (\text{area of } R_1)$. A series of statements can now be made. The area of R_2 is between

$$2 \cdot (\text{area of } R_1) \qquad \text{and} \qquad 3 \cdot (\text{area of } R_1),$$
$$(2.6) \cdot (\text{area of } R_1) \qquad \text{and} \qquad (2.7) \cdot (\text{area of } R_1),$$
$$(2.64) \cdot (\text{area of } R_1) \qquad \text{and} \qquad (2.65) \cdot (\text{area of } R_1).$$

The numbers in these statements satisfy the inequalities

$$2 \quad < 3,$$
$$2.6 \quad < 2.7,$$
$$2.64 < 2.65.$$

This set of inequalities would determine the real number corresponding to P (further inequalities might well be needed). Does this seem to suggest that if α is the real number corresponding to P, then the area of R_2 should be $\alpha \cdot (\text{area of } R_1)$? This should now be assumed as an area property.

Property 9. Let $ABCD$ and $EFGH$ be two rectangles with AD congruent to EH. If these rectangles are labeled R_1 and R_2, respectively, then

$$\text{area of } R_2 = \alpha \cdot (\text{area of } R_1),$$

where α is the real number on a number scale which, with AB as unit, is set up on $\overrightarrow{EF}$ so that zero corresponds to E.

Now we are ready to discuss the concept of the area of a general rectangular region R (see Fig. 12–8). Suppose that a unit for measuring the length of

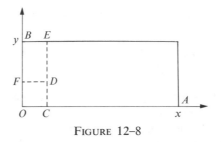

FIGURE 12–8

line segments has been chosen and that, with respect to this unit, the sides of R have lengths x units and y units. Establish a number scale on $\overrightarrow{OA}$ such that O corresponds to zero and OC is the chosen unit length; then x is the real number corresponding to A in this scale. Hence, by Property 9,

$$\text{area of } R = x \cdot (\text{area of } OCEB).$$

Since a number scale can be established on any ray, it can be established on $\overrightarrow{OB}$ with O corresponding to zero and OF of length 1 unit; the number corresponding to B is y. Again by Property 9,

$$\text{area of } OCEB = y \cdot (\text{area of } OCDF).$$

Hence

$$\text{area of } R = x\,[y \cdot (\text{area of } OCDF)] = xy \cdot (\text{area of } OCDF).$$

Now, $OCDF$ is a square with sides of length 1 unit. Apparently this square region would be a convenient unit for measuring the area of a rectangular region. We now choose this square region as the unit and then define the area of a rectangular region in terms of this unit.

Definition. *Area of a rectangular region.* The area of a region determined by a rectangle whose sides are of length x units and y units is xy square units.

If R is a rectangle whose sides are 4.1 units and 6.2 units in length (i.e., if R is a 4.1 by 6.2 rectangle, relative to the chosen unit), then the area of R is 25.42 square units. In a rough sense, 25.42 is the number of unit squares needed to cover the given rectangle; expressed in another way, 25.42 is the measure of the area. The measure of the area is the product of the measures of a pair of adjacent sides; in this example, $25.42 = 4.1 \times 6.2$. If the rectangle were 4.1 in. by 6.2 in., the unit for area measurement would be a one-inch square region; the area would be 25.42 sq. in.; the measure of the area, in square inches, is 25.42. If the unit for measuring the lengths of the sides were a mile, then the area unit would be a square mile.

PROBLEM SET 12–5

1. (a) Is an ellipse a simple closed curve?
    (b) Is a parabola a simple closed curve?
    (c) Do the curves of parts (a) and (b) determine closed regions?

2. What commonly used phraseology does Property 7 replace?

3. Let C represent the closed region enclosed by the outer curve of the illustration below. Using Property 8, write a relationship between C, A_1, A_2, and A_3.

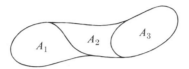

4. Referring to Fig. 12–6, show by the properties of this section that area $ABCD = 10 \cdot$ (area $AEFD$).

5. Two rectangles, R_1 and R_2, have the same altitude. The base of R_1 is AB, and the base of R_2 is AC, where A, B, and C lie on a line. The area of $R_2 = \alpha \cdot$ (area of R_1). Explain precisely what α is.

6. (a) What is the distinction between "a one-inch square" and "one square inch"?
    (b) What is the measure of the area of a 2-ft square, in square feet? in square inches?
    (c) What is the distinction between "a two-foot square" and "two square feet"?

7. Without actually computing the areas, devise a scheme for comparing the areas of two rectangles, one 3 units × 6 units and the other 1.5 units × 9 units.

12–6 VOLUME OF A CLOSED RECTANGULAR PARALLELEPIPED

A sphere is defined as the set of all points in space which lie at a fixed distance, r units, from a given point called the center of the sphere. The set of points whose distance from the center is less than r units is the *interior* of the sphere; the sphere itself is the *boundary* of its interior. The union of the sphere and its interior is called a *closed* spherical region. Both a cylinder and a cone, as described in elementary work, would determine closed regions, and a box-like surface called a rectangular parallelepiped would also determine a closed region. This parallelepiped is determined by six planes, as shown in Fig. 12–9. Opposite planes are parallel and adjacent planes are perpendicular, so that $ABCD$ is a rectangle. There are six *faces*, each of which is a rectangular region such as $ABCD$; adjacent faces intersect in an *edge*. The closed region determined by the rectangular parallelepiped is the simplest closed region in space.

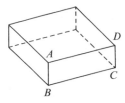

FIGURE 12–9

Intuitively, we know that these closed regions in space have size; we use the term "volume" when we speak of this size. The volumes of two closed regions can probably be best compared by actual measurement. What precisely is this volume, and how can it be measured? Our attention will be restricted to closed regions determined by rectangular parallelepipeds.

It should not be necessary to give all the details of this discussion, since it is similar to that of the last section.

DISCUSSION EXERCISES

1. State a property for volume which is similar to Property 6.

2. State a property for volume which is similar to Property 7.

3. State a property for volume which is similar to Property 8.

4. Sketch three congruent rectangular parallelepipeds, denoting each by R_1. Place them side by side, in nonoverlapping positions but with congruent faces abutting, so as to form a larger parallelepiped. How could the volume of this larger parallelepiped be expressed? Justify your answer by referring to a property.

5. Explain how to obtain a parallelepiped whose volume is
   (a) $(3.1) \cdot$ (volume of R_1),   (b) $(3.4) \cdot$ (volume of R_1).

6. Given a rectangular parallelepiped, R, which has one face congruent to a face of R_1, explain how to express the volume of R in terms of the volume of R_1.

7. Did you prove your result in Exercise 6, or is it a property whose truth should be postulated?

The answer to Exercise 6 above should be similar to Property 9 of the previous section. This answer should yield the desired result immediately. Suppose that a rectangular parallelepiped is given, with edges of length x units, y units, and z units (see Fig. 12–10). This presupposes that a unit of length has been chosen. A parallelepiped will be named by stating a pair of its opposite vertices; for example, the parallelepiped OP in Fig. 12–10 is the large parallelepiped. Using the unit of length OB, mark a number scale on $\overline{OA}$; that OB is the unit of length is denoted by the symbol 1 under the B.

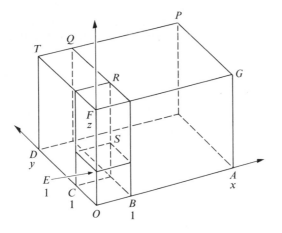

FIGURE 12–10

Now in this scale the length of OA is x units. A plane through B parallel to the face OT determines parallelepiped OQ. By the result of Exercise 6 above,

$$\text{volume of } OP = x \cdot (\text{volume of } OQ).$$

Construct a scale on $\overrightarrow{OD}$ such that the length of OC is 1 unit; then the number corresponding to D is y. A plane through C parallel to the face OG determines the parallelepiped OR, and

$$\text{volume of } OQ = y \cdot (\text{volume of } OR).$$

Construct a scale on $\overrightarrow{OF}$ such that OE is of unit length; parallelepiped OS is determined by a plane through E parallel to the base. Now,

$$\text{volume of } OR = z \cdot (\text{volume of } OS),$$

so that, using the three "volume" statements, we have

$$\text{volume of } OP = x \cdot y \cdot z \cdot (\text{volume of } OS).$$

Note the "shape" of parallelepiped OS; it is a *cube*, the length of each edge being 1 unit. This cube is a convenient unit for measuring volume, since it can be used to express the volume of *any* closed rectangular parallelepiped. If the volume of this unit cube is called a *cubic unit*, then we can state the following definition.

Definition. *Volume of a closed rectangular parallelepiped.* If a rectangular parallelepiped has edges of lengths x units, y units, and z units, then the volume of the closed region determined by this parallelepiped is xyz cubic units.

If the unit of length is the foot, then the corresponding unit of volume is the cubic foot; the cubic centimeter is used for volume if length is measured in centimeters.

If a volume is stated as *w* cubic units, then the *measure* of that volume, in the stated cubic unit, is *w*. Hence, for a closed rectangular parallelepiped,

the measure of the volume = the product of

the measures of the lengths of the edges.

For a parallelepiped of edges 3 in., 4 in., and 5 in.,

the volume = $3 \cdot 4 \cdot 5$ cu. in. = 60 cu. in.,

the measure of the volume, in cu. in., is 60,

$60 = 3 \cdot 4 \cdot 5 =$ product of the measures, in inches, of the edges.

In Property 8, the phrase "sum of the areas" was used. We know what the sum of two numbers means, but this concept does not apply directly to the "addition" of areas. If we define addition of measurements as

x units $+$ y units $= (x + y)$ units,

where the units are the same throughout, then we are free to use such terminology. Note that it is the numbers which are actually added; these numbers are the measures. For example,

2 sq. cm $+$ 7 sq. cm $= (2 + 7)$ sq. cm,

4 cu. mi $+$ 3 cu. mi $= (4 + 3)$ cu. mi.

PROBLEM SET 12–6

1. Let the base of a rectangular parallelepiped be a rectangle which is x units by y units, and let the altitude be z units and the area of the base A square units.
   (a) Show that the measure of the volume is $A \cdot z$.
   (b) Write two different expressions for the volume.
   (c) Find the area of the parallelepiped.
2. Explain the distinction between "nine cubic inches" and "a nine-inch cube."

12–7 ANGLES

What is an angle? Before reading further try to give a definition of an angle. Reflect and deliberate!

You probably had difficulty giving a definition. You may have sketched a diagram such as the drawing in Fig. 12–11(a) as a representation of an angle. You may even have indicated an arc such as that shown in Fig.

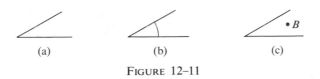

FIGURE 12-11

12-11(b). What is the angle? Is it the pair of rays, or is it the set of all points on the rays together with points such as *B* in Fig. 12-11(c)?

Most people have only an intuitive notion of angle, this having been considered sufficient in many geometry and trigonometry courses. Recently an attempt has been made to define this concept precisely even at the elementary level.

Suppose we have two rays which have a common endpoint but which do not lie on the same line. Then the set of all points on these rays is called an *angle*. For example, the set of all points on $\overrightarrow{OP}$ and $\overrightarrow{OQ}$, in each of the above diagrams, is an angle; thus the angle is the union of $\overrightarrow{OP}$ and $\overrightarrow{OQ}$. The point *O*, which is common to the rays, is termed the *vertex* of the angle. The angles could be denoted by $\angle POQ$ or $\angle QOP$, the vertex always being named second.

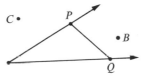

Are either of the points *B* or *C* in the above figure part of the angle? No, since they are not on the rays. If *P* and *Q* are any points on the given rays, one on each ray, a line segment *PQ* is determined. The set of *all* points on all such line segments will be called the *angular region* determined by the given angle. The point *B* is in this region, as are also the points *P* and *Q*. The concept of set subtraction, as defined in Chapter 3, can be used to define the *interior* of an angle as

$$\text{(the angular region)} - \text{(the angle)}.$$

The angle is the *boundary* of the angular region. Hence *B* is a typical point in the interior of the angle. Similarly, the *exterior* of the angle can be defined as

$$\text{(the whole plane)} - \text{(the angular region)}.$$

Thus *C* is a typical point in the exterior of the angle.

It should be expected that certain properties of angles will have to be assumed so that we will have a basis for our thinking.

Property 10.   In any desired position there is an angle congruent to a given angle.

What commonly used language does this property make precise?   Now, given the two angles *ABC* and *DEF* (see figure below), there is an angle, ∠*GBC*, which is congruent to ∠*DEF* (*G* is on the same "side" of the line containing $\overrightarrow{BC}$ as is the point *A*.)   If *G* is in the interior of ∠*ABC*, as in the figure below, then ∠*DEF* is "smaller" than ∠*ABC*; if *A* is in the interior of ∠*CBG*, then ∠*DEF* is "larger" than ∠*ABC*.   Draw a diagram illustrating this last case.   This gives a means of comparing two angles as to "size."   Describe the case where $\overrightarrow{BG}$ coincides with $\overrightarrow{BA}$.

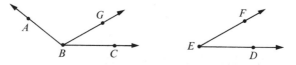

If the endpoint of a ray is on a line and the ray itself is not on the line, two angles are determined, such as ∠*AOB* and ∠*COB* in the figure at the left below.   Two such angles are said to be *supplementary*.   If they are both supplementary and congruent, such as ∠*DOE* and ∠*FOE* in the figure at the right below, each is said to be a *right angle*.   Moreover, in this case the ray is said to be "perpendicular" to the line or, in notation form, $\overrightarrow{OE} \perp \overleftrightarrow{FD}$.

An angle is said to be *acute* if it is "smaller" than a right angle, and *obtuse* if it is "larger" than a right angle (see Problem 6 of the next problem set).

Two angles, such as ∠*ROS* and ∠*SOT* in the figure below, which have a common vertex and exactly one common ray, will be described as *adjacent and nonoverlapping* angles.   This situation can be described more precisely as follows: adjacent nonoverlapping angles have a common vertex and their intersection is a ray.   If ∠*ROS* and ∠*SOT* are acute, adjacent, and non-

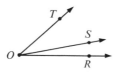

overlapping, then the union of the angular regions *ROS* and *SOT* is the region *ROT*; that is,

region *ROS* ∪ region *SOT* = region *ROT*,

if *S* and *T* lie on the same side of the line determined by $\overrightarrow{OR}$. Moreover, if ∠*ROS* is congruent to ∠*SOT*, as in the figure below, it will be said that ∠*ROT* has been *bisected;* the ray $\overrightarrow{OS}$ is the *angle bisector*. It could be said that $\overrightarrow{OS}$ separates the region *ROT* into two congruent angular regions whose union is the region *ROT*. This is a special case of the following property.

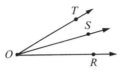

Property 11. For any counting number *n* and any angle ∠*AOB*, there are *n* congruent, adjacent, nonoverlapping angles, the union of whose angular regions is the angular region *AOB*.

For simplicity we may say that the angle has been "subdivided" into *n* congruent parts. This agreement and Property 11, which is one of the postulates, enable us to say that an angle may be "subdivided" into any desired number of congruent, adjacent angles.

PROBLEM SET 12–7

1. What is the union of an angle and its interior?

2. What is the union of an angle, its interior, and its exterior?

3. Consider two line segments which have a common endpoint and do not lie on the same line.
    (a) Is their union an angle? Why?
    (b) Do the segments determine an angle? If so, describe the angle.

4. Consider two adjacent, nonoverlapping angles.
    (a) Is their union an angle? Why?
    (b) Sketch an example where the union of their regions would not be an angular region.
    (c) If the angles are acute, is the union of their regions an angular region?

5. Is your answer to Problem 4(c) based on intuition or knowledge, at this stage?

6. The definitions of "acute angle" and "obtuse angle" in the textual material are somewhat intuitive. Phrase precise definitions of these concepts.

12–8 ANGLE MEASUREMENT

Property 11 yields the basis of angle measurement. Apply it to a right angle for $n = 90$. The "small" angle so determined will be called a *degree*, and its region will be called a *degree region*; the union of 90 adjacent, nonoverlapping degree regions is a right angle region. This degree is a unit of angle measurement. Using this unit, we say that the measurement of a right angle is 90 degrees, or the measure, in degrees, of a right angle is 90. If an angular region were the union of five adjacent, nonoverlapping degree regions, then the measurement of the corresponding angle would be 5 degrees (abbreviated 5°), and its measure, in degrees, would be 5.

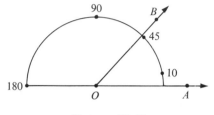

FIGURE 12–12

With this choice of unit, a scale for angle measurement, such as that shown in Fig. 12–12, can be set up as follows. Construct a semicircle of any radius. There is a unit degree angle with its vertex at center O and with its "lower" ray on $\overrightarrow{OA}$. Its "upper" ray intersects the circle in a point with which the number 1 will be associated (this angle is not shown in Fig. 12–12). If ten unit angles are placed in adjacent nonoverlapping positions, a point is determined on the circle with which the number 10 will be associated. Continuation of this procedure yields a scale from 0 to 180 (note that 0 and 180 do not correspond to angles!). For an angle to be measured, there is a congruent angle, $\angle AOB$, which has its vertex at O, one ray on $\overrightarrow{OA}$, and the other ray intersecting the semicircle. If, for example, the ray $\overrightarrow{OB}$ of $\angle AOB$ intersects the semicircle at P_{45}, then $\angle AOB$ is a 45° angle. If $\overrightarrow{OB}$ intersects between P_{45} and P_{46}, as in Fig. 12–12, then we must subdivide further, as in previous measurement problems.

The measure of a 5° angle equals the sum of the measures of the five unit angles, since $5 = 1 + 1 + 1 + 1 + 1$. This exemplifies the first of two general properties which are needed.

Property 12. If the region of an angle α is the union of two or more angular regions whose interiors do not intersect, then the measure of α is the sum of the measures of the angles associated with the "smaller" regions.

Property 13. Congruent angles have the same measure.

By Property 11 there are ten congruent adjacent angles, the union of whose regions is a degree region. By Property 13 these angles have the same measure, say m. Now, by Property 12,

$$m + m + m + \cdots \text{ to 10 terms } = 1,$$

so that $10m = 1$ and $m = 0.1$. Hence, a degree angle has been subdivided into 10 angles, each of which has measure 0.1; each of these angles is a 0.1° angle. If the unit angle determined by P_{45} and P_{46} is subdivided into ten 0.1° angles, points $P_{45.1}, P_{45.2}, \ldots, P_{45.9}$ are determined on the circle. If ray $\overrightarrow{OB}$ of the angle being measured intersects the circle in one of these points, say $P_{45.6}$, then $\angle AOB$ is said to be a 45.6° angle. If it does not intersect at one of these points, further subdivision can take place exactly as occurred for the number line. The above procedure indicates how a number scale can be set up on a semicircle, this scale ranging from 0 to 180. If we now postulate that corresponding to each point on a semicircle there is a real number between 0 and 180, inclusive, a definition of angle measurement (using a degree as unit) can be given.

Definition. *Angle measurement in degrees.* If the vertex of $\angle AOB$ is at the center of a semicircle whose diameter is on $\overrightarrow{OA}$ and if $\overrightarrow{OB}$ intersects the semicircle in a point whose corresponding number is t, then

$\angle AOB$ is a $t°$ angle;   the measure of $\angle AOB$, in degrees, is t.

If a unit other than the degree is chosen, then the scale would range from 0 to some number other than 180. For instance, if a degree is "subdivided" into 60 congruent angles, each such part is called a *minute*. This means that a right angle is "subdivided" into $90 \times 60 = 5400$ parts, so that the scale on the semicircle would range from 0 to 10,800. (Remember that the semicircle determines two right angles at its center.) Likewise, if a minute is "subdivided" into 60 congruent angles, each called a *second*, the scale will range from 0 to 648,000. The preceding definition is valid for angle measurement using either of these scales, if the word "degree" is replaced by "minute" or "second." Other units are possible and are used for special purposes.

PROBLEM SET 12–8

1. Use $n = 125$ in Property 11 as applied to a right angle to define a unit for angle measurement; call this unit a "squen."
   (a) State the scale range for the "squen."
   (b) State the measure, in "squens," of a right angle.
   (c) Write an equation which will give the equivalence relationship between degrees and "squens."
   (d) Find the measure, in "squens," of an 18° angle; a 45° angle; a 120° angle.
   (e) Find the degree measurement of an angle whose measure, in "squens", is 200; is 15; is 90.

2. Write inequalities for the measure, in degrees, of an acute angle A; an obtuse angle B.

3. If α and β are supplementary angles, find $m(\alpha) + m(\beta)$, where $m(\alpha)$ denotes the measure of α.

4. Is there an angle α such that $m(\alpha) = 180$? Why?

5. Using the concept of measure of an angle, show that there is an angle whose measure is the sum of the measures of any two given acute angles. (Compare with Problem 5 of the preceding problem set.)

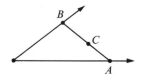

6. Suppose that an angle is defined as follows: If two rays have a common endpoint and if A is any point on one ray and B is any point on the other ray, then the angle determined by these rays is the set of all points on all segments such as AB. Using this definition of angle, answer the following questions.

   (a) Is C on the angle?
   (b) Are A and B on the angle?
   (c) If α and β are any adjacent, nonoverlapping acute angles, is the union of α and β an angle?
   (d) How can a 5° angle be described in terms of union?

7. Write Properties 11 and 12 in terms of the definition of angle in Problem 6.

8. What concept in the text is the counterpart of an angle as defined in Problem 6?

9. Would the definition of angle in Problem 6 have served equally well for a discussion of measurement?

CHAPTER 13

Measurement in Practice

13-1 SOME DIFFICULTIES WHICH ARISE

The discussions of the previous chapter should have given us some understanding of what we will call "mathematical measurement." In practice, several quite different concepts must also be taken into consideration. These concepts can be grouped under several headings.

(a) The reality of a physical length. What is the length of this sheet of paper? There are bound to be irregularities in the edges of the sheet, caused by the cutting process, so that in actuality there is no such thing as *the* length of the sheet. However, it is convenient to speak of this mythical "true" length, and we shall do so. A number used as the measure of this "true" length is, in some sense, an average of many numbers, each of which is the measure of the length of some mathematical line segment. In practice, therefore, uncertainty as to meaning exists even before measurement begins.

(b) Imperfections of instruments. A scale of some sort is used to measure this "true" length. Take two scales, or rulers, which are supposedly alike, and compare them as closely as you can. You will probably find that although they are nearly alike, yet they are not exactly alike, due to imperfections of manufacture. These imperfections are bound to introduce a type of "error" into a measurement. We shall assume that we are using a scale which conforms to suitable standards, and hence can disregard this type of "error."

(c) Zeroing error. When we measure the length of a segment, we place the zero mark of the scale at one end of the segment. Can the placement of the zero point be exact? Since vision is involved, this alone would make such placement inexact; if the zero point is placed several times, there is little likelihood that the result would be the same each time. This error can be eliminated by using a "hook rule." As shown below, this type of rule has a device at the zero point which fits snugly against one end of the segment *AB* to be measured.

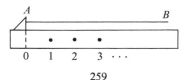

(d) Reading error. Finally, a reading on the scale must be made. Here both judgment and vision, neither of which is completely reliable, are involved in determining which mark on the scale is closest to the "true" length.

By reason of the above discussion an actual measurement may only be an approximation of the "true" length. Whatever answer is given, error is involved — not the kind of "error" due to a mistake made by the operator (which is always possible, of course) but error that is inherent in the nature of measurement. Herein lies the vast distinction between a part of the real world and a mathematical model of that part; the mathematical model of the previous chapter describes only in part the problem of measuring a physical attribute, such as length or volume. However, the use of a model considerably enhances our ability to understand the real world, if the model is correctly applied and interpreted. Successful use of a mathematical model depends on correct mathematical operations, say arithmetic or algebra, and on a correct translation from the real world to the model.

To avoid some, but not all, of these difficulties, you may well say "take several measurements and then compute the average." It is by doing just this and then applying certain ideas from a discipline known as statistics that progress can be made. Most of this is beyond the limits of our present knowledge; hence, we must be satisfied, at present, with just a brief glimpse into the subject of error analysis.

13–2 PRECISION AND GREATEST POSSIBLE ERROR

Suppose that we have a ruler which is based on the inch as unit and which has marks only at points $\frac{1}{4}$ in. apart. This type of ruler will be called a "one-fourth inch ruler." It may be considered that the unit used in constructing this ruler is $\frac{1}{4}$ in. If, using this ruler, we state that the measurement of segment AB is $3\frac{1}{4}$ in., we merely mean that the length of AB is closer to $3\frac{1}{4}$ in. than to either 3 in. or $3\frac{2}{4}$ in. This is illustrated in the following diagram which shows the segment AB and a portion of the $\frac{1}{4}$-in. ruler. The points C and D are the midpoints of the respective segments of length $\frac{1}{4}$ in.; they do not appear on the scale but are reference points in our minds. Since B lies between C and D, the "true" length lies between $3\frac{1}{8}$ in. and $3\frac{3}{8}$ in. Another way to state this is that B cannot lie more than $\frac{1}{8}$ in. in either direction from the $3\frac{1}{4}$-in. mark on the scale. If B had been any point between positions C and D, the same result, $3\frac{1}{4}$ in., would have been given as the measurement. If you think that B lies over the $3\frac{1}{8}$-in. mark, C, then you may choose either 3 in. or $3\frac{1}{4}$ in. as the measurement.

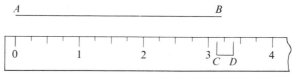

The measurement considered above is said to be *precise to the nearest* $\frac{1}{4}$ in. Further, it is said that the *greatest possible error* in the measurement is $\frac{1}{8}$ in., since B lies between $3\frac{1}{4} - \frac{1}{8}$ in. and $3\frac{1}{4} + \frac{1}{8}$ in.; that is, the "true" length will differ from $3\frac{1}{4}$ in. by no more than $\frac{1}{8}$ in. Note that the greatest possible error (abbreviated GPE) is half the unit size being used. In the preceding discussion and in the rest of the chapter it is assumed that there is no zeroing error; this would be the case if a hook rule were used.

DISCUSSION EXERCISES

1. Consider measurement with a half-inch ruler.
    (a) How precise is such a measurement?
    (b) What is the GPE?
    (c) What could be said about the "true" length of a segment whose measurement is reported as $6\frac{1}{2}$ in.?

2. What unit size should be used so that the GPE would be $\frac{1}{16}$ in.?

3. A measurement correct to the nearest 0.5 in. is said to be more precise than a measurement correct only to the nearest inch. Supply the appropriate words in the following sentences.
    (a) When using a $\frac{1}{8}$-in. ruler, a measurement will be ——— precise than when using a $\frac{1}{4}$-in. ruler.
    (b) As the unit used gets smaller, measurements become ——— precise.
    (c) As the GPE becomes smaller, the precision ——— (increases or decreases).

When the result of a measurement is to be written, how can the precision involved be indicated? The simplest, yet probably least used, method involves the GPE. A length read as $3\frac{1}{4}$ in., using a $\frac{1}{4}$-in. ruler, could be written as $3\frac{1}{4} \pm \frac{1}{8}$ in. This notation means that the length is between $3\frac{1}{4} - \frac{1}{8}$ in. and $3\frac{1}{4} + \frac{1}{8}$ in. Likewise, a measurement with a $\frac{1}{8}$-in. ruler which is read as $2\frac{3}{8}$ in. could be written $2\frac{3}{8} \pm \frac{1}{16}$ in. It follows that when a measurement is written $7\frac{1}{2} \pm \frac{1}{8}$ in., the GPE is $\frac{1}{8}$ in. and the measurement is precise to the nearest $\frac{1}{4}$ in. This indicates that a $\frac{1}{4}$-in. scale has been used. It should be pointed out that some writers use the notation $x \pm c$, where c represents something other than the GPE; such will not be the case here.

If measurements are written in fractional form, another device can be used. Let us agree that $2\frac{3}{4}$ in. will indicate precision to the nearest $\frac{1}{4}$ in. and that $3\frac{5}{16}$ in. will indicate precision to the nearest $\frac{1}{16}$ in. There is one difficulty which arises from use of this agreement: usually fractions are simplified (for example, $3\frac{2}{4}$ is written as $3\frac{1}{2}$); hence, when using the above agreement we must avoid such simplification. When a $\frac{1}{8}$-in. ruler is used, a measurement of $5\frac{6}{8}$ in. must be left in that form; in this instance, a measurement written as 3 in. would not indicate the proper precision, so it should be written as $3\frac{0}{8}$ in.

In scientific work the decimal form of a numeral is often used in writing a measurement. Let us agree, in general, that precision will be indicated by the place value of the right-hand digit. Accordingly,

$$\left.\begin{array}{r} 6.37 \text{ ft} \\ 637 \text{ ft} \\ 6.00 \text{ ft} \end{array}\right\} \text{ indicates precision to the nearest } \left\{\begin{array}{r} 0.01 \text{ ft} \\ 1 \text{ ft} \\ 0.01 \text{ ft} \end{array}\right.$$

The last measurement, 6.00 ft, may cause some wonderment; however, the two zeros would have been omitted if they did not indicate something. One situation which gives trouble is where zeros appear at the right-hand end of a numeral, yet to the left of the decimal point. What precision is involved in writing 12,000 ft? According to the above agreement, the measurement 12,000 ft should mean precision to the nearest foot. If this is true, how would precision to the nearest 10 ft or the nearest 100 ft be indicated? This difficulty can be overcome by modifying the agreement as follows: when zeros appear at the right-hand end of a numeral for a *counting number*, precision is indicated by the right-hand nonzero digit. Accordingly, 12,000 ft would indicate precision to the nearest 1000 ft. If it is desired to indicate greater precision, special marks or notation for the GPE could be used. For example,

$$\left.\begin{array}{r} 120\overline{0}0 \text{ ft} \\ 1200\underline{0} \text{ ft} \\ 12000 \pm 50 \text{ ft} \\ 12.00 \times 10^3 \text{ ft} \end{array}\right\} \text{ indicates precision to the nearest } \left\{\begin{array}{r} 10 \text{ ft,} \\ 1 \text{ ft,} \\ 100 \text{ ft,} \\ 10 \text{ ft.} \end{array}\right.$$

In the last example precision is indicated by the zeros to the right of the decimal point; the power of 10 then produces the proper number; this precision could also be indicated by writing $120\overline{0}0$ ft.

PROBLEM SET 13–2

1. State the precision indicated in each measurement below.

   (a) $5\frac{3}{4}$ ft   (b) 6.27 mi   (c) $4\frac{6}{8}$ in.

   (d) $4\frac{0}{16}$ ft   (e) 3.400 cm   (f) 400 ft

   (g) $6\overline{0}0$ mi   (h) $0.04 \pm \frac{1}{200}$ in.   (i) 400 ± 5 mi

   (j) 6.270 in.   (k) 0.005 in.   (l) 15,000 mi

2. For each measurement given in Problem 1, state the GPE and write the measurements between which the "true" length lies.

3. Four greatest possible errors are given below; in each case find the precision of measurement.

   (a) 0.05 ft   (b) $\frac{1}{32}$ in.   (c) 0.12 in.   (d) 50 mi

4. If a $\frac{1}{8}$-in. ruler is used, could a measurement be given as $4\frac{3}{16}$ in.? Why, or why not?

5. If a $\frac{1}{10}$-in. ruler is used, could a measurement be written as 2.34 in. or 6.785 in.? Why, or why not?

6. What type ruler must be used in order to write a measurement as 6.3 ft? 7.02 ft?

7. (a) Are the measurements 13.1 in. and 1.1 ft equally precise? Why?
   (b) Would it be correct to convert 1.1 ft to (12×1.1) in. $= 13.2$ in. to determine the precision? Why?
   (c) Which measurement in part (b) is the more precise? Why?

13–3 RELATIVE ERROR

It may be felt that knowledge as to the precision of a measurement indicates how "good" the measurement is. Sometimes this is true; at other times the use of another type of error analysis, known as "relative error," is at least convenient. The *relative error* of a measurement is the ratio of the number involved in the GPE to the number involved in the measured length; more precisely,

$$\text{relative error} = \frac{\text{measure of GPE}}{\text{measure of length}}.$$

To exemplify this concept, consider the two measurements 16.14 in. and 1.14 in. which have the same precision and, hence, the same GPE of $\frac{1}{200}$ in., or 0.005 in. For the measurement 16.14 in.

$$\text{relative error} = \frac{0.005}{16.14} \approx 0.0003,$$

and for 1.14 in.

$$\text{relative error} = \frac{0.005}{1.14} \approx 0.0044.$$

To interpret these numbers, we will rewrite the equation defining relative error as

$$\text{measure of GPE} = (\text{relative error}) \cdot (\text{measure of the length}).$$

Using this form of the equation, we have, for example,

$$\text{measure of GPE} = (0.0003) \cdot (\text{measure of length}),$$

that is,

$$\text{GPE} = (0.0003) \cdot (\text{the measured length}).$$

Also, we have

$$\text{measure of GPE} = (0.0044) \cdot (\text{measure of length}),$$

that is,

$$\text{GPE} = (0.0044) \cdot (\text{the measured length}).$$

Intuitively, we may feel that because 0.0003 is smaller than 0.0044, then the first measurement is better than the second; whether or not this is so will be considered in the next two sections.

Earlier it was noted that precision can be determined by the place value of the right-hand digit in the decimal numeral for the measure. What is it that determines relative error? To obtain an answer to this question, let us compare several measurements, say 123 in., 12.3 in. and 1.23 in. For these measurements the relative errors are $0.5/123$, $0.05/12.3$, and $0.005/1.23$, respectively. Since each of these ratios is $5/1230$, these measurements have equal relative errors. Hence the position of the decimal point does not seem to be a determining feature for relative error, as it was for precision.

Now compare the relative errors for measurements of 1.2 in., 1.23 in., and 1.234 in.; these are, respectively,

$$\frac{0.05}{1.2} \approx 0.04, \qquad \frac{0.005}{1.23} \approx 0.004, \qquad \frac{0.0005}{1.234} \approx 0.0004.$$

Accordingly, relative error seems to depend on the number of digits in the measure. We will not pursue this topic into a discussion of the "significance of digits," since, as it will turn out, our primary interest is in precision.

The word "accuracy" has not been used and will not be used in this text. In normal discourse accuracy and precision are usually used as synonyms. Such is not the case in technical work, where the word "accuracy" is used to denote the "trueness" of a measurement. The "trueness" of a measurement is not the same as the relative error; this we cannot discuss further since somewhat advanced tools are needed for the discussion.

PROBLEM SET 13–3

1. Find the relative errors for each of the following measurements, and then arrange the measurements in order of decreasing relative error.
   (a) 27.1 in.   (b) 3.5 in.   (c) 0.071 in.   (d) 23.42 in.

2. The measurements 6 in., 6.2 in., 6.18 in., and 6.184 in. are arranged (a) in order of _____ [increasing or decreasing] precision? (b) in order of _____ [increasing or decreasing] GPE? (c) in order of _____ [increasing or decreasing] relative error?

13-4 ADDITION AND SUBTRACTION INVOLVING MEASUREMENTS

Sometimes a carpenter desires to find the distance between two points which are farther apart than the length of his measuring rule. In such a case he must "break" the distance into two or more parts, measure each part separately, and then "add" the measurements. You will recall that earlier the notion of 12 in. + 16 in. was discussed; it was stated that actually the measures, 12 and 16, are to be added to find the total measure of the final result. It would seem reasonable that the carpenter would use the same precision for each measurement, since he would probably use the same measuring device. For example, he might be interested in finding $45\frac{8}{16}$ in. + $22\frac{3}{16}$ in.; if he were to read the first numeral as $45\frac{1}{2}$ in., he would mentally interpolate "correct to the nearest $\frac{1}{16}$ in." According to this argument the measurements being added will have the same GPE. Let us find the GPE involved in the above sum. Since

$$45\tfrac{8}{16} - \tfrac{1}{32} < \{\text{measure of "true" first length}\} < 45\tfrac{8}{16} + \tfrac{1}{32}$$

and

$$22\tfrac{3}{16} - \tfrac{1}{32} < \{\text{measure of "true" second length}\} < 22\tfrac{3}{16} + \tfrac{1}{32},$$

then

$$45\tfrac{8}{16} + 22\tfrac{3}{16} - (\tfrac{1}{32} + \tfrac{1}{32}) < \begin{Bmatrix} \text{measure of} \\ \text{"true"} \\ \text{total length} \end{Bmatrix} < 45\tfrac{8}{16} + 22\tfrac{3}{16} + (\tfrac{1}{32} + \tfrac{1}{32}).$$

Accordingly, the GPE of the sum is $2(\frac{1}{32})$ in., that is, twice the GPE of the original measurements. Show that if three measurements had been involved, the GPE of the sum would be three times the GPE of the original measurements. Returning to the example, we could write the result as $67\frac{11}{16} \pm \frac{1}{16}$ in. Would an answer $67\frac{11}{16}$ in. convey the correct information? Why?

The above example illustrates the following principle:

The GPE of a sum of measurements is the sum of the GPE's of the individual measurements.

Hence, in general, the GPE of a sum is larger than the GPE of any single measurement in that sum. Consequently, a length obtained by computation involving additions is less precise than the individual measurements.

If a rectangle is measured as $3\frac{1}{4}$ in. by $5\frac{2}{4}$ in., then the perimeter of the rectangle is $17\frac{2}{4}$ in. $\pm \frac{4}{8}$ in.; this could be written $17\frac{1}{2} \pm \frac{1}{2}$ in. (why?). This discussion should point up the fact that when measurements are involved in computations, the precision of the computed result cannot be taken for granted, but rather must be investigated.

The situation is not as simple as the preceding discussion may seem to indicate. Suppose that several measurements are involved in an addition;

in some cases the error involved (i.e., the "true" length minus the measured length) may be positive, while in other cases it may be negative. When the measurements are added, these errors would tend to offset each other, so that the error involved in the computed sum might be considerably less than the GPE. No attempt will be made to do more than point out this situation, since much greater background is necessary for a discussion of it.

It is unlikely that anyone would be interested in adding 123 in. and 0.123 in., even though these measurements have the same relative error. Since the second measurement is smaller than the GPE of the first, the result of the addition would not mean much. However, one might well be interested in adding 123 in. and 12.3 in., if the individual measurements were made with the same instrument. In that case we would expect to be equally precise, so that the first measurement should be written as 123.0 in. rather than 123 in. If, for some reason, measuring instruments of different precision are used to obtain 123 in. and 12.3 in., either of the following two modes of procedure could be used.

(a) Compute and use both GPE's to obtain

$$(123 \pm 0.5 \text{ in.}) + (12.3 \pm 0.05 \text{ in.}) = 135.3 \pm 0.55 \text{ in.}$$

(b) "Round off" the 12.3 to 12, that is, use the lesser precision for both measurements, to obtain

$$123 \text{ in.} + 12 \text{ in.} = 135 \text{ in.}$$

Usually, when measurements are to be added they should be equally precise.

In the preceding paragraph, 12.3 in. was "rounded" to 12 in., that is, the number was "rounded" to the nearest one. In general, one "rounds off" a number to the nearest digit in a specified position, for example,

12.48   to the nearest 0.1 is   12.5,

12.43   to the nearest 0.1 is   12.4,

12.346   to the nearest 0.1 is   12.3.

These examples should be clear from the statement of what is desired. However, if 12.45 is to be rounded to the nearest 0.1, there is no reason for preferring 12.4 over 12.5 as the result. Since there is no mathematical reason for making a choice, it must be made arbitrarily. We choose the number whose last digit is even; in the above example, choose 12.4, since 4 is even. For the same reason, 12.35 would be "rounded up" to 12.4. With this choice, sometimes you "round up," and sometimes you "round down"; hence there is more chance of the "ups" balancing the "downs" in a sequence of "round offs" than if the choice were always made in one direction. The above arbitrary rule has the sanction of a commission appointed to make recommendations on such matters; it may be different from your previous practice.

If, in the last example above, the digits of 12.346 had been "rounded off" one at a time, the results would have been 12.35 first, then 12.4. This is not in accord with the result 12.3 stated previously; moreover, 12.3 is correct, since $12.346 = 12.3 + 0.046$, and $0.046 < 0.050$.

Subtraction will be discussed in the problems below.

PROBLEM SET 13-4

1. In each of the following problems write the answer so as to indicate the GPE. "Round off" where necessary.
    (a) 14.2 in. + 16.7 in. + 5.4 in.
    (b) $5\frac{4}{8}$ lbs + $12\frac{3}{8}$ lbs + $8\frac{7}{8}$ lbs.
    (c) 3.02 ft + 11.435 ft + 7.813 ft.

2. (a) When 7.347 is "rounded" to the nearest 0.1, why is the result 7.3 rather than 7.4?
    (b) "Round off" 0.1348 and 4.6853 to the nearest 0.01.

3. The sides of a rectangle are measured as $14\frac{3}{8}$ in. and $9\frac{7}{8}$ in. Find the perimeter of the rectangle, and show the GPE.

4. The sides of a triangle are measured to be 14.1 ft, 11.7 ft, and 19.2 ft. Find the GPE for the calculated perimeter.

5. In each of the following questions and statements pertaining to the difference 7 in. − 4 in., assume that 7 in. and 4 in. were determined by measurement.
    (a) Can $7 - 4$ be written as $7 + (-4)$? Why?
    (b) Write an inequality involving the GPE in the measurement 4 in. (see ideas used in addition).
    (c) Since $4 - 0.5 < 4 < 4 + 0.5$, does it follow that $-(4 + 0.5) < -4 < -(4 - 0.5)$? What property was used?
    (d) Show how this leads to $7 + (-4) - (0.5 + 0.5) <$ computed measure $< 7 + (-4) + (0.5 + 0.5)$.
    (e) What is the GPE for the computed difference 7 in. − 4 in.?

6. Find the GPE for each of the following computed differences.
    (a) 17.2 lbs − 5.4 lbs
    (b) $23\frac{1}{4}$ ft − $15\frac{2}{4}$ ft
    (c) 3.24 mi − 1.57 mi
    (d) 21.73 in. − 18.61 in.

7. If x and y are the measures of lengths, each having a GPE whose measure is e, show that the GPE for $x - y$ is $2e$.

13–5 HOW "GOOD" IS A MEASUREMENT?

To consider the question "How 'good' is a measurement?" we must define what is meant by "good"; this, as we shall see, calls for another question, "good for what?"

In the preceding section, when addition of measurements was of interest, it appeared that the "goodness" of a measurement was dependent upon precision, rather than upon relative error. Two measurements, such as 123 in. and 12 in., which have the same precision but different relative errors, were considered equally "good." On the other hand, two measurements, such as 123 in. and 12.3 in., which have different precision but the same relative errors, were not considered equally "good."

Are there situations in which measurements would be considered equally "good" because they have the same relative error but differing degrees of precision? What is done with measurements after they are made? They can be compared, of course. If Smith measures a certain distance as $123 \pm \frac{1}{4}\, mi$ and Jones measures another distance as $123 \pm \frac{1}{4}\, in.$, the relative error in each case is the same, $0.25/123$. Since, in each case, the GPE is $(0.25/123) \cdot$ (measured length), these might be considered as equally "good." However, the distances involved are so different that there seems to be little point in making a comparison. If the two distances had not been too different from each other, there would have been reason to make a comparison, but when relative errors are equal,

$$\frac{\text{measure of GPE of first measurement}}{\text{measure of first measurement}}$$

$$= \frac{\text{measure of GPE of second measurement}}{\text{measure of second measurement}}.$$

Since the denominators are nearly equal, the numerators are also nearly equal. Once again, therefore, in a case of real interest it is the GPE which is the governing feature.

Suppose you were interested in measuring the time taken by a jet plane to travel from New York to Chicago and comparing it with the time taken by an automobile to travel the same distance. Measuring their times to the nearest minute, say, (i.e., being equally precise) would hardly seem reasonable. Intuitively, it would seem that measurement of the plane's time to the nearest minute might be comparable to the nearest fifteen minutes for the car. In this case relative error, rather than precision, would determine the "goodness" of the measurement.

To repeat, how "good" a measurement is and how the "goodness" is to be determined depends on how the measurement is to be used.

13-6 PRECISION INVOLVED IN MULTIPLICATION

We have seen that when measured quantities are "added", the GPE of the result is larger than that of the measurements. The effect on the GPE when a multiplication is involved can be illustrated by considering the area of a closed rectangular region. To find the area of such a region, the lengths of the sides are found by measurement and the area is then computed by a multiplication. Suppose that 6 in. and 9 in. are the measured lengths of the sides of a rectangle, correct to the nearest inch, and that L in. and W in. represent the "true" length and width, respectively. Then

$$5.5 < W < 6.5 \quad \text{and} \quad 8.5 < L < 9.5.$$

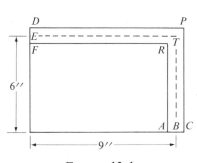

FIGURE 13-1

Now, LW sq. in. is the "true" area of the rectangular region, and 54 sq. in. is the computed area of that same region. As indicated in Fig. 13-1, we could consider the given rectangular region as lying between two other rectangular regions, which are 5.5 in. by 8.5 in. and 6.5 in. by 9.5 in., respectively. Hence

$$5.5 \times 8.5 < \text{measure of "true" area} < 6.5 \times 9.5,$$

$$46.75 < \text{measure of "true" area} < 61.75.$$

Now, the measure of the computed area is $6 \cdot 9 = 54$, and the measure of the "true" area is LW, so that

$$46.75 = 54 - 7.25 < LW < 54 + 7.75 = 61.75.$$

The number 7.75 is the difference between 61.75 and 54; similarly, 7.25 is the difference between 54 and 46.75. The numbers 7.75 and 7.25 will be referred to as differences. Note that these differences are not equal. Also, since $54 - 7.75 < 54 - 7.25$ (why?), then

$$54 - 7.75 < LW < 54 + 7.75.$$

This last inequality was obtained so that the differences would be equal, and hence the GPE could be determined. Accordingly, the "true" area can be expressed as 54 ± 7.75 sq. in., so that the GPE for the computed area is 7.75 sq. in. This can be interpreted as meaning that the "true" area differs from 54 sq. in. by no more than 7.75 sq. in. Expressed in another way, the error involved in stating that the area is 54 sq. in. is no more than 7.75 sq. in.

The GPE determined above is much larger than might have been anticipated. The reason for this can be seen by multiplying 6.5 by 9.5 in expanded form:

$$(6 + 0.5)(9 + 0.5) = 6(9) + 6(0.5) + 9(0.5) + (0.5)^2$$
$$= 54 + (6 + 9)0.5 + 0.25.$$

Here, the original GPE of 0.5 is multiplied by 15 to give the major part of the resulting GPE. In what sense is 15(0.5) the "major part" of the resulting GPE?

Moreover, the reason for the original differences being unequal can be seen by comparing the above computation with the following:

$$(6 - 0.5)(9 - 0.5) = 54 - (6 + 9)0.5 + 0.25$$
$$= 54 - [15(0.5) - 0.25].$$

Accordingly, the original differences are $15(0.5) + 0.25$ and $15(0.5) - 0.25$.

The multiplication of two numbers has an exact result. Certainly 7.9×5.4 is equal to 42.66, in the true sense of equality. It is only when there is some reason for knowing or suspecting that 7.9 and 5.4 are inexact that the product may be inexact. Certainly this will be true if 7.9 and 5.4 result from measurements. It will also be true if they result from "rounding off." If 7.9 and 5.4 are obtained from 7.92 and 5.37 by "rounding off," then 7.9 and 5.4 are precise to the nearest 0.1; with this in mind, the preceding ideas can be applied to find the GPE in 7.9×5.4.

ILLUSTRATIVE EXAMPLE. The numbers 7.32 and 4.75 were obtained by measurement; round them to the nearest 0.1. Then compute the product and find the GPE of the computed product.

Solution. The "rounded" numbers are 7.3 and 4.8. The computed product is $7.3 \times 4.8 = 35.04$. Now, the "actual" numbers are $a = 7.3 \pm 0.05$ and $b = 4.8 \pm 0.05$, so that

$$7.25 < a < 7.35 \qquad \text{and} \qquad 4.75 < b < 4.85.$$

Accordingly,

$$(7.3 - 0.05)(4.8 - 0.05) < ab < (7.3 + 0.05)(4.8 + 0.05),$$
$$35.04 - 0.6025 < ab < 35.04 + 0.6075.$$

Since $35.04 - 0.6075 < 35.04 - 0.6025$, then the last inequality can be replaced by

$$35.04 - 0.6075 < ab < 35.04 + 0.6075.$$

Hence $ab = 35.04 \pm 0.6075$, so that the GPE of the computed product is 0.6075.

Error analysis is very important for persons working with statistical or computing problems. In such situations the analysis can be quite complicated, and for that reason we have attempted to discuss only the introductory aspects of these problems.

PROBLEM SET 13–6

1. Interpret each of the following geometrically in terms of the diagram in Fig. 13–1.

    (a) the difference 7.75 sq. in.,

    (b) the difference 7.25 sq. in.

    (c) the difference between 7.75 sq. ins. and 7.25 sq. in.

2. (a) In the preceding discussion the area of the inner rectangular region, 5.5 in. by 8.5 in., was "replaced" by $(54 - 7.75)$ sq. ins. Why was this replacement made?

    (b) Could the area of the outer rectangular region have been replaced by $(54 + 7.25)$ sq. in.? Why?

3. For each of the following rectangles the lengths of the sides were found by measurement. Find the computed area and the GPE of the computed area. Then express the "true" area in terms of a GPE.

    (a) 3.2 ft by 8.7 ft   (b) $2\frac{7}{8}$ in. by $5\frac{3}{8}$ in.

    (c) 15 cm by 22 cm   (d) $5\frac{2}{4}$ mm by $7\frac{9}{4}$ mm

4. Assume that the following numbers were obtained by "rounding off." Find the GPE for each of the computed results, and express the answer using GPE.

    (a) $67.32 + 45.98$ (b) $43.2 - 28.9$ (c) 14.3×11.8

    (d) 3.24×5.67 (e) 11.6×8.7 (f) 4.6×7.3

5. Given two numbers A and B with GPE's of a and b, respectively, show that the GPE of the computed product is $aB + bA + ab$.

CHAPTER 14

Mathematical Systems

When a person deals with familiar things, he is very apt to overlook important details; also, he may have difficulty in recognizing the full importance of certain concepts. To discuss ideas similar to the familiar but in an unfamiliar context usually serves to clarify them and to set forth related ideas.

We are familiar with several types of numbers (e.g., integers and rational numbers) and several types of operations with these numbers (e.g., addition and multiplication). In fact we are so familiar with some of them that we tend to lose sight of important properties. The seemingly strange ideas presented in some of the following pages are anything but trivial; they are very important in some areas of mathematics and its applications. However, for us their importance is mainly to clarify certain concepts.

14–1 DAY OF THE WEEK COMPUTATION

What day of the week is 25 days from today? Of course, you could determine the day by counting off 25 days on your fingers. Presumably a better scheme has occurred to you by this time. Since 25 days is 3 weeks and 4 days, the question is the same as asking for the day which is 4 days from today. If today is Tuesday, then the answer should be Saturday. The number of exact weeks involved makes no difference; only the "fractional" part of a week is important. Similarly, 90 days from a Sunday is the same as 6 days from a Sunday, i.e., a Saturday.

According to the division theorem, any whole number can be divided by 7 so as to obtain a remainder r, $0 \leq r \leq 6$; it is these remainders which are of interest in a situation such as that outlined above. Determining the answer to the above questions could be facilitated still further as follows: assign the numbers from 0 to 6 to the days of the week, in sequence, starting with any day desired. Suppose that the assignment is made thus:

Sun.	Mon.	Tues.	Wed.	Thurs.	Fri.	Sat.
0	1	2	3	4	5	6

Then the number of the day which is 25 days after Tuesday should be $2 + 4$, that is, four days after the day whose number is 2. The result, 6, and Saturday correspond in the table. Fine! But what is the day 26 days after Tuesday? Here $2 + 5$ is needed, but no day has the number 7 assigned to it; the day "7" could be thought of as one week after day 0. The symbol "7" for a day is not needed if we write $2 + 5 = 0$. Obviously, whole weeks are being disregarded every time they arise. With the same thought in mind, we have $2 + 6 = 1$, $5 + 4 = 2$, and $4 + 3 = 0$.

This sort of calculation appears artificial at first glance, but often it is useful. Essentially, a new operation is being defined. The fact that this operation is "different" and "new" might be emphasized by introducing a new symbol, such as $\oplus$ or $\triangle$, for the operation. This we shall not bother doing at the moment. Other possible addition combinations should be obtained and assembled in a table such as Table 14–1.

Table 14–1

Addition (day of the week)

	0	1	2	3	4	5	6
0	0	1	2	3	4	5	6
1	1	2	3	4	5	6	0
2	2	3	4	5	6	0	1
3	3	4	5	6	0	1	2
4	4	5	6	0	1	2	3
5	5	6	0	1	2	3	4
6	6	0	1	2	3	4	5

The two top rows by themselves constitute what is often called the "zero addition table," since they yield $0 + 0$, $0 + 1$, $0 + 2$, ..., $0 + 6$. Likewise, the top and fourth rows, by themselves, constitute the "two addition table," yielding $2 + 0$, $2 + 1$, $2 + 2$, ..., $2 + 6$. This table is used in a fashion similar to that discussed in Chapter 1. The entries to the right of and below the ruled lines constitute the *body of the table*.

PROBLEM SET 14–1

1. Using the number-day assignments of this section find the day which is (a) 37 days after a Monday, (b) 102 days after a Friday, (c) 69 days after a Wednesday, (d) 43 days after a Sunday, (e) 365 days after a Thursday.

2. Assign 0 to Wednesday, 1 to Thursday, and so on; with this new assignment of numbers answer the questions of Problem 1.

3. Were the answers the same to Problems 1 and 2? Does the assignment of numbers to days seem to make any difference?

4. Show how to find the following addition combinations, which appear in Table 14–1.

(a) 4 + 5   (b) 6 + 2   (c) 4 + 4

14–2 MODULAR ADDITION

The addition table of the previous section resulted from a decision to consider only the remainders r, $0 \leq r \leq 6$, when whole numbers are divided by 7. The arithmetic resulting from this decision is called "modular arithmetic," and the notation "modulo 7" is used to denote the basic divisor. To indicate that 12 and 19 have the same remainder when divided by 7, the notation $12 \equiv 19(\bmod 7)$ is used. This can be read "12 is equivalent to 19, mod 7." (Even though the wording "12 is congruent to 19, mod 7" is more usual in mathematics, the former wording will be adopted here.) When the word "remainder" is used in connection with division by 7, it will be implied that $0 \leq r \leq 6$.

Now, by the division theorem, for each whole number x there is a unique number r such that $x = 7q + r$, $0 \leq r \leq 6$. Hence each whole number x is equivalent to one and only one number r, $0 \leq r \leq 6$, modulo 7. Since $25 = 3 \cdot 7 + 4$, then $25 \equiv 4(\bmod 7)$; likewise, $42 = 6 \cdot 7 + 0 \equiv 0(\bmod 7)$, and $125 = 17 \cdot 7 + 6 \equiv 6(\bmod 7)$. Accordingly,

$$25 + 42 = (3 \cdot 7 + 4) + (6 \cdot 7 + 0)$$
$$= (3 + 6)\, 7 + (4 + 0)$$
$$\equiv 4 + 0 \;(\bmod 7)$$
$$\equiv 4 \;(\bmod 7).$$

Thus, the sum of 25 and 42, modulo 7, is the same as the sum of 4 and 0, modulo 7. This exemplifies the fact that Table 14–1 gives a complete description of possible results when two whole numbers are added, modulo 7.

Since counting proceeds as 0, 1, 2, 3, 4, 5, 6, 0, 1, 2, 3, 4, 5, 6, 0, 1, etc., in this arithmetic modulo 7, it could be considered that we are using a clock with seven positions marked on its face. The clock hand jumps from one position to the next, rather than moving smoothly, as an ordinary clock hand does.

Naturally, division by 12 or 5 or 9, for example, could be considered just as readily as division by 7. This would lead to addition tables modulo 12, modulo 5, or modulo 9, respectively (see problems below).

PROBLEM SET 14–2

1. Find two whole numbers which are truth values for each of the following.
   (a) $x \equiv 3(\text{mod } 7)$ (b) $x \equiv 5(\text{mod } 7)$
   (c) $x \equiv 1(\text{mod } 7)$ (d) $x \equiv 0(\text{mod } 7)$

2. Are the following sentences true or false? Why?
   (a) $25 \equiv 11(\text{mod } 7)$ (b) $13 \equiv 23(\text{mod } 7)$
   (c) $43 \equiv 65(\text{mod } 7)$ (d) $50 \equiv 28(\text{mod } 7)$

3. Perform the following additions, modulo 7.
   (a) $13 + 19$ (b) $(30 + 52) + 17$
   (c) $40 + (15 + 28)$ (d) $15 + 25$
   (e) $128 + 233$ (f) $197 + 634$

4. Consider arithmetic modulo 5.
   (a) Are $23 \equiv 48(\text{mod } 5)$ and $17 \equiv 29(\text{mod } 5)$ true or false?
   (b) What set of remainders would be used in this arithmetic?
   (c) Find $1 + 3$, $2 + 4$, and $3 + 3(\text{mod } 5)$.
   (d) Construct an addition table, modulo 5.
   (e) Is $3 + 4 \equiv 4 + 3(\text{mod } 5)$?
   (f) Find a truth value for $3 + x \equiv 3(\text{mod } 5)$.
   (g) Find a truth value for $3 + x \equiv 0(\text{mod } 5)$.

5. Perform the following additions, modulo 5.
   (a) $17 + 23$ (b) $33 + 51$ (c) $21 + 47$ (d) $92 + 69$

6. Devise a scheme of thought which will give any addition combination, modulo 7, without referring to the addition table. Will a similar scheme work for addition, modulo 5?

7. Use the scheme devised in Problem 6 to find each of the following sums, modulo 12.
   (a) $8 + 13$ (b) $7 + 18$ (c) $46 + 11$
   (d) $34 + 10$ (e) $39 + 26$ (f) $38 + 28$

8. Find the following, modulo 9.
   (a) $17 + 15$ (b) $28 + 36$ (c) $7 + 33$
   (d) $49 + 22$ (e) $16 + 27$ (f) $34 + 18$

9. (a) An ordinary clock could be thought of as measuring time with respect to what modulus?
   (b) What change would you make on an ordinary clock face to bring it in line with the notation used here?

10. Find truth values for each of the following.

(a) $x + 7 \equiv 2(\mod 8)$ (b) $x + 10 \equiv 2(\mod 12)$
(c) $x + 5 \equiv 1(\mod 6)$ (d) $x + 7 \equiv 3(\mod 9)$
(e) $x + 4 \equiv 0(\mod 7)$ (f) $x + 2 \equiv 1(\mod 10)$

14–3 MODULAR MULTIPLICATION

Since

$$25 \times 38 = (3 \cdot 7 + 4)(5 \cdot 7 + 3)$$
$$= (15 \cdot 7^2 + 20 \cdot 7 + 9 \cdot 7) + 4 \cdot 3,$$

it is readily seen that $25 \times 38 \equiv 4 \cdot 3(\mod 7)$; that is, in arithmetic modulo 7 the product of 25 and 38 can be found by taking the product of their remainders. In general, any two whole numbers x and y can be written as $x = q_1 \cdot 7 + r_1$ and $y = q_2 \cdot 7 + r_2$. It follows that

$$x \cdot y = (7q_1 q_2 + q_1 r_2 + q_2 r_1)7 + r_1 r_2$$
$$\equiv r_1 r_2 \,(\mod 7).$$

Hence, r_1 and r_2 have the same effect in multiplication modulo 7 as x and y, respectively. In the example above, $4 \cdot 3$ can be written as $1 \cdot 7 + 5$, so that $4 \cdot 3 \equiv 5(\mod 7)$. Likewise, $2 \cdot 4 \equiv 1(\mod 7)$, and $6 \cdot 6 \equiv 1 \mod 7$. Multiplication combinations such as these are collected in Table 14–2.

Table 14–2

$\times$ or $\cdot$	0	1	2	3	4	5	6
0	0	0	0	0	0	0	0
1	0	1	2	3	4	5	6
2	0	2	4	6	1	3	5
3	0	3	6	2	5	1	4
4	0	4	1	5	2	6	3
5	0	5	3	1	6	4	2
6	0	6	5	4	3	2	1

If we started with 2, added 2, again added 2, and continued in this fashion, would we obtain the entries in the column under the number 2? Since we would obtain these entries, we know that

$$2 \cdot 2 = 2 + 2, \quad 3 \cdot 2 = 2 + 2 + 2, \quad 4 \cdot 2 = 2 + 2 + 2 + 2, \text{ etc.}$$

Hence, as might be expected, multiplication by 2 can be thought of in terms of addition. Check this for multiplication by 3, by 4, etc.

PROBLEM SET 14-3

1. Perform the following operations, modulo 7.
   (a) 22 × 46
   (b) 34 × 53
   (c) 624 × 589
   (d) 403 × 215
   (e) (17 + 24)82
   (f) 27 + (16 × 49)
   (g) (53 + 62)(28 + 19)
   (h) (27 + 16) 49

2. Find the following.
   (a) 6 × 7(mod 12)
   (b) 4 × 11(mod 12)
   (c) 9 × 10(mod 12)
   (d) 8 × 9(mod 12)

3. Form a table for multiplication, modulo 12.

4. Will the scheme devised in Problem 6 of the previous problem set enable us to perform a multiplication without using a table?

5. Perform the following operations.
   (a) 16 × 21(mod 12)
   (b) 43 × 26(mod 12)
   (c) 89 × 76(mod 12)
   (d) 19 × 47(mod 12)
   (e) 21 × 48(mod 5)
   (f) 49 × 24(mod 5)
   (g) 17 × 42(mod 9)
   (h) 81 × 46(mod 9)
   (i) 32 × 51(mod 6)
   (j) 17 × 41(mod 6)

6. Find truth values for the following.
   (a) $2x \equiv 1$(mod 5)
   (b) $2x \equiv 5$(mod 7)
   (c) $3x + 2 \equiv 5$(mod 7)
   (d) $3x - 1 \equiv 5$(mod 5)
   (e) $2x + 1 \equiv x + 4$(mod 7)
   (f) $5x + 2 \equiv 2x + 4$(mod 5)

14-4 OPERATION. PROPERTIES OF AN OPERATION

Let us define the set $S = \{0, 1, 2, 3, 4, 5, 6\}$, without considering where the elements of S come from, and then write down Table 14-3, without considering its possible origin. Now choose any two elements of S, say 4 and 5. By reading the table in the usual manner, another number, in this

Table 14-3

$\oplus$	0	1	2	3	4	5	6
0	0	1	2	3	4	5	6
1	1	2	3	4	5	6	0
2	2	3	4	5	6	0	1
3	3	4	5	6	0	1	2
4	4	5	6	0	1	2	3
5	5	6	0	1	2	3	4
6	6	0	1	2	3	4	5

case 2, can be obtained. Phrased in another way, for each pair of elements of S the table determines a unique third number in S. This is what we mean when we say that the table defines a *binary operation* for the set S. The operation is "binary" in the sense that from *two* numbers the table determines a result. For example,

from 2 and 5 the table determines 0;

from 4 and 4 the table determines 1.

If this operation is denoted by $\oplus$ (read "circle plus"), then, for example,

$$6 \oplus 6 = 5 \quad \text{and} \quad 2 \oplus 4 = 6.$$

The notation $\oplus$, rather than the simpler notation $+$, is used for emphasis and to make us realize that this is different from "ordinary addition."

The operation of "ordinary addition" for rational numbers is also a binary operation, since for each pair of rational numbers the ordinary addition combinations yield a rational number. For example, $\frac{1}{2} + \frac{1}{3}$ yields $\frac{5}{6}$, and $\frac{3}{7} + \frac{2}{7}$ yields $\frac{5}{7}$.

For contrast, consider the idea of a unary operation. A good example for ordinary whole numbers is the squaring operation, by which

$$\text{to 3 corresponds } 3^2 \quad \text{and} \quad \text{to 25 corresponds } 25^2,$$

for instance. For each single number the operation produces another number; the word "single," as used here, describes the essence of the term "unary," whereas, the essence of "binary" is "two-ness."

In substance, for the set S Table 14–3 defines a binary operation. This operation has certain properties, most of which have been encountered before.

(a) Closure. Look in the body of Table 14–3, where each entry is a member of the set S. Whether we are performing $3 \oplus 3$, $2 \oplus 5$, or $6 \oplus 0$, the result is always a member of S. The fact that $a \oplus b$ is always in S, no matter which members of S are represented by a and b, is stated by saying that S is closed with respect to the operation $\oplus$.

(b) Commutativity. Is $2 \oplus 4 = 4 \oplus 2$? Is $5 \oplus 4 = 4 \oplus 5$? Try other combinations; the answer is "yes" in each case. Must we try each possible combination to determine whether or not the operation is commutative? To answer this question, construct the main diagonal of the body of Table 14–3 (mental construction will suffice); this is the line passing from the entry in the upper left-hand corner to the entry in the lower right-hand corner. Each entry on this line results from a combination like $x \oplus x$, while each entry which is not on the line results from a combination like

$x \oplus y$, where x and y are different. The entries for $x \oplus y$ and $y \oplus x$ are in like positions on opposite sides of the diagonal (see, for example, $2 \oplus 4$ and $4 \oplus 2$ in Table 14–3). Since the portions of the table on opposite sides of the diagonal are alike, the indication is that $\oplus$ is commutative, i.e.,

$$x \oplus y = y \oplus x, \qquad \text{for all elements } x \text{ and } y \text{ of } S.$$

(c) **Identity.** According to the top row of the body of Table 14–3, $0 \oplus x = x$, for any element x of S. Likewise, the first column of the body of the table yields $x \oplus 0 = x$, for all x of S. For S and $\oplus$, therefore, 0 is an element for which the following statement is true when u is replaced by 0;

$$x \oplus u = x \quad \text{and} \quad u \oplus x = x, \qquad \text{for every element } x \text{ of } S.$$

An element u which has this property is called an *additive identity*, or an identity for the operation $\oplus$. Note that 0 is the only element of S for which this is true.

(d) **Inverse.** Choose any element of S, say 4. Is there an element z of S for which $4 \oplus z = 0$? Certainly $z = 3$ will serve. Can z be any other element of S? Is $z \oplus 4 = 0$? Try, in turn, each of the other elements of S, in place of 4. For each element x of S, there is an element z in S, such that

$$x \oplus z = 0 \quad \text{and} \quad z \oplus x = 0.$$

This could be written $x + z = u = x + z$, where u is the additive identity. The element z is called the *additive inverse* of x, for the operation $\oplus$. The fact that in the table 0 appears in the row opposite 5 indicates that 5 has an additive inverse; the inverse can be found by noting the column in which 0 appears. Does 0 appear in each row of the table? What is indicated by the fact that 0 does appear in each row? The additive inverse of x will be denoted by ^-x; thus $^-4 = 3$ and $^-6 = 1$.

(e) **Associativity.** Is $(2 \oplus 4) \oplus 3 = 2 \oplus (4 \oplus 3)$? Try several other examples of the same type. It appears that

$$x \oplus (y \oplus z) = (x \oplus y) \oplus z, \qquad \text{for all } x, y, \text{ and } z \text{ of } S.$$

That this is true can be established by testing all possible combinations of x, y, and z. As might be expected, it is said that the *associative* property holds for $\oplus$.

All of these properties have been encountered in connection with ordinary numbers and ordinary operations. Problems concerning such properties appear in the next problem set.

For the set S we state the following definition.

Definition. *Subtraction.* For any elements x and y of S,

$$x \ominus y = x \oplus {}^-y.$$

Thus, $2 \ominus 5 = 2 \oplus {}^-5 = 2 \oplus 2 = 4$. Subtraction is a binary operation on S, since for any x and y in S, the operation $x \ominus y$ determines a unique number in S. Since this operation uses the inverse of y for finding $x \ominus y$, it is often called the inverse operation to addition.

A *mathematical system* is a set for which there is a binary operation defined on the set. As will be seen later, more than one binary operation may be defined on a set. Certainly the set S together with the operation $\oplus$ is a mathematical system; it could be denoted by $S\oplus$.

It should be noted that the system $S\oplus$ is not quite the same as arithmetic, modulo 7. They are related, since the table for $S\oplus$ is the same as Table 14–1, used in modular arithmetic. Since such numbers as 27 and 13 do not have meaning in $S\oplus$, then $27 \oplus 13$ is meaningless. However,

$$27 + 13 \equiv 6 + 6 \equiv 5 (\text{mod } 7)$$

is meaningful in modular arithmetic.

PROBLEM SET 14–4

1. Find the following for the mathematical system $S\oplus$.
   (a) $^-6$, $^-2$, $^-1$
   (b) $5 \ominus 3$, $2 \ominus 6$, $1 \ominus 5$, $3 \ominus 4$

2. For the mathematical system $S\oplus$, find a truth value for $x \oplus 2 = 1$. Is this truth value unique?

3. For the mathematical system $S\oplus$, find the truth sets for the following equations.
   (a) $x \oplus 6 = 3$ (b) $x \ominus 3 = 4$
   (c) $x \ominus 5 = 2$ (d) $x \ominus 6 = 1$

4. Does $2 \oplus 3 = 5$ show that 2 is not an additive identity for the system $S\oplus$? Why?

5. Given the set $T = \{3, 4, 5\}$ and Table 14–4.
   (a) Is $\triangle$ a binary operation on T? Why?
   (b) Is T closed with respect to $\triangle$? Why?
   (c) Is $\triangle$ commutative? Why?
   (d) Is $T \triangle$ a mathematical system?
   (e) Is there an identity for $\triangle$? If so, name it.
   (f) Does 3 have an inverse? If so, what is it?
   (g) Does 4 have an inverse? If so, name it; if not, state why.

Table 14–4

$\triangle$	3	4	5
3	3	4	5
4	4	5	4
5	5	4	4

6. Does Table 14–5 define a binary operation on {3, 4, 5}? Why?

7. Refer to the table previously constructed for addition, modulo 5 (see Problem 4 of Problem Set 14–2).

Table 14–5

	3	4	5
3	3	4	5
4	4	5	6
5	5	6	3

   (a) List the elements of the set used there. Label this set V.
   (b) State why the table defines a binary operation on V.
   (c) Is $V \oplus$ a mathematical system?
   (d) Is V closed with respect to $\oplus$? Why is it not necessary to state this fact?
   (e) Is $\oplus$ commutative? Why?
   (f) Does $V \oplus$ have an identity? If so, name it.
   (g) Does each element of $V \oplus$ have an inverse? If so, list the inverse for each element.

8. Construct the multiplication table, modulo 6.
   (a) Does this table define an operation on {0, 1, 2, 3, 4, 5}? Why?
   (b) Find all the elements which have inverses for this operation.
   (c) Find all elements which do not have inverses.
   (d) Find $2 \cdot 3$. In what way does this system differ from those encountered previously?

9. Consider C = {all counting numbers} and "ordinary addition."
   (a) Is "ordinary addition" a binary operation? Why?
   (b) Is $C+$ a mathematical system?
   (c) Is C closed with respect to $+$?
   (d) Does $C+$ contain an identity? Why?
   (e) Would it be meaningful to ask "does 3 have an additive inverse?" Why?

10. Let W = {all whole numbers}, and let $+$ denote "ordinary addition."
   (a) How does $W+$ differ from $C+$ so far as properties are concerned?
   (b) Does each element have an additive inverse?
   (c) Describe the smallest system which contains $W+$ and in which each element would have an additive inverse.

11. Given the set U = {x, y, z, w} and Table 14–6.

Table 14–6

$\square$	x	y	z	w
x	z	w	x	y
y	w	x	y	z
z	x	y	z	w
w	y	z	w	x

   (a) Is $U \square$ a mathematical system?
   (b) Is there an identity for $\square$? If so, name it.
   (c) For each element that has an inverse, find it.
   (d) Is $\square$ commutative?
   (e) Describe how it could be determined whether or not $\square$ is associative?

12. Refer to Table 14–2 and denote the operation defined by that table by $\odot$ (read "circle times" or "circle dot").
   (a) Is S closed with respect to $\odot$?

    (b) Does the system $S\odot$ have an identity for $\odot$? If so, name it.

    (c) Is $\odot$ commutative?

    (d) Which elements have an inverse with respect to $\odot$? In each case where it exists, name the inverse.

    (e) Which elements do not have an inverse?

13. Let $A = \{$all $3k$, where k is any whole number$\}$.

    (a) Is A closed with respect to "ordinary" addition?

    (b) Upon what property is the answer to (a) based?

    (c) Does $A+$ have an identity? If so, what is it?

    (d) Which elements, if any, have additive inverses?

    (e) Could the restriction on k be changed so that each element would have an additive inverse? If so, how?

14. Let $B = \{$all 3^k, where k is any whole number$\}$.

    (a) Is B closed with respect to ordinary addition? Show why.

    (b) Is B closed with respect to ordinary multiplication? Upon what is the answer based?

    (c) Does $B\cdot$ have an identity? If so, name it.

    (d) Which elements of $B\cdot$ have inverses?

    (e) How could the restriction on k be modified so that every element of the resulting system would have a multiplicative inverse? To answer this, you will need an idea not discussed in this book.

14–5 SYSTEMS WITH TWO OPERATIONS

In Problem 12 above it should have been noted that the system $S\odot$ has the properties of (a) closure, (b) commutativity, (c) identity (1 is an identity for $\odot$), and (d) inverse (every element except 0 has an inverse for $\odot$). In this system the term *multiplicative identity* should be used for the element 1. The notation for the *multiplicative inverse* of x is x^{-1}; hence $3^{-1} = 5$ and $4^{-1} = 2$. Since the same set is used for both $S\oplus$ and $S\odot$, it might simplify procedures if S, $\oplus$, and $\odot$ were considered together as a single "package." This will be denoted by $S\oplus\odot$. Certainly $S\oplus\odot$ is a mathematical system, the only difference between it and systems discussed previously being that it has two operations instead of one. This system has all the properties of $S\oplus$ together with those of $S\odot$.

The sets C and W, which were defined in the preceding problem set, and $I = \{$all integers$\}$, together with "ordinary addition and multiplication" denoted by $+$ and $\cdot$, respectively, will likewise determine systems $C+\cdot$, $W+\cdot$, and $I+\cdot$. The properties of these systems with respect to $\cdot$ should be determined (see the following set of problems).

If a mathematical system has two operations, the question arises as to whether there is any interaction between them. For each of the systems $C+\cdot$, $W+\cdot$, $I+\cdot$, and $R+\cdot$, where R represents the set of rational numbers, the distributive property of multiplication with respect to addition was discussed in previous chapters. This property states that $x \cdot (y + z)$ is another numeral for $x \cdot y + x \cdot z$. In computing $x \cdot (y + z)$, the addition is performed first, and then the sum $y + z$ is multiplied by x. In computing $x \cdot y + x \cdot z$, the multiplications are performed first, and then the products $x \cdot y$ and $x \cdot z$ are added. Hence, the distributive property does relate multiplication and addition; it gives two alternative orders in which these operations may be performed, either $x(y + z)$ or $xy + xz$.

Would the distributive property hold in $S \oplus \odot$? Let us try an example; since

$$3 \odot (4 \oplus 5) = 3 \odot 2 = 6$$

and

$$(3 \odot 4) \oplus (3 \odot 5) = 5 \oplus 1 = 6,$$

then $3 \odot (4 \oplus 5) = (3 \odot 4) \oplus (3 \odot 5)$. This example checks the validity of the distributive property in a particular case. Is this a proof of the distributive property? Of course not! Other cases could and should be checked; there are 169 such cases according to one method of listing them! Due to the fact that in $S \oplus \odot$ the operations are defined entirely in terms of tables, the validity of such properties as the distributive and associative properties can be proved only by recourse to checking all possible cases. In a system such as $R + \cdot$, where the operations are defined not by tables but rather in terms of certain sentences, a property such as the distributive property can be proved by using these sentences. This latter method was used in earlier chapters.

PROBLEM SET 14–5

1. The system $V \oplus$, where $V = \{0, 1, 2, 3, 4\}$, was considered previously. Now consider $V \oplus \odot$. Find the properties of $V \oplus \odot$ with respect to $\odot$.

2. Consider $I + \cdot$.
   (a) Find $^-5$, $^-(-3)$, $^-(-12)$, and $^-0$.
   (b) What elements have additive inverses?
   (c) Find the multiplicative identity.
   (d) Does 3 have a multiplicative inverse? Why?
   (e) Name each element which does have a multiplicative inverse, and show the inverse of each.

3. State the defining property of the additive identity. What was this property called in previous chapters?

4. State the defining property of the multiplicative identity. What was this property called in previous chapters?

5. As previously, let $R = \{$all rational numbers$\}$; let $+$ and $\cdot$ represent the addition and multiplication operations as defined for rational numbers.

(a) Find $(\frac{3}{1})^{-1}$, $(\frac{7}{6})^{-1}$, $(-\frac{3}{2})^{-1}$, and $(-\frac{1}{4})^{-1}$ in $R + \cdot$.

(b) In $R + \cdot$ which elements have a multiplicative inverse?

(c) Is there any element which does not have a multiplicative inverse? If so, what is it?

(d) Find $(x/y)^{-1}$. For what elements does this exist?

(e) What was $(x/y)^{-1}$ called in the chapter on rational numbers?

6. In Section 14–4 a definition of subtraction was given for $S\oplus$.
   (a) Could this definition be used in $C + \cdot$ or $W + \cdot$? Why?
   (b) Could this definition be used in $I + \cdot$ or $R + \cdot$? Why?

7. (a) Phrase a definition of $r \div s$, where r and s belong to R, in terms of a concept introduced in this section.
   (b) Could the definition given in the answer to part (a) be used in I, the set of integers? Why?

8. Show that there are 169 cases to be checked in order to establish the distributive property for $S\oplus\odot$, assuming that both $\oplus$ and $\odot$ are commutative. [*Hint:* Show that $x = 0$, y and z being arbitrary, can be treated as a single case. Then count the remaining cases, assuming commutativity.

14–6 SYSTEMS, CONTINUED

The system $S\oplus\odot$ differs in one significant aspect from the systems obtained by using the sets C, W, I, and R. In Chapter 2 we introduced the sets S_1, S_2, S_3, etc. These sets are *finite* sets, and any set which matches one of these sets, S_i say, is a finite set. Hence, each natural number is associated with a finite set. The set S used in this chapter matches S_7; hence S is finite. Accordingly, $S\oplus\odot$ would be a *finite system*, with seven elements. Likewise, $V\oplus\odot$ would be a finite system of five elements.

Is C a finite set? That is, does there exist some specific natural number n, such that C matches S_n? Since S_n matches the subset of elements 1, 2, 3, ..., n of C and since $n + 1$, a member of C, does not appear in this matching, then we have not obtained a matching of C with S_n. It can be shown that for any attempt to match C with S_n, there will always be at least one element of C "left over." Hence C is not a finite set; as noted previously, it is called an *infinite* set. Now C is a proper subset of W, so that W would also be an infinite set. For similar reasons, I and R are infinite sets. Accordingly, $I + \cdot$ and $R + \cdot$ are infinite systems.

Both the finite system $S\oplus\odot$ and the infinite system $R + \cdot$ have *all* the properties which have been under discussion. A system which has these properties is called a *field*.

There is an important pattern linking the systems developed from the sets C, W, I, and R, the details of which have entered into many of the problems in the last two or three problem sets.

(1) The system $C + \cdot$ does not have an additive identity.

(2) The system $W + \cdot$ does have an additive identity, 0; however, 0 is the only element which has an additive inverse.

(3) Each element of the system $I + \cdot$ has an additive inverse. Subtraction is now meaningful for each pair of elements, and I is closed with respect to subtraction. There is a multiplicative identity, but only 1 and -1 have multiplicative inverses.

(4) Each nonzero element of the system $R + \cdot$ has a multiplicative inverse. Hence division, except by 0, can be introduced, and R is closed with respect to division.

Accordingly, $R + \cdot$ is the smallest of the above systems within which addition, subtraction, multiplication, and division (except by 0) can be performed at will, the result again being in the set.

In Chapter 3, $a - b$ was defined for some pairs of elements a and b in C. Since it is not defined for all pairs, $a - b$ does not satisfy the definition of binary operation used in this chapter. It is convenient to extend the definition of binary operation to cover such cases; when this is done it is necessary to discuss closure. The set C would not be closed with respect to subtraction. Similarly, I is not closed with respect to division.

For $S \oplus \odot$ the result of any of the four operations of addition, subtraction, multiplication, and division is again in S. Division has not been discussed for this system, but an example will suffice to show the procedure:

$$6 \div 5 = 6(5^{-1}) = 6 \cdot 3 = 4.$$

The real numbers have not been mentioned in the discussion of systems; this may seem curious, since, as indicated in Chapter 11, they are an extension of the rational numbers. The reason for this omission is that no precise definitions of addition, multiplication, etc. were given for the real numbers; only examples which might lead toward such definitions were given. When the definitions are introduced, it can be shown that the set of real numbers, together with $+$ and $\cdot$, will be a system for which all the properties which have been under discussion hold. For instance, every real number has an additive inverse and, also, every real number except zero has a multiplicative inverse.

PROBLEM SET 14-6

1. Consider the sentence $x + r = s$. In each case below discuss whether or not the sentence has truth values for all r and s. If it does not have such for all r and s, find a pair r, s for which there is a truth number and a pair for which there is no truth number.

   (a) r and s in $C + \cdot$ (b) r and s in $W + \cdot$ (c) r and s in $I + \cdot$

   (d) r and s in $R + \cdot$ (e) r and s in $S \oplus \odot$

2. Repeat Problem 1 for the sentence $r \cdot x = s$.

3. Assume that $\triangle$ denotes a binary operation for a set Z. Under what condition would the sentence $x \triangle a = b$ have a truth value in Z, where a and b are given elements of Z?

4. In terms of the ideas discussed in the last paragraph of the textual material, what can be said about the truth sets of the following sentences, where r and s are real numbers?

    (a) $x + r = s$ (b) $rx = s$

5. In $R + \cdot$, both $x + t = s$ and $rx = s$, where $r \neq 0$, have a solution. Show that the solution, in each case, is unique. [*Hint:* Assume two solutions and argue to a conclusion.]

14–7 SYSTEMS OF A MORE GENERAL TYPE

The mathematical systems discussed heretofore have numbers as elements. In many cases these numbers are those of "ordinary" arithmetic. Moreover, the operations of the systems were "ordinary" except for a system such as $S \oplus \odot$. Need this be so, or are there systems whose properties are like those discussed but whose elements and operations are of a seemingly different nature?

Table 14–7

*	I	H	V	R
I	I	H	V	R
H	H	I	R	V
V	V	R	I	H
R	R	V	H	I

Consider Table 14–7. Certainly this table defines a binary operation on a set. Let us denote the set by $P = \{I, H, V, R\}$ and the operation by $*$. Now $P*$ is a mathematical system, even though, for the moment, no meaning is associated with the elements I, H, V, and R. Moreover, P is closed with respect to $*$, the element I is an identity for $P*$, and each element of P has an inverse in P. Find the inverses of H, V, and R. Is $*$ a commutative operation?

Let us attempt to give $P*$ meaning in the sense that I, H, V, and R would represent specific elements and $*$ would represent a specific operation. To do this, we construct a rectangle and label its vertices as indicated in Fig. 14–1. This rectangle is to be rotated about the dotted lines as axes of rotation. With this in mind, we will find it helpful to think of the rectangle as being cut out of paper and to think of numerals as being placed on the

FIGURE 14–1

back of the paper at each vertex, so that, for example, the numerals 1 are back-to-back. These numerals are used only for the purpose of identifying specific vertices, so that the motion of the vertices, due to rotations, can be followed.

Now we rotate the rectangle through 180° about the horizontal dotted line; this actually flips the rectangle over, so that the former back of the paper is now the up side. In this new position the rectangle "coincides with itself," the vertices having changed positions as follows:

1	to the position formerly held by	2,
2	to the position formerly held by	1,
3	to the position formerly held by	4,
4	to the position formerly held by	3.

This movement of the rectangle will be denoted by H. Similarly, the rotation of the rectangle through 180° about the vertical dotted line as axis will carry

$$1 \text{ to } 4, \quad 4 \text{ to } 1,$$
$$2 \text{ to } 3, \quad 3 \text{ to } 2.$$

This movement of the rectangle into itself will be denoted by V.

It should be possible to apply various movements to the rectangle in succession. For instance, consider the effect of applying H, then again H. This should yield the following changes in position:

$$1 \text{ to } 2 \text{ then to } 1, \quad \text{or} \quad 1 \text{ to } 1;$$
$$2 \text{ to } 1 \text{ then to } 2, \quad \text{or} \quad 2 \text{ to } 2;$$
$$3 \text{ to } 4 \text{ then to } 3, \quad \text{or} \quad 3 \text{ to } 3;$$
$$4 \text{ to } 3 \text{ then to } 4, \quad \text{or} \quad 4 \text{ to } 4.$$

The net effect is to carry the rectangle back to its original position, as though it had never been moved. Would it be overly disconcerting to consider as a movement that which leaves the vertices in original position? This we shall do, denoting the movement by I, if only to be able to say "H followed by H

has the same effect as I." This could be written $H * H = I$, if we let $*$ denote successive application of the given motions. In similar fashion, $V * V = I$.

Referring to Fig. 14–1, visualize a line through point O, perpendicular to the plane of the paper. The rectangle could also be rotated, counterclockwise, about this line through 180°, so as to coincide with itself; this movement, which will be denoted by R, carries

$$1 \text{ to } 3, \quad 3 \text{ to } 1,$$
$$2 \text{ to } 4, \quad 4 \text{ to } 2.$$

Note that $R * R = I$.

Now perform H, then V; that is, find $H * V$. The result is R, since the vertices are moved as follows:

$$1 \text{ to } 2 \text{ to } 3, \quad 3 \text{ to } 4 \text{ to } 1,$$
$$2 \text{ to } 1 \text{ to } 4, \quad 4 \text{ to } 3 \text{ to } 2.$$

Also, $V * H = R$. When all possible combinations are determined, the results should be those given in Table 14–7 at the beginning of this section.

Thus, *the elements of set P have been described as rotations of a rectangle*, not numbers, and *the operation has been described as "successive application" of these rotations*, i.e., one rotation followed by another. Each element of P carries the rectangle into itself. The set P is the set of all rigid motions of the rectangle into itself. The operation $*$ links these motions in the sense that it enables us to state what happens when one motion is followed by another.

The system $P*$ illustrates the fact that in a mathematical system the elements may be almost anything. The important requirement is that it be possible to define an operation on the set.

Curious though $P*$ may seem to be, it is of considerable importance in certain areas of mathematics. For us it should indicate that mathematics deals with concepts which are more general than those of the arithmetic of our early experience. A close study of the properties of a system often enables us to develop new ideas; some of these new ideas may turn out to be important.

PROBLEM SET 14–7

1. For the square below, define H and V as they were defined for the rectangle in Fig. 14–1. Use the diagonal lines as axes of rotation through 180°, and denote the corresponding rotations by D_1 and D_2. Let R denote the counterclockwise rotation through 90° about a line perpendicular to the plane of the square and passing through its center. Let $*$ denote successive application, as before. The lines H, V, D_1, and D_2 should be considered as lying on a sheet of paper parallel to the plane of the square; hence these lines do not shift position under the rotation R.

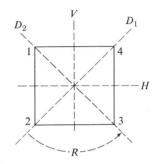

(a) Find $D_1 * D_1$.

(b) Find $R*R$, $R*R*R$, and $R*R*R*R$. These will be denoted by R^2, R^3, and R^4, respectively.

(c) Find the complete "operation table" for $*$ and the set

$$\{I, H, V, D_1, D_2, R, R^2, R^3\}.$$

(d) Show that a mathematical system has been defined.

(e) Is $*$ commutative for this system?

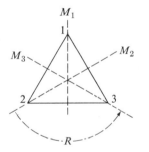

2. For the equilateral triangle shown above, M_1, M_2, and M_3 are the rotations of the triangle through $180°$ about the medians indicated. Let R denote a counterclockwise rotation of the triangle through $120°$ about a line perpendicular to the plane of the paper and passing through the point of intersection of the medians.

(a) Find $M_1 * M_1$. How could it be denoted?

(b) Find $R*R$. Denote this by R^2.

(c) Find $R*R*R$.

(d) Find the operation table for $*$ and the set $\{I, M_1, M_2, M_3, R, R^2\}$.

(e) Find R^{-1} and $M_2{}^{-1}$.

(f) Is $*$ commutative for this system?

CHAPTER 15

Mathematical Method

In the last fourteen chapters considerable space has been devoted to discussing the development of mathematical systems, and many theorems have been proved. Let us now consider some of the basic thought sequences used in those discussions.

15-1 UNDEFINED TERMS. DEFINITIONS. ASSUMPTIONS

When the term "set" was introduced in Chapter 2, it was not defined. Note that the idea of a set was discussed, by means of examples, until it was felt that both reader and writer had a common understanding. The statement "a set is merely a collection of things" could be considered a definition of "set" in terms of the word "collection." However, do we know anything more about "collection" than we do about "set"? We would gain nothing by considering this as a definition, since a definition should explain a new term or concept in terms of something which has "prior meaning."

The question is: can we define everything, or must something be left undefined? We will illustrate the idea that not everything can be defined by considering a dictionary and its usage. The meaning of a word as given in a dictionary can be considered to be the definition of that word. If we looked up the word "set" would we find the word "set" in the definition? Of course not; a word cannot be used to describe itself! Therefore other words must be used in the definition of "set." Consider a dictionary definition of this word and certain other words which appear in that definition.

Set: a collection of things of the same kind.
Collection: an assemblage.
Assemblage: a collection of particular things.

We did not get very far, since the definition of "assemblage" took us back to "collection." A situation of this nature is untenable since we are "thinking in circles." This seems to indicate that a starting point is needed and that this starting point must be accepted as understood.

To be specific, we must agree to accept certain terms without definition; these are the *undefined terms* of our system. Examples of such terms which appear in the discussion of Chapter 2 are "set," "element of a set," and "belonging to a set." Now it is possible to actually define the concept of set union; check the original definition to see that it is phrased in terms of "set," "element of a set," and "belonging to a set."

Note the definition of subtraction for the system $S\oplus$ in Chapter 14; the operation $x \ominus y$ was defined to be $x \oplus {}^{-}y$, both $\oplus$ and ${}^{-}y$ having been defined prior to that time. In this instance a new concept was defined in terms of concepts previously defined.

In making definitions we should keep in mind certain basic ideas. When x^4 is defined to represent $x \cdot x \cdot x \cdot x$, it is merely defined for convenience; the abbreviation x^4 is easier to write than is $x \cdot x \cdot x \cdot x$. However, in defining an operation it is advisable to determine by investigation what might be a suitable definition. For instance, in Section 10–9 it was necessary to define the product of $-a$ by b, where a and b were positive numbers, and it seemed desirable that the distributive and associative properties should hold for negative as well as positive numbers. If this were to be so, it was shown that $(-a)b$ had to be $-ab$. Accordingly, to define $(-a)b$ as $-ab$ became a suitable definition.

The concepts of "matching" and "number" were also undefined in Chapter 2. "Set matching" was described, but we did not say precisely what it was. Can you say what a number (actually, a counting number) is? Try it! When we say that there is a number, called "two" in the English language, such that $n(A)$ is "two" if A matches $\{\Box, \Box\}$, we are really stating a property which might be called "twoness." Moreover, this is based on an underlying principle, or property:

$$n(A) = n(B), \quad \text{if} \quad A \text{ matches } B.$$

Actually this property was assumed to be true. This could be called an *axiom*, or *postulate;* it is one of the "foundation stones" upon which our structure is built.

Hence we started with certain assumptions among which were undefined terms whose meaning we agreed to accept, and axioms whose truth we agreed to accept. It would not seem to be profitable to use as axioms two contradictory statements. This alone indicates that reasonable care must be used in the selection of assumptions. For our purpose the main thing is to realize that everything subsequent to Chapter 2 was based on these, and other, assumptions.

Proofs of properties appeared in Chapter 3. For example, it was proved that addition of numbers is commutative, i.e., that $n(A) + n(B) = n(B) + n(A)$. By the definition of addition of two numbers, the left-hand side is $n(A \cup B)$ and the right-hand side is $n(B \cup A)$, if A and B are disjoint. Hence, the postulate stated two paragraphs back indicates that the desired result will follow if it is known that $A \cup B$ and $B \cup A$ match. This result had been obtained previously; actually, it was proved that $A \cup B = B \cup A$, but equal sets must match. Accordingly, proving the property consists of showing that it follows from the assumptions, definitions, and previously proved properties or theorems. On what must the proof of the first property have been based?

What have we been trying to head toward? Since the proof of any property uses the basic assumptions, it follows that the property is true only insofar as the assumptions are true. Truth in mathematics is relative! It is easy to lose sight of this idea, yet it is vital to a real understanding of mathematics. We are prone to say "such a theorem is true," yet implicit in this statement is the proviso "based on the assumptions which underlie this particular body of mathematics."

It is to be hoped that sometime you will see some of the interesting mathematical structures which come about by changing certain postulates. Not only are the new structures interesting, but many are also useful.

15–2 DIRECT PROOF

When a statement has been proved, that statement is usually called a theorem. In our development of numbers, the commutative property of addition for counting numbers was proved; hence it is a theorem. Several different types of proof have appeared in the course of previous discussions. It is our purpose now to review certain of these and point out their salient features and differences.

The proof outlined in the last section is a simple example of a *direct proof*. The argument proceeds directly from the basic assumptions and definitions to the conclusion. From the assumptions and definitions, we have

$$A \cup B = B \cup A.$$

Then, from the definition of number it follows that

$$n(A \cup B) = n(B \cup A). \tag{1}$$

Also, by the definition of addition of numbers,

$$n(A \cup B) = n(A) + n(B) \tag{2}$$

and

$$n(B \cup A) = n(B) + n(A), \tag{3}$$

since A and B were chosen to be disjoint. Hence

$$n(A) + n(B) = n(B) + n(A). \tag{4}$$

Note the use of the symmetric and transitive properties of equality (see Section 4–5) in the above proof. From (1) and (3) the transitive property yields

$$n(A \cup B) = n(B) + n(A);$$

from (2) the symmetric property gives

$$n(A) + n(B) = n(A \cup B).$$

Hence the transitive property applied to the last two equations produces (4).

Theorem 6–8 of Section 6–6 states that if p is a prime, $(p, a) = 1$; and p divides ab, then p divides b. Many theorems are stated in this form: if "so and so" is true, then "such and such" follows. The "if" portion of this sentence is the hypothesis, i.e., the set of specific assumptions for the theorem. The "then" portion is the conclusion, i.e., the statement which is to be proved. The theorem stated above might be phrased as follows:

Hypothesis: (a) p is a prime,

(b) a and b are counting numbers (implied by context),

(c) $(p, a) = 1$,

(d) p divides ab.

Conclusion: p divides b.

Actually, the hypothesis includes the definition of a prime, the definition of the symbol (p, a), and all basic assumptions from which the counting numbers were developed. This is implied rather than stated; however, such facts must often be recalled when a proof is being analyzed.

Reread the proof of this theorem, noting how each part follows directly from the preceding part or from a theorem proved prior to that stage. Since we now have integers to work with, the form can be simplified somewhat. Since $xp - ya$ can be written $xp + (-y)a = xp + za$ and since $ya - xp$ can be written $(-x)p + ya = wp + ya$, the single statement $1 = wp + za$, for some integers w and z, will suffice. Hence, using the original x and y in place of w and z, we have the following:

(1) From $(p, a) = 1$ it follows that $1 = xp + ya$, for some integers x and y.

(2) From (1) it follows that $b = xpb + yab$.

(3) From p divides ab it follows that $ab = pc$.

(4) From (2) and (3) it follows that $b = (xb + yc)p$.

(5) From the definition of divisibility it follows that p divides b.

Accordingly, this is another example of a direct proof.

15–3   INDIRECT PROOF

In Section 6–1 it was proved that if n is a composite counting number ≤ 100, then n has a prime divisor ≤ 10. In terms of notation introduced for this theorem, it may be phrased as follows:

> Hypothesis: (a) n is a counting number,
>
> (b) $n \leq 100$,
>
> (c) n has prime divisors p and q.
>
> Conclusion: either $p \leq 10$ or $q \leq 10$.

The proof was begun with an assumption:

> the conclusion is false,   i.e., both $p > 10$ and $q > 10$ are true.

Through a sequence of steps, this assumption led to $n > 100$. But this last inequality contradicts part (b) of the hypothesis and hence cannot be true in view of that hypothesis. Where did $n > 100$ come from? It resulted from the assumption that the conclusion is false. Accordingly, that assumption cannot hold, since there are only two possibilities: the assumption holds or does not hold. Hence if the hypothesis is true the conclusion must be true, since the possibility of a false conclusion has been rejected.

The proof discussed above is called an *indirect proof*. Its characteristic feature is that the desired conclusion is assumed to be false and that, in due course, this assumption leads to a contradiction. Then, since the assumption is untenable, the conclusion must be true.

As a second example of an indirect proof let us analyze the proof of Theorem 6–6, which states that there is no largest prime (see Section 6–3). Again the conclusion was assumed to be false, i.e., it was assumed that there is a largest prime, p_r. A counting number N was formed in terms of the primes up to p_r. There were two cases, one where N was prime and the other where N was composite.

(a) Where N was prime, it was shown that $N > p_r$; hence there is a prime larger than p_r, that is, N itself.

(b) Where N was composite, using the definition of N it was shown that none of the primes from 2 to p_r can divide N; but N is divisible by some prime which, by the preceding statement, must be larger than p_r.

In each case we obtained a statement which contradicted the assumption. Since these statements resulted from the assumption, then the assumption cannot hold. Accordingly there cannot be a largest prime.

Frequently both the indirect and the direct forms will appear in a single proof; an example of this is given in Section 15–5.

15–4   MATHEMATICAL INDUCTION.   COUNTEREXAMPLE

In connection with the discussion of "casting out nines" in Section 5–3, it was proved that, for any counting number t, the number 10^t has the form $9z + 1$, where z is a counting number.   Of course this could be tested for various values of t, say from 1 to 1000, but we know that even though this may make us *feel* that the theorem is true, it does not constitute a *proof* that it is true.

To see how easy it might be to think that a statement is true by showing that it holds for several cases, consider $n^2 - n + 41$, where n is a counting number.   For $n = 1, 2, 3, 4, 5, 6, 7$, and 8, you can show very quickly that $n^2 - n + 41$ is a prime.   For $n = 9, 10, 11, \ldots, 40$ it will take more calculation, but in each case $n^2 - n + 41$ is still a prime.   By now you are probably convinced that $n^2 - n + 41$ is a prime for all counting numbers n. Try $n = 41$; for this value of n, $n^2 - n + 41 = 41^2 - 41 + 41 = 41^2$ is not a prime!

How did you overcome this type of difficulty when considering the form of 10^t?   After considering such cases as $t = 1$ and $t = 2$, you showed (see Section 5–3) that

> if 10^k has the form $9v + 1$, then 10^{k+1} has the same form;

that is,

> if a particular power of 10 has the form $9v + 1$, then the "next" power of ten has the same form.

This form of proof is called "mathematical induction."   Such a proof has two parts, both of which must be shown to hold.   In terms of the notation used above these can be phrased as follows.

(a) Show that the statement to be proved is true for $t - 1$.

(b) Show that *if* the statement is true for a general value of t, say k, *then* it is also true for the next counting number, $k + 1$.

In imprecise language it might be said that part (a) gives us a start, while part (b) enables us to proceed from any given step to the next.

Proof by mathematical induction is a property of counting numbers in the sense that it can be attempted when the variable, such as t above, has counting numbers as permissible substitutes.   It is an important and frequently used method of proof (for a second example, see Section 5–4).

Let us return to the statement that $n^2 - n + 41$ is a prime for all counting numbers n.   Note that the assertion is that this statement is true for *all n*. We found a single case, $n = 41$, for which $n^2 - n + 41$ is not a prime. Can we then say that the statement is not true?   Yes, this one *counterexample* is sufficient to show that the statement is false.   There is an important difference between this situation and that discussed at the beginning of this section. If a statement contains the phrase "for all n," we are stating that the truth set is C, the set of all counting numbers:

(a) Showing that specific numbers are in the truth set gives no indication as to whether other numbers are in that set.

(b) Showing that a specific number is not in the truth set means that the "for all n" is not true.

PROBLEM SET 15-4

1. Analyze each of the following proofs to determine whether its type is direct, indirect, or mathematical induction.
   (a) Theorem 6-2 of Section 6-2.
   (b) The unique factorization theorem, Section 6-7.

15-5 PYTHAGOREAN TRIPLES

The area of mathematics known as number theory is concerned with properties of integers. Some of Chapter 5 and all of Chapter 6 are included in this category. Since the positive integers arose first in man's experience, it would be expected that number theory would be among the oldest branches of mathematics.* It is! Many number theory problems are quite simple to state and easy to understand. As an example, consider the problem of finding integer solutions of the equation

$$z^2 = x^2 + y^2.$$

We know that $x = 3$, $y = 4$, $z = 5$ is a solution of this equation; also, $x = 5, y = 12, z = 13$ is a solution, or a *truth triple*. Are there other truth triples? Can we find all truth triples? Because of the relationship of the above equation to the Pythagorean theorem of geometry, any solution of it is called a *Pythagorean triple;* such a triple could be written (x, y, z). Hence $(3, 4, 5)$ and $(5, 12, 13)$ are Pythagorean triples. It is not difficult to determine all solutions, as we will see shortly.

In 1637, the French mathematician Fermat stated as a theorem that

$x^n + y^n = z^n$ has no solutions in integers if n is a counting number > 2, except for the trivial case $(0, 0, 0)$.

The solution of this equation for $n = 2$ is our Pythagorean triple problem. To date no one has proved the statement for general $n > 2$, though many

* *The World of Mathematics*, Simon and Schuster, pp. 498–518. A general discussion of some number theory problems.

have tried. For this reason it should be called "Fermat's conjecture" rather than "Fermat's last theorem," the name by which it has been known for many years. It is interesting to note that the statement has been proved true for all $n < 4000$. If this makes you feel that the general statement is probably true, you are not alone; however, "feeling" and "proving" are two very different things.

Now let us return to Pythagorean triples.

(a) Since $(3, 4, 5)$ is a Pythagorean triple (abbreviation, Pt), then for any combination of signs $(\pm 3, \pm 4, \pm 5)$ is a Pt. As this example indicates, we might just as well restrict our attention to (x, y, z), where x, y, and z are positive or zero; Pt with other signs can then be found by simple sign changes.

(b) If $x = 0$, show that z must be $\pm y$ and that $(0, y, \pm y)$ is a Pt. Similarly for $y = 0$. This takes care of cases where either x or y is 0. Henceforth we restrict x, y, and z to be positive.

(c) If r, s, and t have a gcd of d, then $r = r_1 d$, $s = s_1 d$, $t = t_1 d$, where r_1, s_1, and t_1 have gcd 1. Now

$$r^2 + s^2 = t^2 \quad \text{can be written} \quad r_1^2 d^2 + s_1^2 d^2 = t_1^2 d^2,$$

so that

$$r_1^2 + s_1^2 = t_1^2.$$

Hence, if (r, s, t) is a Pt, then (r_1, s_1, t_1) is also a Pt. Show that if (r_1, s_1, t_1) is a Pt, then (r, s, t) is also a Pt. A Pt in which the numbers are positive and have a gcd of 1 is called a *primitive* Pythagorean triple (abbreviated pPt). This discussion should show that if all pPt are known, then all other Pt can be formed from them. Thus our attention will be concentrated on finding pPt.

The proof of the following theorem is a fine example of "interplay" between direct and indirect proof.

Theorem. Every primitive Pythagorean triple (x, y, z) has the form

$$x = 2uv, \quad y = u^2 - v^2, \quad z = u^2 + v^2,$$

where u and v are positive integers satisfying the conditions

(1) u and v are relatively prime,
(2) $u > v$,
(3) of u and v, one is even and the other is odd.

The proof of this theorem will be broken into several parts to delineate ideas.

(a) No two of x, y, and z are even. To prove this, let x and y, say, be even. Since $x^2 + y^2 = z^2$, then z is even. But then (x, y, z) would not be primitive. (Why?) The same result would follow from assuming that x and z or y and z are both even. The assumption has led to a contradiction. Hence the assumption is false, and so the desired statement has been proved true. Here is an indirect proof as part of a larger proof.

(b) x and y are not both odd. To prove this, assume they are both odd by letting $x = 2r + 1$ and $y = 2s + 1$; then

$$x^2 + y^2 = (2r + 1)^2 + (2s + 1)^2$$
$$= 4(r^2 + r + s^2 + s) + 2.$$

Hence $x^2 + y^2$ is even but is not divisible by 4. But $x^2 + y^2 = z^2$, so that z is even; also, $z = 2t$ implies $z^2 = 4t^2$, hence z^2 is divisible by 4. Is there a contradiction here? If so, what is it? Has the desired result been proved? What form of proof was used?

(c) Combining parts (a) and (b), we see that one of x and y is even, and the other is odd. Would it make any difference which of x and y is chosen to be even? It would not, since, for example, it is immaterial whether we write $(3, 4, 5)$ or $(4, 3, 5)$ as the solution. Let us choose x to be even. This choice explains the difference between the forms of x and y in the statement of the theorem.

Why does it follow that z is odd? At this stage we have x even, y and z both odd.

(d) Now, $x^2 = z^2 - y^2 = (z - y)(z + y)$, so that $z - y$ and $z + y$ enter naturally into the problem. Since z and y are both odd, then $z + y$ and $z - y$ are both even. Hence, let $z + y = 2r$ and $z - y = 2s$, where r and s are positive integers. Explain why s is positive.

It is desired to prove that r and s are relatively prime. Solve the following pair of equations for z and y, by adding corresponding sides and then subtracting corresponding sides:

$$z + y = 2r, \qquad z - y = 2s.$$

The result is $z = r + s$, and $y = r - s$. Now, let q be a prime that divides both r and s. Why does q divide both z and y? The equation $x^2 = z^2 - y^2$ then shows that q^2 divides x^2. As a result, q divides x^2 and hence x. What theorem was used to show that q divides x? Accordingly, q would divide each of x, y, and z, thus contradicting the hypothesis that (x, y, z) is primitive. As a result, r and s do not have a common prime divisor, so that r and s are relatively prime.

(e) Since x is even, then $x = 2t$, where t is a counting number. Using this result together with the notation introduced in part (d), we can write $x^2 = (z - y)(z + y)$ as

$$(2t)^2 = (2s)(2r).$$

Hence

$$t^2 = rs,$$

where r and s are relatively prime.

Let us work for the moment with a numerical example. Let $t = 2^2 \cdot 3 \cdot 5^3$. Then $t^2 = 2^4 \cdot 3^2 \cdot 5^6$, so that we want to express $2^4 \cdot 3^2 \cdot 5^6$ as $r \cdot s$. Now consider how the various factors 2, 3, and 5 can appear in r and s. Since we must be able to write

$$2^4 \cdot 3^2 \cdot 5^6 = (\ \ ) \cdot (\ \ ) = r \cdot s,$$

and since r and s are relatively prime, then if a factor 2 appears in the first set of parentheses, it cannot appear in the second. Accordingly, all four factors 2 must appear in one set of parentheses and none in the other. Similarly for the other primes. As a result, $(2^4 \cdot 5^6)(3^2)$ is one possible factorization as $r \cdot s$, but $(2^4 \cdot 5^5)(5 \cdot 3^2)$ is not possible. That is, both r and s must be perfect squares.

The general result can be proved as follows. Let w be a prime divisor of r, so that

$$w \text{ divides } t^2 \qquad \text{(why?)},$$

$$w \text{ divides } t \qquad \text{(why?)}.$$

Now let the highest power of w which divides t be w^c; then $t = w^c \cdot k$, where $(k, w) = 1$. Consequently, $t^2 = w^{2c}k^2$, so that w^{2c} divides t^2, and no higher power of w divides t^2. Hence w^{2c} divides rs and, as in the example, w^{2c} must divide r (why?). No higher power of w could divide r (why?). Since this is true for each prime divisor of r, then r must be a perfect square. Likewise, s is a perfect square.

(f) According to the preceding work, $r = u^2$ and $s = v^2$, where u and v are positive integers. Then

$$t^2 = u^2 v^2,$$

so that

$$t^2 - u^2 v^2 = 0,$$

$$(t - uv)(t + uv) = 0.$$

Hence

$$t - uv = 0 \qquad \text{or} \qquad t + uv = 0 \qquad \text{(why?)}.$$

Consequently, $t = uv$ or $t = -uv$; but since t, u, and v are all positive, then $t = uv$.

(g) The equations $\quad x = 2t, \quad y = r - s, \quad$ and $\quad z = r + s \quad$ now yield

$$x = 2uv, \qquad y = u^2 - v^2, \qquad z = u^2 + v^2.$$

(h) That u and v are relatively prime follows from the fact that $r = u^2$ and $s = v^2$ are relatively prime. This proves property (1) of the theorem.

(i) Since $y > 0$ and $y = r - s$, then $r > s$; thus $u^2 > v^2$, so that $u > v$. (Prove that $u^2 > v^2$ implies $u > v$.) This proves property (2) of the theorem.

(j) Now $z = u^2 + v^2$, and z is odd. If u and v are both even then z is even (why?); this is a contradiction. If u and v are both odd, then z is even (why?); again, this is a contradiction. Hence one of u and v must be odd and the other must be even. This is property (3) of the theorem.

This completes the proof of the theorem. It is a direct proof when taken as a whole, even though indirect proofs were used for some parts.

Now substitute $x = 2uv$, $y = u^2 - v^2$, and $z = u^2 + v^2$ into $x^2 + y^2 = z^2$. Then

$$x^2 + y^2 = 4u^2v^2 + (u^4 - 2u^2v^2 + v^4)$$
$$= u^4 + 2u^2v^2 + v^4$$

and

$$z^2 = (u^2 + v^2)^2 = u^4 + 2u^2v^2 + v^4,$$

so that, for any integers u and v, the resulting values of x, y, and z form a Pt. For instance,

if $u = 6$, $v = 4$, then $(x, y, z) = (48, 20, 52)$ is a Pt, though not primitive;
if $u = 7$, $v = 5$, then $(x, y, z) = (70, 24, 74)$ is a Pt, though not primitive;
if $u = 7$, $v = 6$, then $(x, y, z) = (84, 13, 85)$ is a pPt.

PROBLEM SET 15–5

1. Using the pPt $(8, 15, 17)$, find two other Pt.

2. Find three pPt.

3. Is $(40, 75, 85)$ a pPt? Why or why not?

15–6 PROOF OF THE DIVISION THEOREM

In Section 5–2 the division theorem was discussed. An intuitive argument was given which made the theorem seem plausible even though no actual proof was attempted. We will now give a proof, which is based on the following property.

Property. Every nonempty set of counting numbers has a least element.

For the set $\{3, 5, 8, 10, 12\}$ it is evident that 3 is the least element. The set of common multiples of 4 and 6 could be written $\{12, 24, 36, \ldots\}$, and it might be considered evident that 12 is the least member of the set. However, if one is to consider the set of common multiples of x and y, even though it is known that xy and $2xy$ are members of the set, it is not evident that there is a least member. Moreover, proof must not be based on intuition.

Where does the property stated above come from? Is it a theorem? Is it a postulate? The answers to these questions depend on how we start to develop the number system. For certain basic postulate systems it is a theorem, that is, it can be proved. A proof will not be attempted here; hence for our purpose it will be considered a postulate.

In Chapter 5 the division theorem was stated only for counting numbers. We now state it for integers.

Division Theorem. For any integers a and b, where $b > 0$, there exist integers q and r such that

$$a = qb + r, \qquad 0 \le r < b.$$

Proof. The numbers $a - xb$, where x is any integer, are themselves integers; the first question is whether or not we can say definitely that at least one of these is positive or zero. Let us start with some examples:

if $a = 3, b = 4$, then $3 - 4x$ is positive for $x = 0$;
if $a = -3, b = 4$, then $-3 - 4x$ is positive for $x = -2$;
if $a = 0, b = 4$, then $0 - 4x$ is positive for $x = -1$ and zero for $x = 0$.

In each example there is a value of x for which $a - xb$ is non-negative, i.e., positive or zero. Now consider the general case where a and b are any integers, $b > 0$.

If $a > 0$, then $a - (-a)b = a + ab = a(1 + b)$ is positive, since both a and $1 + b$ are positive (why is $1 + b > 0$?); hence, $a - xb$ is positive for $x = -a$.

If $a < 0$, then $a - (a)b = a(1 - b)$ is positive or zero, since $a < 0$ and $1 - b \le 0$ [$1 - b \le 0$, since $b \ge 1$ follows from $b > 0$]; hence, $a - xb$ is positive or zero for $x = a$.

If $a = 0$, then $0 - (-1)b = b$ is positive; hence $a - xb$ is positive for $x = -1$.

Accordingly, no matter what a is, there exists an integral value of x for which $a - xb$ is positive or zero. Hence the set $A = \{$all numbers $a - xb$, where x is an integer and $a - xb \ge 0\}$ is a set of non-negative integers which is nonempty. It is "nonempty" because we have shown that there exists an integer of the form $a - xb$ which is positive or zero.

Now, either 0 is a member of A or it is not. If 0 is a member of A, then for $x = $ (some integer q), $a - xb = a - qb$ is 0. Thus $a = qb + 0$. The integers q and $r(=0)$ needed in the theorem have been determined.

Suppose that 0 is not a member of A; then A is a set of positive integers, and A is nonempty. By the property stated at the beginning of this section, A must have a least element. Denote this element by r, and let it be given by $x = q$. Accordingly, $a - qb = r$, that is, $a = qb + r$, and $r > 0$ (why is $r > 0$?).

Now it must be shown that $r < b$. Assuming that $r \geq b$, we have

$$a - (q + 1)b = a - (qb + b)$$
$$= (a - qb) - b < a - qb = r$$

and

$$a - (q + 1)b = (a - qb) - b$$
$$= r - b \geq 0.$$

If $r - b$ were zero then $a - (q + 1)b = 0$ so that zero is a member of A. This contradicts the hypothesis stated in the preceeding paragraph, so that $r \neq b$. Accordingly, $a - (q + 1)b$ is a member of A (since it is >0 and has the proper form), which is $<r$. This contradicts the previous statement that r is the least member of A. Hence the statement $r \geq b$ is false; therefore $r < b$.

Consequently, it has been shown that q and r can be determined so that $a = qb + r$, where $0 \leq r < b$. You will recall that in Section 5–2 it was shown that the numbers q and r are unique.

Again an indirect proof appeared as part of an over-all direct proof. A proof of the above type is sometimes called an "existence proof"; the existence of q and r was proved without actually showing what they are.

Answers to Selected Problems

1. (a) $*\triangle\triangle|||$ (c) $**\triangle\square|||$ (e) $****\triangle\triangle\square\square||$
   (g) $****\triangle|$ (i) $***\triangle\triangle\triangle\triangle|$
2. (a) Five "crunches"   (b) $\sim\triangle\triangle\square||$
3. (a)

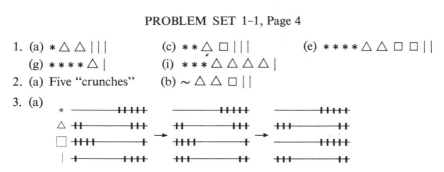

4. The second; fewer steps, because fewer beads to manipulate.
5. No, position of symbol has no effect on number represented.

PROBLEM SET 1–3, Pages 6–7

1. (a) $\cap\cap\cap$
      $\cap\cap$ $||$ or $\cap|\cap\cap|\cap\cap$ (c) 999 $\cap\cap\cap\cap|||||$
                                                                 $\cap\cap\cap||||$

   (e) $\oint ?\, ?\, ?\, 999$ $\cap\cap|||$
                              $\cap\cap|||$

3. Delete symbols if there are enough; otherwise convert a symbol, e.g., convert $\cap$ to $|||||\ |||||$, then delete.
4. (a) CCLVII   (c) CCCCLXIIII or CDLXIV   (e) MDCCCCL or MCML
5. $X = VV$, etc.
6. "Sweep together," convert, write.
7. (a) CXCIV   (c) CMXII   (e) XXX   (g) XXV
8. Cannot merely "sweep together" symbols.
9. Convert to additive form first.
10. (a) CXLIII
11. Five beads on each I, X, C, or M wire and two beads on each V, L, or D wire; one less bead on each wire is possible.

PROBLEM SET 1–4, Page 9

1. (a) ❮ ▼ ▼   (b) Six hundred two
2. (a) ▼, ❮ ▼ ▼   (c) ▼, ❮ ▼ ▼   or ▼ ▯ ❮ ▼ ▼
   (e) ▼ ▼, ▼, ▼ ▼ ▼
3. (a) ▼, ▼   (b) ▼ ▯ ▼

PROBLEM SET 1–5, Page 11

3. (a)

4. (a) Place 32 on frame, then add 32.
   (c) Place 32, then add 32 nine times, or place 32 on wires one position up.
   (e) Place 10 × 32, then add 32 twice.

5. (a) Place 15, then remove four 1 beads.

6. (a) Place 15, subtract 5, again subtract 5, etc.; count number of subtractions.

7. Subtract sixties.

8. (a) Subtract sixties, then sixes.

PROBLEM SET 1–6, Pages 14–15

1. 34(five)   2. (a) 4 fives + 2   3. (a) 100   (c) 441

4. (a)
$$
\begin{array}{r}
② ① \\
2\ 4 \\
(+)\ 3\ 2 \\
\hline
1\ 1\ 1
\end{array}
$$
   ① 4 + 2 = 1 five + 1
   ② (2 + 3 + 1)fives = 1 twenty-five + 1 five

   (c) 401 (five)   (e) 12330 (five)   (g) 21 (five)   (i) 232 (five)

PROBLEM SET 1–7, Page 16

1. (a) (2 fives + 4)3 = (1 five + 1)fives + (2 fives + 2)
                    = 1 twenty-five + (1 + 2)fives + 2 = 132 (five)
   (c) 1243 (five)

2. (a) 4011 (five)   (c) 3242030 (five)   (e) 122300 (five)   (g) 24143141 (five)

PROBLEM SET 1–8, Page 18

1. (a) 1232 (seven)   (c) 10026 (seven)   (e) 341 (seven)   (g) 63360 (seven)
   (i) (6 forty-nines + 5 sevens + 4) − (4 forty-nines + 3 sevens + 2)
          = (6 − 4)forty-nines + (5 − 3)sevens + (4 − 2) = 222 (seven)
   (k) 121 (seven)

2. (a) 1233(twelve)　　　(c) 113E4(twelve)　　　(e) 328(twelve)

　 (g) 2E593(twelve)　　　(i) 2T4(twelve)　　　(k) 615(twelve)

3. (a) 11000(two)　　　(c) 11110(two)　　　(e) 111(two)

4. (a) More basic operation combinations to learn.

PROBLEM SET 1–9, Page 20

1. (a) 45(ten)

　 (c) In decimal scale notation: $3 \cdot 1728 + 10 \cdot 144 + 4 \cdot 12 + 11 = 6683$(ten).

　 (e) 64(ten)　　(g) 17176(ten)

2. (a) $943 = 6 \cdot 144 + 79 = 6$ (one hundred forty-fours) + 6 twelves + 7
　　　　 $= 667$(twelve)

　 (c) 1560(seven)　　(e) 111001111(two)　　　(g) 57E4(twelve)

3. (a) Six or greater　　(b) Six

4. (a) 390(twelve)　　(c) 422(five)

5. (a) Twenty　　(c) Twelve

PROBLEM SET 2–3, Pages 26–27

3. (a) $n\{$all numbers between 2 and 9$\} = n(S_6) = 6$

4. (b) Six

5. (a) A matches S_5; hence $n(A) = n(S_5) = 5$.

6. (a) No　　(b) Match

7. (a) $6 = n\{$a set which matches $S_6\}$

8. (a) No, a set cannot equal a number.　　(b) $n(A) = 5$

9. X matches S_4.

10. (d) $3 \cdot 2$ ways　　(f) $3 \cdot 2 \cdot 1$ matchings

11. (a) $4 \cdot 3 \cdot 2 \cdot 1 = 24$　　(b) $5 \cdot 4 \cdot 3 \cdot 2 \cdot 1 = 120$

PROBLEM SET 2–5, Pages 30–31

3. (b) $4 = n(S_4)$ and $6 = n(S_6)$; S_4 matches a proper subset of S_6; thus $4 < 6$.

4. (b) No.

5. (c) $2 \cdot 2 = 4$　　(e) No, not directly.

6. (b) $2^5 = 32$

7. $0 = n(\Phi)$, and Φ matches a proper subset of S_3.

PROBLEM SET 2–6, Page 32

1. (a) C(ardinal)　　(c) C, O(rdinal)　　(e) C, O　　(g) O, C　　(i) C　　(k) O, O

PROBLEM SET 3–2, Pages 37–38

1. (a) $\{a, b, c, d, x, r, z\}$, disjoint   (c) {ball, bat, dog, house, rabbit}, not disjoint

5. (a) {man, house, car}

6. (b) $n(A) + n(B) = 4 + 4 \neq n(A \cup B) = 7$

7. (a) $5 + 2 = n(S_5) + n(S_2)$; choose A to match S_2, such that S_5 and A are disjoint, say $A = \{6, 7\}$; hence $5 + 2 = n(S_5) + n(A) = n(S_5 \cup A) = n\{1, 2, 3, 4, 5, 6, 7\} = n(S_7) = 7$.

8. (a) $7 + 0 = 7$

10. (a) $B \cup D \subseteq A$; if some are red-haired, say, then $B \cup D \subset A$.   (b) Yes.
    (d) If statement in (b) is true.

11. (a) Yes.   (b) True only if no person takes both subjects.   (c) Smallest is 7, if $A \subseteq B$; largest is 12, if A and B are disjoint.

PROBLEM SET 3–3, Page 43

1. (a) If $B = \{4, 5, 6, 7\}$, then $3 + 4 = n(S_3) + n(B) = n(S_3 \cup B)$; handle right side of equation similarly; show that $S_3 \cup B = B \cup S_3$.

2. (d) No.

3. Yes, unless such an effect as rate of breathing at end is considered.

4. No, $x + y$ will result in some unpainted ends, if sawcuts are necessary.

8. Use disjoint sets.

9. (a) L.S. (left side) $= [(3 + 4) + 2] + 5$, by A_a; $= [2 + (3 + 4)] + 5$, by C_a; $= [2 + (4 + 3)] + 5$, by C_a; $= [(2 + 4) + 3] + 5$, by A_a; $= (2 + 4) + (3 + 5)$, by A_a;   several orders of steps are possible.

PROBLEM SET 3–4, Pages 46–47

1. (c) Be certain to show that $S_2 \times S_5$ matches S_{10}.

2. (a) Set   (b) Number   (c) M   (d) M   (e) F, even though they match   (f) T

6. (a) Yes, definition of multiplication has no limitation on sets.   (b) No, sets must be disjoint.

PROBLEM SET 3–6, Page 52

1. (a) L.S. $= 0 \cdot t = 0$, and R.S. $= r \cdot 0 = 0$; hence L.S. $=$ R.S. (right side)

2. (a) L.S. $= 4[(3 \cdot 7)8]$, by A_m; $= 4[8(3 \cdot 7)]$, by C_m;
   $= (4 \cdot 8)(3 \cdot 7)$, by A_m; $= (4 \cdot 8)(7 \cdot 3)$, by C_m;
   $= [(4 \cdot 8)7]3$, by A_m; $= [7(4 \cdot 8)]3$, by C_m;
   $= [(7 \cdot 4)8]3$, by A_m; $= (7 \cdot 4) \cdot (8 \cdot 3)$, by A_m;
   other orders of steps are possible.

3. $1 \cdot r = n(S_1) \cdot n(S_r) = n(S_1 \times S_r) = n(S_r) = r$, since $S_1 \times S_r$ matches S_r.

4. (d) Solution of equations such as $(x - 2)(x - 5) = 0$.

5. Only by performing calculations.

PROBLEM SET 3–7, Pages 55–56

2. Use commutative property.

4. (c) L.S. $= 5 \cdot 10 + (4 + 3) \cdot 10$, by D_+; $= [5 + (4 + 3)]10$, by D_+;
$= [(5 + 4) + 3]10$, by A_a.

5. (c) Show that (a) is false by computation and (b) is true by distributive property.

PROBLEM SET 3–8, Pages 59–60

2. (a) {book}.   (c) Impossible, since $\{8, 2, 7\}$ is not a subset of $\{1, 2, 8, 3, 5\}$.
(e) $\{5, 7, 9, 11\}$

3. (a) No, $S_8 - S_5$ matches S_3.   (b) Yes.

4. (a) $9 - 6 = n(S_9) - n(S_6) = n(S_9 - S_6) = n\{7, 8, 9\} = 3$, since $\{7, 8, 9\}$ matches S_3.

6. (a) $6 = 8 - 2$ or $2 = 8 - 6$ (c) $9 = 5 + 4$

8. No set which matches S_8 can be a subset of S_3.

PROBLEM SET 3–9, Page 63

1. (a) $42 = 6 \cdot 7$ (c) $28 \div 7 = 4$ or $28 \div 4 = 7$

3. (a) $3 + 6$ is meaningless at this stage.   (b) Part (a) shows that "$x \div y = y + x$, for all x and y" is *not* true since there is one case in which it is *not* true.

PROBLEM SET 4–2, Pages 68–69

1. (a) 2245   (c) 248   (e) 1511   (g) 11646

2. Properties A_a and C_a

3. Check digit positions separately; digits are the same in the sums of each part.

4. (a) 1532 (seven)   (b) 13772 (twelve)   (c) 10011010 (two)

7. Property of numbers

PROBLEM SET 4–3, Pages 70–71

3. (a) 5^{19} (c) 4^{47} (e) x^{30} (g) r^{79} (i) x^{a+b} (k) $y^{s+t+u+w}$

PROBLEM SET 4–4, Pages 74–75

4. (a) $8(7 \cdot 10^2 + 2 \cdot 10 + 4) = (8 \cdot 7)10^2 + (8 \cdot 2)10 + 8 \cdot 4$
$= (5 \cdot 10 + 6)10^2 + (1 \cdot 10 + 6)10 + (3 \cdot 10 + 2)$
$= 5 \cdot 10^3 + (6 + 1)10^2 + (6 + 3)10 + 2 = 5792$

(c) 7190   (e) 12231   (g) 58588

5. $(48 \cdot 6)10$

6. (c) $(3415 \cdot 4)10^3$ (e) $(56 \cdot 73)10^5$

7. (b) $(X + V + I + I)V = L + XXV + V + V = LXXXV$
   (d) $(XXVII)(V + I) = (XXVII)V + (XXVII)I = CLXII$
   (e) $\overline{X}DCCXL$ and $\overline{CXXX}MMMDCCCLXXV$

9. (a) 255046(seven)   (c) 3T3568(twelve)   (e) 304431(five)   (g) 100010001(two)

PROBLEM SET 4–5, Page 78

1. (a) L.S. $= [(8 + 9) - 5] - 3$, by PP$_2$; $= [(9 + 8) - 5] - 3$, by C$_a$;
   $= [9 + (8 - 5)] - 3$, by PP$_1$; $= [(8 - 5) + 9] - 3$, by C$_a$;
   $= (8 - 5) + (9 - 3)$, by PP$_1$.

3. $(x - y) - z = a$ implies that $a = (x - y) - z$, by symm. prop.; then
   $x - (y + z) = a$ and $a = (x - y) - z$ imply that
   $x - (y + z) = (x - y) - z$, by trans. prop.

PROBLEM SET 4–6, Pages 81–82

1. (b) $(7 \cdot 10 + 3) - (5 \cdot 10 + 4) = (6 \cdot 10 + 1 \cdot 10 + 3) - (5 \cdot 10 + 4)$
   $= (6 \cdot 10 + 13) - (5 \cdot 10 + 4)$
   $= (6 \cdot 10 - 5 \cdot 10) + (13 - 4)$
   $= (6 - 5)10 + (13 - 4)$
   $= 1 \cdot 10 + 9 = 19$

2. (b) $[(7 \cdot 10 - 5 \cdot 10) - 1 \cdot 10] + [10 + (3 - 4)]$
   $= [7 \cdot 10 - (5 \cdot 10 + 1 \cdot 10)] + (13 - 4) = (7 - 6)10 + (13 - 4)$

6. (a) Add 6972 to 1672.

7. (a) 81445   (c) 11315

9. (a) 104(five)   (c) 11(three)   (e) 20(three)

PROBLEM SET 4–7, Page 84

1. (a) $672 - 13 \cdot 43 = 113$ (13 is a guess); $(672 - 13 \cdot 43) - 2 \cdot 43 = 27$;
   $672 - (13 + 2)43 = 27$; quotient is 15, remainder is 27.
   (c) $2614 - 34 \cdot 75 = 64$; quotient is 34, remainder is 64.

2. (a) 4900   (c) 6280

4. (a) 3200   (b) 3200, 6400, and 9600

5. When the result of subtraction $< y$.

6. (a) $(9104 - 100 \cdot 87) - 4 \cdot 87 = 56$; $9104 - (100 + 4)87 = 56$; quotient
   is 104, remainder is 56.   (c) $60105 - 2226 \cdot 27 = 3$.
   (e) $604873 - 926 \cdot 653 = 195$

7. (a) $134 = 12 \cdot 11 + 2$ (b) $x = q \cdot y + r$

PROBLEM SET 4–9, Pages 89–90

1. (a) 2700   (c) $b = 3$; divide 89 by 27.   (d) $b \cdot g = 3 \cdot 2700 = 300 \cdot 27$

2. (a) Subtract $500 \cdot 18$, then $20 \cdot 18$.   (c) Subtract $300 \cdot 35$, then $20 \cdot 35$.

3. (c) 7   (d) No, since $7 \cdot 67$ is too large.   (e) 6

4. (a) $b \cdot 83 \leq 672$, $c \cdot 8 \leq 67$, $c = 8, b = 8$ (d) $c = 9, b = 7$

5. (a) At step three, $c = 10$, $b = 7$, subtract $700 \cdot 28$; at step four, subtract $70 \cdot 28$.   (c) $q = 34, r = 191$ (e) $q = 44, r = 553$ (g) $q = 579$, $r = 1294$

9. (a) 230(seven)   (b) $q = 23$(seven), $r = 1$

10. (a) $q = 16$(seven), $r = 14$(seven)   (c) $q = 11$(three), $r = 0$
    (e) $q = 114$(eight), $r = 54$(eight)   (g) $q = 114$(twelve), $r = 4T$(twelve)

PROBLEM SET 5–1, Page 93

1. (a) 1011110(two)   (c) 11010100(two)

2. (a) $(2^5 + 0 \cdot 2^4 + 2^3 + 0 \cdot 2^2 + 2 + 1)51$
   $$= 2 \cdot 816 + 0(2 \cdot 408) + 2 \cdot 204 + 0(2 \cdot 102) + 2 \cdot 51 + 51$$

3. (a) 11214   (c) 21210   (e) 7560

4. (a) First method; since there are fewer terms in base two representation, then there are fewer multiplications.   (b) Double the larger number.

6. Terminates when quotient is zero.

8. (a) 1264(seven)   (c) 3234(six)   (e) 6666(seven)

PROBLEM SET 5–2, Pages 97–98

1. *Hint:* represent product by $n(n + 1)(n + 2)(n + 3)$.

3. (a) *Hint:* four cases, according as n has the form $4k$, $4k + 1$, $4k + 2$, or $4k + 3$.

4. (c) Even or odd since whole number has form $2k$ or $2k + 1$.

5. No, since remainders are less than divisor, quotient and remainder must be unique.

PROBLEM SET 5–3, Page 102

1. (a) $9(4 \cdot 111 + 3 \cdot 11 + 2) + (4 + 3 + 2 + 8)$

2. (a) 0   (c) 1

3. (a) $R_9(763) + R_9(482) = R_9(7 + 5) = 1 + 2$
   (c) $R_9(743) - R_9(528) = R_9(5) - R_9(6) = R_9(14 - 6) = 8$
   (e) $R_9(78) \cdot R_9(845) = R_9(6 \cdot 8) = R_9(48)$
   (g) $R_9(85) \cdot R_9(43) + R_9(22)$

310   ANSWERS TO SELECTED PROBLEMS

4. (a) No error indicated; $R_9(n)$ is 0 for each side of equation.
   (c) Error indicated.   (e) Error indicated.

5. (a) $R_9(87 \cdot 87 + 73) = 1,$ $R_9(7642) = 1$; no error indicated.

PROBLEM SET 5–4, Page 105

1. (a) $7(100,001 - 1) + 6(9999 + 1) + 4(1001 - 1) + 8(99 + 1)$
   $+ 9(11 - 1) + 7$
   $$= 11(7 \cdot 9091 + 6 \cdot 909 + 4 \cdot 91 + 8 \cdot 9 + 9)$$
   $$+ [(6 + 8 + 7) - (7 + 4 + 9)]$$

2. (a) 7   (c) $R_{11}(1 + 0 + 5 + 2) - R_{11}(3 + 4 + 7) = 8 - 3 = 5$

3. (a) Error indicated.   (c) No error indicated.

4. R_9(L.S.) $= 5; R_9$(R.S.) $= 5$, no error indicated. R_{11}(L.S.) $= 6; R_{11}$(R.S.) $= 6$, result probably correct; multiplication shows shift of one digit two places.

PROBLEM SET 6–1, Page 109

1. 13 is the largest prime needed.

2. (a) Composite; 11 divides 209.   (c) Prime; not divisible by a prime ≤ 23.
   (e) Composite; 23 divides 667.

PROBLEM SET 6–2, Page 113

1. (a) Not divisible by 3, since $3 + 4 + 7 + 2$ is not divisible by 3; divisible by 4, since 4 divides 72; divisible by 8, since 8 divides 472; not divisible by 11, since $(11 + 2 + 4) - (7 + 3)$ is not divisible by 11.   (c) Not divisible by 8, 9, or 11.

3. (a) $2^3 \cdot 11 \cdot 13$ (c) $2^2 \cdot 3^2 \cdot 11^2$ (e) $11 \cdot 1931$

6. 13(seven) represents a number divisible by 5, yet 5 does not divide the ones digit.

7. 11(eight) is divisible by 3, yet $1 + 1$ is not divisible by 3.

9. Replace 9 by 6.

12. (a) If $N = 2k$, then $1 = 2(k - 3 \cdot 5 \cdot 7 \cdots 97)$.

PROBLEM SET 6–4, Page 115

1. (a) $\{r\}$ (c) $\{2, 3, 4, \ldots, 9\}$

2. A

PROBLEM SET 6–5, Page 118

1. (a) $\{1, 2, 4, 7, 14, 28\} \cap \{1, 3, 7, 9, 21, 63\} = \{1, 7\}$; gcd is 7.   (c) 9

2. (a) $179 = 3 \cdot 58 + 5,$ $58 = 11 \cdot 5 + 3,$ $5 = 1 \cdot 3 + 2,$ $3 = 1 \cdot 2 + 1,$
   $2 = 2 \cdot 1 + 0$; gcd is 1.   (c) 1   (e) 9

3. (a) $7 = 16 \cdot 217 - 15 \cdot 231$
   (c) $7 = 16 \cdot 910 - 63 \cdot 231$; $x = 16$, $y = 63$

PROBLEM SET 6–6, Page 120

1. (a) $(17, 47) = 1$; $1 = 4 \cdot 47 - 11 \cdot 17$
   (c) $(31, 77) = 1$; $1 = 5 \cdot 31 - 2 \cdot 77$

2. (a) $375 = 5k$; since 3 divides $375 = 5k$, then 3 divides k; $k = 3t$, $375 = 5(3t) = 15t$. (c) $1350 = 25k$; 3 divides 1350, 3 divides k; $1350 = 25(3t) = 75t$. (e) $1410 = 2k$; 3 divides 1410, $k = 3t$, $1410 = 6t$; 5 divides 1410, $t = 5r$; $1410 = 30r$

5. Yes; $n = 15k$; thus 14 divides k, since $(14, 15) = 1$.

PROBLEM SET 6–8, Page 124

1. (a) $\{14, 28, 42, \ldots\} \cap \{21, 42, \ldots\} = \{42, 84, \ldots\}$; lcm is 42.

2. (c) Any counting number   (d) 1

3. (b) $k = 7t$ (c) $5 \cdot 3 \cdot 7$

4. (a) $3^2 \cdot 5^4 \cdot 7^3$ (c) $5^2 \cdot 7 \cdot 11 \cdot 13$ (e) $2^3 \cdot 3^2 \cdot 5 \cdot 7 \cdot 11^2$ (g) $5^4 \cdot 13^2$

6. (a) A common multiple of m and n has form $2 \cdot 3 \cdot 5^2 \cdot 7k$; k must have the form $2 \cdot 3 \cdot t$; $t = 1$ gives $2^2 \cdot 3^2 \cdot 5^2 \cdot 7$ as lcm   (c) $2^3 \cdot 3^3 \cdot 5^2 \cdot 7$

PROBLEM SET 7–1, Pages 129–130

1. (a) $\frac{43}{22}$ (c) No reduction   (e) No reduction

2. (a) x^2/z^2 (c) u^2w^4/v^2z (e) $(x - y)/(x + y)$

3. (a) No.

4. (a) $108/(5^2 \cdot 6)$ and $115/(5^2 \cdot 6)$ (c) $105/(2 \cdot 7^3)$ and $48/(2 \cdot 7^3)$
   (e) $70/(3^2 \cdot 5 \cdot 29)$ and $63/(3^2 \cdot 5 \cdot 29)$

5. (a) Numerator $5 \cdot 7^3 \cdot 11^2$ (c) Denominator $2^2 \cdot 3 \cdot 5 \cdot 7^2$

6. (a) Fractions become $110/(3 \cdot 7 \cdot 11)$ and $112/(3 \cdot 7 \cdot 11)$; no, since new numerators are unequal.   (c) No; new numerators are 105 and 110.

7. (a) Yes, if $b = d$.   (b) Yes, if $a = c$; otherwise no. To give a similar answer to part (a), Problem 12(b) of Problem Set 7–5 is needed.   (c) $a = c$.

PROBLEM SET 7–2, Pages 132–133

3. (a) $\frac{2}{3} + \frac{3}{5} = (10 + 9)/15$

4. (a) $11/(3 \cdot 5) + 7/(4 \cdot 5) - 44/(3 \cdot 5 \cdot 4) + 21/(4 \cdot 5 \cdot 3)$
   $$= (44 + 21)/(3 \cdot 4 \cdot 5) = 65/(3 \cdot 4 \cdot 5) = 13/(3 \cdot 4)$$
   (c) $133/(3 \cdot 3 \cdot 5 \cdot 29)$ (e) $559/(5 \cdot 7 \cdot 11)$; reduce fractions first.
   (g) $(rz + sx)/xyz$ (i) $(ub^2 + va^2c)/a^3b^3c^2$
   (k) $[a(x + y) + b]/(x + y)^2$

6. (a) L.S. $= (\frac{3}{7} + \frac{2}{3}) + \frac{1}{4}$, by C_a; $= \frac{3}{7} + (\frac{2}{3} + \frac{1}{4})$, by A_a; $= \frac{3}{7} + (\frac{1}{4} + \frac{2}{3})$, by C_a

7. (b) $(a/b + c/b) + e/b = a/b + (c/b + e/b)$, by A_a;   hence   define $a/b + c/b + e/b$ as either of the expressions involving parentheses.

PROBLEM SET 7–3, Page 136

1. (a) L.S. $= \frac{2}{7} + \frac{1}{2}(\frac{2}{3} + \frac{4}{5})$, by C_a; $= \frac{2}{7} + \frac{1}{2}(\frac{4}{5} + \frac{2}{3})$, by C_a;
   $= \frac{2}{7} + (\frac{1}{2} \cdot \frac{4}{5} + \frac{1}{2} \cdot \frac{2}{3})$, by D_+; $= \frac{2}{7} + (\frac{4}{5} \cdot \frac{1}{2} + \frac{1}{2} \cdot \frac{2}{3})$, by C_m;
   $= \frac{2}{7} + \frac{4}{5} \cdot \frac{1}{2} + \frac{1}{2} \cdot \frac{2}{3}$, by Problem 7 of Problem Set 7–2.
   (c) L.S. $= \frac{1}{2} + 0 = \frac{1}{2}$, by mult. and add. properties of zero;
   R.S. $= \frac{1}{2} \cdot 1 = \frac{1}{2}$, by E_1 and prop. of one.

2. (a) 5/3   (c) 20/429   (e) $(7 \cdot 31)/(6 \cdot 20)$
   (g) 0   (i) 8/15   (k) y^2/x^2
   (m) $(y^2 + x^2)/y^2$ (o) 41/7   (q) 29/6
   (s) 65/6

PROBLEM SET 7–5, Pages 139–140

1. (a) So that $a - c$ will be a whole number. (b) So that d/c will be a fraction.

2. (a) $(23 \cdot 13)/(7 \cdot 13) - (17 \cdot 7)/(13 \cdot 7) = (299 - 119)/(7 \cdot 13) = 180/91$
   (c) $11/(2 \cdot 3 \cdot 5)$ (e) $\frac{151}{55}$ (g) $\frac{2}{15}$

3. (b) No.

5. (a) $\frac{4}{7} \cdot r = \frac{5}{4}$; $(\frac{4}{7} \cdot \frac{7}{4}) \cdot \frac{5}{4} = \frac{5}{4}$; $\frac{4}{7}(\frac{7}{4} \cdot \frac{5}{4}) = \frac{5}{4}$; $r = \frac{7}{4} \cdot \frac{5}{4}$
   (c) $(12 \cdot 5)/(7 \cdot 11)$ (e) $\frac{16}{125}$

6. (a) Multiply "numerator" and "denominator" of the "four-tiered" fraction by $\frac{7}{4}$; answer is $(17 \cdot 7)/(3 \cdot 4)$.
   (c) $(5 \cdot 12)/(7 \cdot 11)$ (e) $\frac{35}{44}$ (g) $xy/1 = xy$ (i) $uvx/1 = uvx$

7. (a) No; first is $\frac{12}{7}$, second is $\frac{3}{7}$.

9. (a) $x = (17 \cdot 43)/(22 \cdot 43) = 731/(22 \cdot 43)$ and
   $y = (35 \cdot 22)/(43 \cdot 22) = 770/(43 \cdot 22)$; $x < y$
   (c) $x < y$

PROBLEM SET 7–6, Pages 144–145

1. (a) $\frac{19}{8} = (2 \cdot 8 + 3)/8 = (2 \cdot 8)/8 + \frac{3}{8} = 2 + \frac{3}{8} = 2\frac{3}{8}$; by div. th., def. of add. of fractions and E_1
   (c) $3 + \frac{8}{13} = 3\frac{8}{13}$

2. (a) $7 + \frac{4}{11} = \frac{77}{11} + \frac{4}{11} = \frac{81}{11}$ (c) $\frac{89}{7}$

3. (a) $(15 \cdot 29)/(7 \cdot 4)$ (c) $\frac{119}{60}$ or $1\frac{59}{60}$ (e) $\frac{187}{5}$ or $37\frac{2}{5}$
   (g) $\frac{598}{35}$ (i) $\frac{26}{37}$

4. (a) $(4 + \frac{2}{3}) + (3 + \frac{1}{2}) = (4 + 3) + (\frac{2}{3} + \frac{1}{2}) = 7 + \frac{7}{6} = 8\frac{1}{6}$, by C_a and A_a
   (c) $11\frac{13}{20}$ (e) $(7 - 2) + (\frac{5}{8} - \frac{1}{3}) = 5\frac{7}{24}$ (g) $3\frac{13}{30}$
   (i) $10 + \frac{16}{15} = 10 + 1\frac{1}{15} = 11\frac{1}{15}$ (k) $10\frac{11}{35}$
5. (i) $\frac{22}{5} + \frac{20}{3} = \frac{166}{15}$ (l) $\frac{14}{3} - \frac{23}{8} = \frac{43}{24}$
6. Use of improper form is shorter.

PROBLEM SET 7–7, Page 146

1. Treat $\frac{11}{6}$ as eleven of the one-sixth parts or as $1 + \frac{5}{6}$.

PROBLEM SET 7–8, Page 150

1. (a) $7 + \frac{6}{10} + \frac{3}{100} + \frac{5}{1000} = (7000 + 600 + 30 + 5)/1000 = \frac{7635}{1000}$
   (c) $180,013/10,000$ (e) $17,639/100,000$
2. (a) $(1 \cdot 10^3 + 7 \cdot 10^2 + 6 \cdot 10 + 4)/10^4 = 1/10 + 7/10^2 + 6/10^3 + 4/10^4$
   $= 0.1764$
   (c) 1.73024
3. (a) $7 + \frac{6}{11} = 7 + \frac{60}{11} \cdot \frac{1}{10} = 7 + (5 + \frac{5}{11})\frac{1}{10} = 7.5 + \frac{50}{11} \cdot \frac{1}{100}$
   $= 7.54 + \frac{60}{11} \cdot \frac{1}{100} = 7.545 + \frac{5}{11} \cdot \frac{1}{100} \approx 7.545$
   (c) Nearer to 0.417 than to 0.416   (e) 0.444
4. Obtained $0.5714285 + (5/7)(1/10^7)$; no zero remainder obtained and no such remainder can be obtained later, since remainder terms will be similar to the previous remainder terms.
5. (a) 0.71; $\frac{3}{7} \cdot \frac{1}{100} < \frac{1}{2} \cdot \frac{1}{100}$ (c) 0.917; remainder term $> \frac{1}{2} \cdot \frac{1}{1000}$
6. (a) 0.3125; remainder term is zero.   (c) $3.0375 + 0$
7. (a) $3 + 2 \cdot \frac{1}{7} + 4 \cdot (1/7^2) + 6 \cdot (1/7^3)$
   (b) 0.1(seven), 0.4(seven), and 0.6(seven)
   (c) $(1 \cdot 7^2 + 2 \cdot 7 + 2)/7^2 - 1.22$(seven)
8. (a) $6 \cdot \frac{1}{12} = 0.6$(twelve)   (b) 0.8(twelve)   (c) 2.4(twelve)

PROBLEM SET 7–9, Page 156

1. (a) $1 \cdot 10 + (6 + 1) + (3 + 7)\frac{1}{10} + (2 + 3)\frac{1}{100} + 5 \cdot \frac{1}{1000}$, by C_a and A_a;
   $(3 + 7)\frac{1}{10} = 1 + 0 \cdot \frac{1}{10}$; 18.055
   (c) $(4 - 2) + (3 - 8)\frac{1}{10} + (2 - 1)\frac{1}{100} + (0 - 3)\frac{1}{1000}$;
   $(2 - 1) \cdot \frac{1}{100} = (1 + 1 - 1)\frac{1}{100} = (1 - 1)\frac{1}{100} + \frac{10}{1000}$;
   $4 - 2 = (1 + 3 - 2) = (3 - 2) + 10 \cdot \frac{1}{10}$;
   problem becomes $(3 - 2) + (13 - 8)\frac{1}{10}$
   $+ (1 - 1)\frac{1}{100} + (10 - 3)\frac{1}{1000} = 1.507$
   (e) 8.211 (g) 0.389 (i) 4.036

2. (a) $(6713 \times 154)(1/10^5) = 10.33802$ (c) 0.0949365
   (e) 422.5364   (g) 8.65296

3. (a) $(98476 \div 1223)\frac{1}{10} = (80 + \frac{636}{1223})\frac{1}{10} \approx 8.1$; $\frac{636}{1223} \cdot \frac{1}{10} > \frac{1}{2} \cdot \frac{1}{10}$
   (c) $(1350 \div 892)\frac{1}{100} \approx 0.02$ (e) 3268

4. (a) 0.58; $\frac{1}{2} < \frac{484}{748} < 1$ implies that $\frac{1}{2} \cdot \frac{1}{100} < \frac{484}{748} \cdot \frac{1}{100} < \frac{1}{100}$; remainder
   term is nearer to 0.01 than to 0.

5. (a) No; the symbol $\approx$ should be used.

PROBLEM SET 7–10, Pages 157–158

1. (a) No; 6.72×10^9

2. (a) 6.89×10^{11} (c) $5 \times 1/10^{10}$ (e) $2.6 \times 1/10^8$

3. (a) $2.686 \times 1/10^9$

5. $3.69538848 \times 10^{13}$ mi $\approx 3.6953885 \times 10^{13}$ mi

PROBLEM SET 8–2, Pages 161–162

1. (a) $(3n - 2)/3 + 4$ (c) $(x + 7)(x + 3)$

2. (c) A number is increased by 4, and the result is multiplied by $\frac{1}{2}$; 7 is then
   added to the resulting number.

3. (a)

x	1	2	3	4	5
$3x - 2$	1	4	7	10	13

(better to display this in a column with x on the left.)

(c)

x	2	2	5	5
y	2	5	2	5
$(x + 2y - 3)/4$	$\frac{3}{4}$	$\frac{9}{4}$	$\frac{3}{2}$	3

4. (a) $x = 4$ (c) $u = 2$ and $v = 3$,   or $u = 3$ and $v = 1$

PROBLEM SET 8–4, Pages 167–168

1. (a) Table of values of $2x + 1$ shows that 3 is a truth value and the only such
   value.
   (c) $\{0, 1, 2, 3, 4\}$ (e) $\{0, 1, 2, 3, 5, 6, 7, 8\}$ (g) $\{0, 1, 2, 3\}$

3. (a) 5 is a truth number. (b) No; there may be other truth numbers. (c) Truth
   set is empty.

4. (a) If there is a truth number, 5 is the only possibility.
   (c) Truth set is $\{5\}$, if 5 is in the substitution set.
   (d) Truth set is $\{5\}$.

5. (a) If there is a truth number, $3x - 2 + 2 - x = x + 2 - x$, $2x = 2$,
   $\frac{1}{2}(2x) = \frac{1}{2} \cdot 2$, $x = 1$, and 1 is the only possibility; for $x = 1$,
   L.S. $= 3 - 2 = 1$,   R.S. $= 1$, 1 is a truth number; truth set is $\{1\}$.
   (c) $\{\frac{5}{2}\}$ (e) $\{\frac{3}{2}\}$ (g) $\{\frac{8}{3}\}$

9. The union of the truth sets is the substitution set.

10. Let A be the truth set of $2x - 1 = 3 - x$; (substitution set) $-A$ is truth set
    of inequality.

11. (a) {All fractions except $\frac{4}{3}$}   (c) {All fractions except $\frac{12}{1} = 12$}

PROBLEM SET 8–6, Page 173

1. (a) If $3x < 11$, then $x < \frac{11}{3}$; try 0, 1, 2, and 3; truth set is $\{0, 1, 2, 3\}$.
   (c) $\{0, 1, 2, 3, 4, 5, 6, 7\}$

2. If $3x + 2 > 12$, then $x > \frac{10}{3}$; if $x > \frac{10}{3}$, then $3x + 2 > 12$; truth set
   is {all fractions $> \frac{10}{3}$}.

3. {all fractions $< \frac{17}{4}$}; must show that if $x < \frac{17}{4}$, then $4x - 7 < 10$.

4. (a) $\{5, 6, 7, 8\}$ (c) Φ (e) {all fractions $< \frac{9}{2}$}
   (g) {all whole numbers ≥ 9}

PROBLEM SET 9–1, Pages 175–176

1. (a) 5.3 cents   (b) 65(5.3) cents $= 344.5$ cents   (c) $5.3x$ cents

2. (a) In 1 min it goes $\frac{12}{13}$ mi; in 28 min it goes $28(\frac{12}{13})$ mi.
   (b) $12t/13$ mi   (c) $42(\frac{13}{12})$ min   (d) $13y/12$ min

3. (b) $\frac{65}{4}$ servings   (c) Yes; $60\frac{4}{5}$ oz required.

4. Large package, by $\frac{1}{12}$ cent per oz.

5. $58\frac{2}{3}$ ft per sec

6. Approx. 20.5 m.p.h.

7. (a) 1 in. $\sim$ 30 mi   (c) $y/30$ in.

8. (a) Different numerals for same number. (b) Equivalent to, i.e., same length
   of time but different units.

PROBLEM SET 9–2, Pages 180–182

2. 34 per row

3. Let $x =$ number of plants Harry places per row; $12x + 9(x + 7) = 714$;
   Jim planted 38 per row.

4. (a) 14 in. by 21 in.   (c) 14 in. by 21 in.

5. 11 suits

6. 1330; let $x =$ number of seniors.

8. Let Charles run x ft per sec; $50x = 55(x - 2)$; 5 sec

9. 3.5 ft

10. $5000, $12000, $15000

11. 4500 sq. ft

12. 1750

13. 84

15. 20 min

16. $17\frac{1}{3}$ min and $23\frac{1}{3}$ min

17. 40 lbs

18. 42(five)

20. (b) $x + 5$ m.p.h. downstream and $x - 5$ m.p.h. upstream

21. 36 mi

22. 630 mi

PROBLEM SET 9–3, Page 184

1. (a) $x/7 = \frac{11}{14}$; $x = \frac{11}{2}$ (c) $\frac{16}{3}$

2. (a) $\frac{7}{12}$ (c)$\frac{5}{4}$

3. $\frac{17}{22}$

5. $2,950,000

7. 34(approx.)

PROBLEM SET 9–4, Pages 187–188

1. (c) $\frac{74}{1000}$ (e) $\frac{1}{300}$

2. (a) $5(12\frac{1}{2})/8(12\frac{1}{2}) = 62.5/100$ or $\dfrac{5(100)}{8} \cdot \dfrac{1}{100} = 62.5/100 = 62.5\%$

   (c) $133\frac{1}{3}\%$;   (e) $91\frac{7}{23}\% \approx 91\%$;   (g) 0.79% (approx.)   (i) 497% (approx.)

3. (a) $\frac{3}{100}y = 47$; $y = \frac{4700}{3}$ or $1566\frac{2}{3}$ (c) $\dfrac{5.2}{100}\, 160 = w$; $w = 8.32$

   (e) $(0.5/100)x = 48$; $x = 9600$

4. $\frac{17}{54} = \frac{1700}{54} \cdot \frac{1}{100} \approx 31.5\%$

5. 180

7. $240

9. Let $x\%$ be the rate of interest; $440 + (x/100)(440) = 12(38.68)$; $x \approx 5.5\%$

11. Sale price $= 1.04$ (original price)

12. 23% (approx.)

13. Let sales $= \$x$; salesman's net receipts $= \frac{60}{100}(\frac{9}{100}x)$; net receipts/sales $= \frac{60}{100}(\frac{9}{100}x) \div x = 5.4\%$

14. (b) $0.03x + 0.04y$

15. $36\frac{4}{11}$ lbs of 2.5% milk, or approx. 36 lbs.

PROBLEM SET 10–1, Page 192

2. (c) Assumption is false; r is irrational.

3. (c) $1 < \sqrt{2} < 2$ (e) $1.4 < \sqrt{2} < 1.5$ (f) Segment within which $\sqrt{2}$ lies is smaller.   (h) Rational   (k) Yields approximations to $\sqrt{2}$, as close as is desired.

4. $\sqrt{3} \approx 1.73$

PROBLEM SET 10–3, Pages 195–196

2. (a) 11   (c) $^-(\frac{5}{3})$

3. (a) $^-5$ (d) $\frac{5}{11}$

4. (a) 4 or $^-4$ (c) 0

5. None

6. (a) Positive   (c) Negative

7. (a) No; zero is different from both the positives and the negatives.
   (c) Negative, if r is positive; positive, if r is negative

8. (a) 3   (b) $^-5$

PROBLEM SET 10–4, Page 199

3. (a) $|^-8| + |^-3| = 8 + 3 = 11$ (c) $|^-5| - |3| = 5 - 3 = 2$
   (e) $\frac{5}{2} - \frac{1}{3} = \frac{13}{6}$ (g) $\frac{5}{4}$
   (i) 3.02

4. (a), (c), (e), and (g) negative; (i) positive

5. (a) $^-(8 - 6) = ^-2$ (c) $^-(\frac{4}{5} + \frac{6}{7}) = ^-(\frac{58}{35})$ (e) $\frac{22}{21}$
   (g) $|\text{sum}| = |\frac{2}{3} - \frac{2}{3}| = |0| = 0$; sum $= 0$ (i) $\frac{1}{8}$

6. (a) $^-(|r| + |s|)$ (b) $r - |s|$ (c) 0   (d) $^-(|s| - r)$ (e) $r + 0 = r$
   (f) $^-(|r| + 0) = ^-|r|$

PROBLEM SET 10–5, Page 202

1. (a) $(-\frac{2}{3} + \frac{2}{3}) + \frac{7}{5} = 0 + \frac{7}{5} = \frac{7}{5}$, by A_a, Th. 10–5, Th. 10–4
   (c) $-\frac{3}{4} + (\frac{3}{4} + \frac{4}{3})$, by C_a;   proceed as before, to $\frac{4}{3}$.

2. (a) L.S. $= (-5 + 6) + 11 = -5 + (6 + 11)$, by C_a and A_a;   also
   L.S. $= 11 + (6 - 5) = 11 + 1 = 11 + 1 = 12$ and
   R.S. $= -5 + 17 = 17 - 5 = 12$
   (c) $-a + a = 0$, by Th. 10–3; or let $u = -(-a)$, then $-u + u = 0$.

3. (a) $^-(|-\frac{4}{5}| + |-\frac{6}{7}|) = {}^-(\frac{4}{5} + \frac{6}{7}) = -\frac{58}{35}$
   (c) $[11 + (-7)] + (-6) = (11 - 7) + (-6) = 4 + (-6) = -(6 - 4) = -2$
   (e) $^-10\frac{1}{6}$

5. (a) $(x + 2) + (-2) = -7 + (-2);\ x + [2 + (-2)] = -9;\ x + 0 = -9;$
   $x = -9$ is the only possible solution; show that -9 is a truth number.
   (c) $[w + (-4)] + 4 = -11 + 4;\ w = -7$ (e) $w = \frac{11}{3}$

PROBLEM SET 10–7, Page 205

1. (a) $-8 + [-(-4)] = -8 + 4 = -(8 - 4) = -4;$ on the number line
   add 4 to $^-8$.   (c) 3   (e) $-\frac{2}{9}$

2. (a) Positive. (b) No; need information concerning absolute values.

3. (a) $-\frac{3}{2} - (-\frac{5}{2}) = 1 > 0;$ hence $-\frac{3}{2} > -\frac{5}{2}$
   (c) $-\frac{7}{2} - (-\frac{7}{9}) = -\frac{49}{18} < 0;$ hence $-\frac{7}{9} > -\frac{7}{2}$

4. (a) $\frac{8}{14} < \frac{9}{14} < \frac{10}{14}$

6. (a) $\frac{40}{15} + (-\frac{63}{15}) = -\frac{23}{15}$ (c) $-\frac{31}{10}$ (e) $\frac{19}{10}$ (g) $2\frac{1}{4}$ (i) $5\frac{19}{28}$ (k) $-\frac{89}{10}$

PROBLEM SET 10–8, Page 207

2. $\{-\frac{17}{12}\}$

3. (a) $\{-2\}$ (c) $\{\frac{11}{3}\}$

4. (a) $-\frac{2}{3} + [-(\frac{3}{4} - \frac{7}{8})]$, by def. of sub.; $= -\frac{2}{3} + [\frac{7}{8} - \frac{3}{4}]$, by Th. 10–8;
   $= (\frac{7}{8} - \frac{3}{4}) + (-\frac{2}{3})$, by C_a; $= [\frac{7}{8} + (-\frac{3}{4})] + (-\frac{2}{3})$, by def. of sub.;
   $= \frac{7}{8} + [-\frac{3}{4} + (-\frac{2}{3})]$, by A_a; $= \frac{7}{8} + [-\frac{2}{3} - \frac{3}{4}]$, by C_a and def. of sub.

PROBLEM SET 10–9, Page 211

1. (a) $|-3| \cdot |-9| = 3 \cdot 9 = 27$ (c) -2 (e) $-\frac{4}{9}$ (g) 1   (i) $\frac{9}{2} \cdot \frac{23}{3} = \frac{69}{2}$

2. (a) $-\frac{1}{4}$ (c) $x/2y$

3. (a) L.S. $= (-x)(-y) - (-x)z$, by Th. 10–12; $= xy - (-xz)$, by Th.
   10–11; $= xy + xz$, by Th. 10–3 and def. of sub.

4. $(-1)a = -(1 \cdot a) = -a;$ also
   $a + (-1)a = 1 \cdot a + (-1)a = [1 + (-1)]a = 0 \cdot a = 0;$ thus $(-1)a$ is
   the opposite of a since the opposite is unique.

6. (a) L.S. $= 3(-2) + 3 \cdot 4$, by C_m and Th. 10–11; $= 3(-2 + 4)$, by D_+;
   (c) L.S. $= -[-(2 \cdot 4)]$, by Th. 10–11; $= 2 \cdot 4$, by Th. 10–3; $= 4 \cdot 2$,
   by C_m.

7. $3 \cdot 3 \cdot 3 = 27$ cases; may be reduced to eleven cases since, e.g., for $a = 0, b,$
   and c any rational may be treated as one case.

PROBLEM SET 10–11, Pages 215–216

1. (a) $1/(-4) = -1/4$, since $(-4)(-1/4) = 4(1/4) = 1$ (c) $3/2$
2. (b) $(-3)x = 1$
4. (a) $(-4) \cdot (\frac{1}{3}) = -\frac{4}{3}$ (c) $(-\frac{2}{3}) \cdot 4 = -\frac{8}{3}$
7. (a) $-\frac{96}{35}$ (c) $-\frac{3}{10}$ (e) $-\frac{17}{4}$ (g) $-r^2/2s^2$ (i) $-3x/2y^2$ (k) $-v^2$
11. (a) L.S. $= -1/(x - y) = (-1)(-1)/(-1)(x - y) = 1/(y - x)$
   (c) L.S. $= 1 + (-1)/(r - 2s) = 1 + 1/[(-1)(r - 2s)] = 1 + 1/(2s - r)$

PROBLEM SET 11–1, Page 221

1. (a) $2 < 3$, $2.2 < 2.3$, $2.23 < 2.24$, $2.236 < 2.237$; 2.236
   (c) $8 < 9$, $8.4 < 8.5$, $8.42 < 8.43$; 8.43
2. (a) $3 < 4$, $3.4 < 3.5$, $3.43 < 3.44$, $3.430 < 3.431$, $3.4300 < 3.4301$
   (c) $1 < 2$, $1.3 < 1.4$, $1.33 < 1.34$, $1.333 < 1.334$
   (e) $-3 < -2$, $-2.3 < -2.2$, $-2.24 < -2.23$, $-2.237 < -2.236$
   (g) $-9 < -8$, $-8.5 < -8.4$, $-8.43 < -8.42$

PROBLEM SET 11–2, Page 222

1. (a) $1 < 3$, $1.4 < 1.6$, $1.48 < 1.50$, $1.480 < 1.482$
   (c) $3 < 5$, $3.6 < 3.8$, $3.64 < 3.66$, $3.650 < 3.652$
   (e) $0 < 2$, $0.9 < 1.1$, $0.99 < 1.01$, $1.005 < 1.007$
   (g) $-1 < 1$, $0.3 < 0.5$, $0.43 < 0.45$, $0.437 < 0.439$
2. (a) 1.48; next digit is 0, 1, or 2.   (c) 3.65; next digit is 0, 1, or 2.
   (e) 1.00; next digit is 5, 6, or 7.   (g) 0.43; next digit is 7, 8, or 9.

PROBLEM SET 11–3, Page 224

1. (b) $1/0.33 = 3.03 + (1/3300) < 3.03 + (1/100) = 3.04$
   (c) No; $1/0.33 > 3.03$.
2. $80 < 90.9$, $83.000 < 84.084$, $83.30000 < 83.40834$; No, the tenths digit is either 3, 4, or 5.
3. (a) $2 < 6$, $3.08 < 3.45$, $3.1443 < 3.1808$; up to tenths
   (b) $0.3 < 0.8$, $0.462 < 0.510$, $0.46953 < 0.47428$; tenths

PROBLEM SET 11–6, Pages 227–228

2. (a) $3^7 \cdot 4^7$ (c) $u^4 \cdot (v^2)^4 = u^4 \cdot v^2 \cdot v^2 \cdot v^2 \cdot v^2 = u^4 v^8$ (e) 1
   (g) $3^2 \cdot 4^5$ (i) $x^9 \cdot y^9$
3. (a) Multiply numerator and denominator by 5^2; $(7 \cdot 5^2)/10^3$.
   (c) $(13 \cdot 2)/10^2$ (e) $(17 \cdot 2^3)/10^7$
5. (a) 7^{12} (c) $1/11^2$ (e) $1/5^{s-r}$ (g) $x^2 y$ (i) $x^6 y$ (k) 1

PROBLEM SET 11–7, Page 230

1. (a) 85.4025   (c) 23.6875   (e) 6.27456
2. (a) $838/5^3$ (c) $707/(2^3 \cdot 5)$ (e) $2532/5^4$
5. $\frac{4}{7}$ and $\frac{11}{12}$

PROBLEM SET 11–8, Pages 234–235

1. (a) $0.\dot{7}1428\dot{5}$ (c) 0.83 (e) $0.41\dot{6}$
2. (a) $667/99$ (c) $477874/999000 = 238937/499500$
   (e) $13124/9900 = 3281/2475$
3. (a) Nonending, nonrepeating; irrational number
4. (a) Yes; it has a decimal expansion.   (b) No; nonrepeating
5. (b) No; $\frac{22}{7}$ is rational, π is irrational; $\frac{22}{7}$ is an approximation of π.
7. Properties of numerals, since reference is to decimals; hence the decimal system.

PROBLEM SET 12–2, Page 238

1. (a) BC (b) B (c) $\overrightarrow{BC}$ (d) $\overleftrightarrow{AC}$
2. The intersection of two rays, oppositely directed, which have more than one point in common.

PROBLEM SET 12–3, Page 243

1. (b) For example, through any two distinct points one and only one line can be drawn.
2. (c) 6.0, 6.2, 6.4, 6.6, 6.8, 7.0   (d) 6, $6\frac{1}{7}$, etc.
3. (a) Separate segment from 3 to 4 into ten congruent, nonoverlapping segments; then treat $P_{3.4}P_{3.5}$ similarly; $P_{3.42}$ is right endpoint of the second of these segments from $P_{3.4}$.
4. Property 3
5. (a) Measure, in miles, is 3.2.   (c) Length = 6 ft

PROBLEM SET 12–5, Page 249

1. (a) Yes.   (b) No.   (c) Ellipse, yes; parabola, no.
2. On AB construct a triangle (for example) congruent to a given $\triangle CDE$, with C at A.
3. Area of A_1 + area of A_2 + Area of A_3 = area of $(A_1 \cup A_2 \cup A_3)$.
4. $ABCD$ has been separated into ten congruent, nonoverlapping regions; measure of area $ABCD = m + m + m + \cdots$ to ten terms $= 10m$, where $m =$ area of $AEFD$; area of $ABCD = 10 \cdot$ (area $AEFD$).

5. Establish a number scale on $\overrightarrow{AC}$, with origin at A, the unit being AB; α is the number corresponding to C in this scale.

6. (a) "One inch square" describes the shape of a rectangular region; "one square inch" is the area of a rectangular region, not necessarily square (it might not even be rectangular).   (b) 4;   576

PROBLEM SET 12–7, Page 255

1. The angular region determined by the angle

2. The whole plane

3. (b) Yes; segments determine a pair of suitable rays.

4. (a) No; the common ray is part of the union but not part of the angle.
   (b) If the "outside" rays form a line.   (c) Yes.

5. Intuition

PROBLEM SET 12–8, Pages 257–258

1. (a) 0 to 250   (b) 125   (c) $90° = 125$ squens   (d) 25   (e) $144°$

2. $0 < m(A) < 90$; $90 < m(B) < 180$

4. No; the rays lie on a line.

5. $m(\alpha) + m(\beta) < 180$

6. (a) Yes.   (b) Yes.   (c) Yes.   (d) The union of five $1°$ angles

8. Angular region

9. Yes; follow through the development.

PROBLEM SET 13–2, Pages 262–263

1. (a) $\frac{1}{4}$ ft   (c) $\frac{1}{8}$ in.   (e) 0.001 cm   (g) 10 mi   (i) 10 mi   (k) 0.001 in.

2. (a) $\frac{1}{8}$ ft; $5\frac{5}{8}$ ft and $5\frac{7}{8}$ ft   (c) $\frac{1}{16}$ in.; $4\frac{11}{16}$ in. and $4\frac{13}{16}$ in.
   (e) 0.0005 cm; 3.3995 cm and 3.4005 cm   (g) 5 mi; 595 mi and 605 mi
   (i) 5 mi; 395 mi and 405 mi   (k) 0.0005 in.; 0.0045 in. and 0.0055 in.

3. (a) 0.1 ft   (c) 0.24 in.

4. No; too precise for the instrument.

6. $\frac{1}{10}$ ft rule; $\frac{1}{100}$ ft rule

7. (a) No; 0.1 in. $\neq$ 0.1 ft.   (b) No; converted measurement indicates precision of 0.1 in., whereas the precision is (12×0.1) in. $= 1.2$ in.   (c) 13.1 in.; smaller GPE

PROBLEM SET 13–3, Page 264

1. (a) 0.0018   (c) 0.007; in order of (b), (c), (a), (d)

2. (a) Increasing   (b) Decreasing   (c) Decreasing

PROBLEM SET 13–4, Page 267

1. (a) 36.3 ± 0.15 in.   (c) 22.27 ± 0.015 in.

2. (a) Since $0.047 < 0.050$ (b) 0.13 and 4.69

3. $48\frac{1}{2} \pm \frac{1}{4}$ in.

4. 0.15 ft

5. (b) $(4 - \frac{1}{2})$ in. $<$ "true" length $< (4 + \frac{1}{2})$ in.   (e) 1 in.

6. (a) 0.1 lbs   (c) 0.01 mi

PROBLEM SET 13–6, Page 271

1. (a) Area bounded by $ETBCPD$ (b) Area bounded by $FRABTE$
(c) Twice the area of square whose opposite vertices are T and P

2. (a) To express a "true" area in terms of computed area so as to indicate the GPE, the number of sq in. subtracted in one part must equal the number of sq in. added in the other part.   (b) No; this would indicate a GPE of 7.25 sq in., which is too small.

3. (a) "True" area $= (27.84 \pm 0.5975)$ sq ft   (c) (330 ± 18.75) sq cm

4. (a) 113.30 ± 0.01 (c) 168.74 ± 1.3075 (e) 100.92 ± 1.0175

PROBLEM SET 14–1, Pages 273–274

1. (a) Wednesday   (c) Tuesday   (e) Friday

3. Same; no difference

4. (a) $4 + 5 = 1 \cdot 7 + 2$ (b) $6 + 2 = 1 \cdot 7 + 1$ (c) $4 + 4 = 1 \cdot 7 + 1$

PROBLEM SET 14–2, Pages 275–276

1. (a) Use $x = 3 + 7k$, k any integer. (c) Use $x = 1 + 7k$, k any integer.

2. (a) True; $25 = 3 \cdot 7 + 4$, $11 = 1 \cdot 7 + 4$ (c) False; $1 \neq 2$

3. (a) $(1 \cdot 7 + 6) + (2 \cdot 7 + 5) = 3 \cdot 7 + (1 \cdot 7 + 4) = 4 \cdot 7 + 4 \equiv 4 \pmod 7$
(c) $6 \pmod 7$ (e) $4 \pmod 7$

4. (a) True; false   (b) 0, 1, 2, 3, 4   (c) 4; 1; 1   (f) 20

5. (a) $(3 \cdot 5 + 2) + (4 \cdot 5 + 3) = 7 \cdot 5 + 5 = 8 \cdot 5 + 0 \equiv 0 \pmod 5$
(c) $3 \pmod 5$

7. (a) $8 + (1 \cdot 12 + 1) = 1 \cdot 12 + 9 \equiv 9 \pmod{12}$ (c) $9 \pmod{12}$
(e) $5 \pmod{12}$

8. (a) $5 \pmod 9$ (c) $4 \pmod 9$ (e) $7 \pmod 9$

9. (a) Hours: $\pmod{12}$; minutes: $\pmod{60}$ (b) Replace "12" by 0.

10. (a) 3   (c) 2   (e) 3

PROBLEM SET 14–3, Page 277

1. (a) $1 \times 4 \equiv 4 (\mathrm{mod}\ 7)$ (c) $1 (\mathrm{mod}\ 7)$ (e) $2 (\mathrm{mod}\ 7)$ (g) $1 (\mathrm{mod}\ 7)$

2. (a) $6 (\mathrm{mod}\ 12)$ (c) $6 (\mathrm{mod}\ 12)$

5. (a) $0 (\mathrm{mod}\ 12)$ (c) $8 (\mathrm{mod}\ 12)$ (e) $3 (\mathrm{mod}\ 5)$ (g) $3 (\mathrm{mod}\ 9)$
   (i) $0 (\mathrm{mod}\ 6)$

6. (a) Since $1 \equiv 6 (\mathrm{mod}\ 5)$, then $2x \equiv 6 (\mathrm{mod}\ 5)$, so that $x = 3$; in general, $x = 3 + 5t$, for t any integer.   (c) 1   (e) 3

PROBLEM SET 14–4, Pages 280–282

1. (a) 1, 5, and 6   (b) $5 + (^-3) = 5 + 4 = 2$;   3;   3;   6

2. 6; yes, see table.

3. (a) $\{4\}$ (b) $\{0\}$ (c) $\{0\}$ (d) $\{0\}$

4. Yes; if it were an identity, then $2 + 3 = 3$.

5. (a) Yes; $a \triangle b$ is given as a unique element of T, for all a and b in T.
   (b) Yes; part of definition of operation.   (c) Yes, table is symmetric about main diagonal.   (d) Yes.   (e) Yes; 3.   (f) Yes; 3.   (g) No; no truth number for $4 \triangle x = 3$.

4. No; to 4 and 5 corresponds 6, but 6 is not in the set.

5. (f) 0   (g) Yes; $^-0 = 0$, $^-3 = 2$, $^-4 = 1$.

8. (b) 1 and 5   (c) 0, 2, 3, and 4   (d) $2 \cdot 3 = 0$ is an example of a product being zero, yet neither factor is zero.

9. (d) No; no solution of $1 + x = 1$.   (e) No; identity must exist before inverse can be considered.

10. (a) $W+$ has an identity; 0.   (b) Only 0 has an inverse.   (c) Set of integers

11. (b) Yes; z (c) $^-x = x$, $^-y = w$, $^-z = z$, $^-w = y$.   (e) Try all cases; sixty-four such cases, if commutativity is not used.

12. (b) Yes; 1   (d) $^-1 = 1$, $^-2 = 4$, $^-3 = 5$, $^-4 = 2$, $^-5 = 3$, $^-6 = 6$
    (e) 0 only

13. (b) Distributive, and closure of $W+$; $3m + 3n = 3(m + n)$
    (d) 0 is only solution of $x + (^-x) = 0$.   (e) Yes; let k be any integer.

14. (a) No; for example, $3^2 + 3^3 \neq 3^k$, for k some whole number.   (b) Yes; $3^m \cdot 3^n = 3^{m+n}$, and closure in $W+$.   (c) Yes; 1   (d) Only 1   (e) Let k be any integer; $3^{-t} = 1/3^t$ was not discussed previously.

PROBLEM SET 14–5, Pages 283–284

1. $A_\odot$, $C_\odot$ hold; 1 is identity; all elements but 0 have inverse for $\odot$.

2. (a) $-5, 3, 12, 0$ (b) All elements   (c) 1   (d) No; $3x = 1$ has no solution in $I+ \cdot$.   (e) $1^{-1} = 1$ and $(-1)^{-1} = -1$

3. Let u be the additive identity; $u + x = x = x + u$, for all x; prop. of zero.

4. $x \cdot e = x = e \cdot x$, for all x; prop. of one.

5. (a) $\frac{1}{3}, \frac{6}{7}, -\frac{2}{3}, -\frac{4}{1}$ (b) All but $\frac{0}{1}$ (d) y/x if $x \neq 0$ ($y \neq 0$ is implied by the notation)   (e) Reciprocal

6. (a) No; additive inverse is needed.   (b) Yes; additive inverse is meaningful.

7. (a) For $s \neq 0$, $r \div s = r \cdot s^{-1}$ (b) No; only 1 and -1 have multiplicative inverses.

8. In $x(y + z)$ there are 6 possibilities for $a \neq 0$; if b and c are distinct, there are 21 ways to choose them; if $b = c$, there are 7 possibilities. Total number of cases is $1 + 6(21 + 7)$.

PROBLEM SET 14–6, Pages 285–286

1. (a) Not for all; $x + 2 = 5$ does have; $x + 5 = 2$ does not have.   (b) Same as for part (a)   (c) Has, for all r and s.   (d) Same as (c)   (e) Same as (c)

2. (a) $2 \cdot x = 6$ has; $2 \cdot x = 5$ does not have.   (b) Same as (a)   (c) Same as (a)   (d) Has for all r and s, $r \neq 0$.   (e) Same as (d)

3. For all a which have an inverse for $\triangle$; this presumes the existence of an identity.

4. (a) There is a unique truth number for all r and s.   (b) There is a unique truth number for all r and s, $r \neq 0$.

5. If $x_1 + t = s$ and $x_2 + t = s$, then $x_1 + t = x_2 + t$; add $-t$ to both sides to obtain $x_1 = x_2$. Use similar reasoning for $rx = s$.

PROBLEM SET 14–7, Pages 288–289

1. (a) I
   (b) R^2:1 $\to$ 3, 2 $\to$ 4, 3 $\to$ 1, 4 $\to$ 2; R^3: 1 $\to$ 4, 2 $\to$ 1, 3 $\to$ 2, 4 $\to$ 3; $R^4 = I$

(c)

*	I	H	V	D_1	D_2	R	R^2	R^3
I	I	H	V	D_1	D_2	R	R^2	R^3
H	H	I	R^2	R	R^3	D_1	V	D_2
V	V	R^2	I	R^3	R	D_2	H	D_1
D_1	D_1	R^3	R	I	R^2	V	D_2	H
D_2	D_2	R	R^3	R^2	I	H	D_1	V
R	R	D_2	D_1	H	V	R^2	R^3	I
R^2	R^2	V	H	D_2	D_1	R^3	I	R
R^3	R^3	D_1	D_2	V	H	I	R	R^2

(e) No; $D_1 * H \neq H * D_1$

2. (a) I (b) $1 \rightarrow 3$, $2 \rightarrow 1$, $3 \rightarrow 2$ (c) I

(d)

$*$	I	M_1	M_2	M_3	R	R^2
I	I	M_1	M_2	M_3	R	R^2
M_1	M_1	I	R^2	R	M_3	M_2
M_2	M_2	R	I	R^2	M_1	M_3
M_3	M_3	R^2	R	I	M_2	M_1
R	R	M_2	M_3	M_1	R^2	I
R^2	R^2	M_3	M_1	M_2	I	R

(e) R^2; M_2 (f) No; $M_1 * M_2 \neq M_2 * M_1$

Index

4+5+7

1/8   1+2

sed